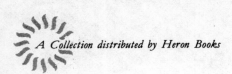

A Collection distributed by Heron Books

CHARLES DICKENS

COMPLETE
WORKS

CENTENNIAL EDITION

Charles Dickens

CHARLES DICKENS

MISCELLANEOUS
PAPERS
II

Distributed by
HERON BOOKS

Edito-Service S.A., Geneva, Publishers

13 002 36 R1

CONTENTS

CONTENTS

MISCELLANIES FROM 'ALL THE YEAR ROUND'
1859-1869

CONTENTS

CONTENTS

MISCELLANIES

FROM

'HOUSEHOLD WORDS'

1850-1859

THAT OTHER PUBLIC

[FEBRUARY 3, 1855]

IN our ninth volume,[1] it fell naturally in our way to make a few inquiries as to the abiding place of that vague noun of multitude signifying many, The Public. We reminded our readers that it is never forthcoming when it is the subject of a joke at the theatre: which is always perceived to be a hit at some other Public richly deserving it, but not present. The circumstances of this time considered, we cannot better commence our eleventh volume, than by gently jogging the memory of that other Public: which is often culpably oblivious of its own duties, rights, and interests: and to which it is perfectly clear that neither we nor our readers are in the least degree related. *We* are the sensible, reflecting, prompt, Public, always up to the mark—whereas that other Public persists in supinely lagging behind, and behaving in an inconsiderate manner.

To begin with a small example lately revived by our friend, the *Examiner* newspaper. What can that other Public mean, by allowing itself to be fleeced every night of its life, by responsible persons whom it accepts for its servants? The case stands thus. Bribes and fees to small officials, had become quite insupportable at the time when the great Railway Companies sprang into existence. All such abuses they immediately and very much to their credit, struck out of their system of management; the keepers of hotels were soon generally obliged to follow in this rational direction; the Public (meaning always, that other one, of course) were relieved from a most annoying and exasperating addition to the hurry and worry of travel; and the reform, as is in the nature of every reform that is necessary and sensible, extended in many smaller directions, and was beneficially felt in many smaller ways. The one persistent and unabashed defyer of it, at this moment, is the Theatre—which

---

[1] *Household Words*, vol. ix. p. 156, in an article entitled 'Where are They?' written by G. A. Sala.

pursues its old obsolete course of refusing to fulfil its contract with that other Public, unless that other Public, after paying for its box-seats or stalls, will also pay the wages of theatre servants who buy their places that they may prey upon that other Public. As if we should sell our publisher's post to the highest bidder, leaving him to charge an additional penny or twopence, or as much as he could get, on every number of *Household Words* with which he should graciously favour that other Public! Within a week or two of this present writing, we paid five shillings, at nine o'clock in the evening, for our one seat at a pantomime; after our cheerful compliance with which demand, a hungry footpad clapped a rolled-up play-bill to our breast, like the muzzle of a pistol, and positively stood before the door of which he was the keeper, to prevent our access (without forfeiture of another shilling for his benefit) to the seat we had purchased. Now, that other Public still submits to the gross imposition, notwithstanding that its most popular entertainer has abandoned all the profit derivable from it, and has plainly pointed out its manifest absurdity and extortion. And although to be sure it is universally known that the Theatre, as an Institution, is in a highly thriving and promising state, and although we have only to see a play, hap-hazard, to perceive that the great body of ladies and gentlemen representing it, have educated themselves with infinite labour and expense in a variety of accomplishments, and have really qualified for their calling in the true spirit of students of the Fine Arts; yet, we take leave to suggest to that other Public with which our readers and we are wholly unconnected, that these are no reasons for its being so egregiously gulled.

We just now mentioned Railway Companies. That other Public is very jealous of Railway Companies. It is not unreasonable in being so, for, it is quite at their mercy; we merely observe that it is not usually slow to complain of them when it has any cause. It has remonstrated, in its time, about rates of Fares, and has adduced instances of their being undoubtedly too high. But, has that other Public ever heard of a preliminary system from which the Railway Companies have no escape, and which runs riot in squandering treasure to an incredible amount, before they have excavated one foot of earth or laid a bar of iron on the ground? Why does that other Public never begin at the beginning, and raise its voice against the monstrous charges of soliciting private bills in Parliament, and

THAT OTHER PUBLIC

conducting inquiries before Committees of the House of Commons—
allowed on all hands to be the very worst tribunals conceivable by
the mind of man? Has that other Public any adequate idea of the
corruption, profusion, and waste, occasioned by this process of misgovernment? Supposing it were informed that, ten years ago, the
average Parliamentary and Law expenses of all the then existing
Railway Companies amounted to a charge of seven hundred pounds
a mile on every mile of railway made in the United Kingdom, would
it be startled? But, supposing it were told in the next breath, that
this charge was really—not seven, but SEVENTEEN HUNDRED POUNDS
A MILE, what would that other Public (on whom, of course, every
farthing of it falls), say then? Yet this is the statement, in so
many words and figures, of a document issued by the Board of Trade,
and which is now rather scarce—as well it may be, being a perilous
curiosity. That other Public may learn from the same pages, that
on the Law and Parliamentary expenses of a certain Stone and
Rugby Line, the Bill for which was lost (and the Line consequently
not made after all), there was expended the modest little preliminary total of one hundred and forty-six thousand pounds! That
was in the joyful days when counsel learned in Parliamentary Law,
refused briefs marked with one hundred guinea fees, and accepted
the same briefs marked with one thousand guinea fees; the attorney
making the neat addition of a third cipher, on the spot, with a
presence of mind suggestive of his own little bill against that other
Public (quite dissociated from us as aforesaid), at whom our readers
and we are now bitterly smiling. That was also in the blessed times
when, there being no Public Health Act, Whitechapel paid to the
tutelary deities, Law and Parliament, six thousand five hundred
pounds, to be graciously allowed to pull down, for the public good,
a dozen odious streets inhabited by Vice and Fever.

Our Public know all about these things, and *our* Public are not
blind to their enormity. It is that other Public, somewhere or
other—where can it be?—which is always getting itself humbugged
and talked over. It has been in a maze of doubt and confusion, for
the last three or four years, on that vexed question, the Liberty of
the Press. It has been told by Noble Lords that the said Liberty
is vastly inconvenient. No doubt it is. No doubt all Liberty is—
to some people. Light is highly inconvenient to such as have their
sufficient reasons for preferring darkness; and soap and water is

5

observed to be a particular inconvenience to those who would rather be dirty than clean. But, that other Public finding the Noble Lords much given to harping betweenwhiles, in a sly dull way, on this string, became uneasy about it, and wanted to know what the harpers would have—wanted to know for instance, how they would direct and guide this dangerous Press. Well, now they *may* know. If that other Public will ever learn, their instruction-book, very lately published, is open before them. Chapter one is a High Court of Justice; chapter two is a history of personal adventure, whereof they may hear more, perhaps, one of these days. The Queen's Representative in a most important part of the United Kingdom— a thorough gentleman, and a man of unimpeachable honour beyond all kind of doubt—knows so little of this Press, that he is seen in secret personal communication with tainted and vile instruments which it rejects, buying their praise with the public money, over- looking their dirty work, and setting them their disgraceful tasks. One of the great national departments in Downing Street is ex- hibited under strong suspicion of like ignorant and disreputable dealing, to purchase remote puffery among the most puff-ridden people ever propagated on the face of this earth. *Our* Public know this very well, and have, of course, taken it thoroughly to heart, in its many suggestive aspects; but, when will that other Public— always lagging behindhand in some out of the way place—become informed about it, and consider it, and act upon it?

It is impossible to over-state the completeness with which *our* Public have got to the marrow of the true question arising out of the condition of the British Army before Sebastopol. *Our* Public know perfectly, that, making every deduction for haste, obstruction, and natural strength of feeling in the midst of goading experiences, the correspondence of the *Times* has revealed a confused heap of mismanagement, imbecility, and disorder, under which the nation's bravery lies crushed and withered. *Our* Public is profoundly ac- quainted with the fact that this is not a new kind of disclosure, but, that similar defection and incapacity have before prevailed at similar periods until the labouring age has heaved up a man strong enough to wrestle with the Misgovernment of England and throw it on its back. Wellington and Nelson both did this, and the next great General and Admiral—for whom we now impatiently wait, but may wait some time, content (if we can be) to know that it is not the tendency of our service, by sea or land, to help the greatest Merit to rise—must do the same, and will assuredly do it, and by that sign ye shall know them. *Our* Public reflecting deeply on these materials for cogitation, will henceforth hold fast by the truth, that the system of administering their affairs is innately bad; that classes and families and interests, have brought them to a very low pass; that the intelligence, steadfastness, foresight, and wonderful power of resource, which in private undertakings distinguish England from all other countries, have no vitality in its public business; that while every merchant and trader has enlarged his grasp and quickened his faculties, the Public Departments have been drearily lying in state, a mere stupid pageant of gorgeous coffins and feebly-burning lights; and that the windows must now be opened wide, and the candles put out, and the coffins buried, and the daylight freely admitted, and the furniture made firewood, and the dirt clean swept away. This is the lesson from which *our* Public is nevermore to be distracted by any artifice, we all know. But, that other Public. What will *they* do? They are a humane, generous, ardent Public; but, will they hold like grim Death to the flower Warning, we have plucked from this nettle War? Will they steadily reply to all cajolers, that though every flannel waistcoat in the civilised, and every bearskin and buffalo-skin in the un-civilised, world, had been sent out in these days to our ill-clad countrymen (and never reached them), they would not in the least affect the lasting question, or dispense with a single item of the amendment proved to be needful, and, until made, to be severely demanded, in the whole household and system of Britannia? When the war is over, and that other Public, always ready for a demonstration, shall be busy throwing up caps, lighting up houses, beating drums, blowing trumpets, and making hundreds of miles of printed columns of speeches, will they be flattered and wordily-pumped dry of the one plain issue left, or will they remember it? O that other Public! If we—you, and I, and all the rest of us—could only make sure of that other Public!

Would it not be a most extraordinary remissness on the part of that other Public, if it were content, in a crisis of uncommon difficulty, to laugh at a Ministry without a Head, and leave it alone? Would it not be a wonderful instance of the shortcomings of that other Public, if it were never seen to stand aghast at the supernatural imbecility of that authority to which, in a dangerous hour, it confided the body and soul of the nation? *We* know what a sight it would be to behold that miserable patient, Mr. Cabinet, specially calling his relations and friends together before Christmas, tottering on his emaciated legs in the last stage of paralysis, and feebly piping that if such and such powers were not entrusted to him for instant use, he would certainly go raving mad of defeated patriotism, and pluck his poor old wretched eyes out in despair ; *we* know with what disdainful emotions we should see him gratified and then shuffle away and go to sleep : to make no use of what he had got, and be heard of no more until one of his nurses, more irritable than the rest, should pull his weazen nose and make him whine—*we* know what these experiences would be to us, and Bless us ! *we* should act upon them in round earnest—but, where is that other Public, whose indifference is the life of such scarecrows, and whom it would seem that not even plague pestilence and famine, battle murder and sudden death, can rouse ?

There is one comfort in all this. We English are not the only victims of that other Public. It is to be heard of, elsewhere. It got across the Atlantic, in the train of the Pilgrim Fathers, and has frequently been achieving wonders in America. Ten or eleven years ago, one Chuzzlewit was heard to say, that he had found it on that side of the water, doing the strangest things. The assertion made all sorts of Publics angry, and there was quite a cordial combination of Publics to resent it and disprove it. But there *is* a little book of Memoirs to be heard of at the present time, which looks as if young Chuzzlewit had reason in him too. Does the ‘smart’ Showman, who makes such a Mermaid, and makes such a Washington’s Nurse, and makes such a Dwarf, and makes such a Singing Angel upon earth, and makes such a fortune, and, above all, makes such a book —does *he* address the free and enlightened Public of the great United States : the Public of State Schools, Liberal Tickets, First-chop Intelligence, and Universal Education ? No, no. That other Public is the sharks’-prey. It is that other Public, down somewhere or other, whose bright particular star and stripe are not yet ascertained, which is so transparently cheated and so hardily outfaced. For that other Public, the hatter of New York outbid Creation at the auction of the first Lind seat. For that other Public, the Lind speeches were made, the tears shed, the serenades given. It is that

THAT OTHER PUBLIC

other Public, always on the boil and ferment about anything or nothing, whom the travelling companion shone down upon from the high Hotel-Balconies. It is that other Public who will read, and even buy, the smart book in which they have so proud a share, and who will fly into raptures about its being circulated from the old Ocean Cliffs of the Old Granite State to the Rocky Mountains. It is indubitably in reference to that other Public that we find the following passage in a book called *American Notes*. 'Another prominent feature is the love of "smart" dealing, which gilds over many a swindle and gross breach of trust, many a defalcation, public and private; and enables many a knave to hold his head up with the best, who well deserves a halter—though it has not been without its retributive operation; for, this smartness has done more in a few years to impair the public credit and to cripple the public resources, than dull honesty, however rash, could have effected in a century. The merits of a broken speculation, or a bankruptcy, or of a successful scoundrel, are not gauged by its or his observance of the golden rule, "Do as you would be done by," but are considered with reference to their smartness. The following dialogue I have held a hundred times:—"Is it not a very disgraceful circumstance that such a man as So-and-So should be acquiring a large property by the most infamous and odious means; and, notwithstanding all the crimes of which he has been guilty, should be tolerated and abetted by your Citizens? He is a public nuisance, is he not?"—"Yes, sir."—"A convicted liar?"—"Yes, sir."—"He has been kicked and cuffed and caned?"—"Yes, sir."—"And he is utterly dishonourable, debased, and profligate?"—"Yes, sir."—"In the name of wonder, then, what is his merit?"—"Well, sir, he is a smart man."'

That other Public of our own bore their full share, and more, of bowing down before the Dwarf aforesaid, in despite of his obviously being too young a child to speak plainly: and *we*, the Public who are never taken in, will not excuse their folly. So, if John on this shore, and Jonathan over there, could each only get at that troublesome other Public of his, and brighten them up a little, it would be very much the better for both brothers.

GASLIGHT FAIRIES

[FEBRUARY 10, 1855]

FANCY an order for five-and-thirty Fairies! Imagine a mortal in a loose-sleeved great-coat, with the mud of London streets upon his legs, commercially ordering, in the common-place, raw, foggy forenoon, 'five-and-thirty more Fairies'! Yet I, the writer, heard the order given. 'Mr. Vernon, let me have five-and-thirty more Fairies to-morrow morning—and take care they are good ones.'

Where was it that, towards the close of the year one thousand eight hundred and fifty-four, on a dark December morning, I over-heard this astonishing commission given to Mr. Vernon, and by Mr. Vernon accepted without a word of remonstrance and entered in a note-book? It was in a dark, deep gulf of a place, hazy with fog—at the bottom of a sort of immense well without any water in it; remote crevices and chinks of daylight faintly visible on the upper rim; dusty palls enveloping the sides; gas flaring at my feet; hammers going, in invisible workshops; groups of people hanging about, trying to keep their toes and fingers warm, what time their noses were dimly seen through the smoke of their own breath. It was in the strange conventional world where the visible people only, never advance; where the unseen painter learns and changes; where the unseen tailor learns and changes; where the unseen mechanist adapts to his purpose the striding ingenuity of the age; where the electric light comes, in a box that is carried under a man's arm; but, where the visible flesh and blood is so persistent in one routine that, from the waiting-woman's apron-pockets (with her hands in them), upward to the smallest retail article in the 'business' of mad Lear with straws in his wig, and downward to the last scene but one of the pantomime, where, for about one hundred years last past, all the characters have entered groping, in exactly the same way, in identically the same places, under precisely the same circumstances, and without the smallest reason—I say, it was in that strange world where the visible population have so completely settled their so-potent art, that when I pay my money at the door I know before-hand everything that can possibly happen to me, inside. It was in the Theatre, that I heard this order given for five-and-thirty Fairies.

And hereby hangs a recollection, not out of place, though not of a Fairy. Once, on just such another December morning, I stood on the same dusty boards, in the same raw atmosphere, intent upon a pantomime-rehearsal. A massive giant's castle arose before me, and the giant's body-guard marched in to comic music; twenty grotesque creatures, with little arms and legs, and enormous faces moulded into twenty varieties of ridiculous leer. One of these faces in particular—an absurdly radiant face, with a wink upon it, and its tongue in its cheek—elicited much approving notice from the authorities, and a ready laugh from the orchestra, and was, for a full half minute, a special success. But, it happened that the wearer of the beaming visage carried a banner; and, not to turn a banner as a procession moves, so as always to keep its decorated side towards the audience, is one of the deadliest sins a banner-bearer can commit. This radiant goblin, being half-blinded by his mask, and further disconcerted by partial suffocation, three distinct times omitted the first duty of man, and petrified us by displaying, with the greatest ostentation, mere sackcloth and timber, instead of the giant's armorial bearings. To crown which offence he couldn't hear when he was called to, but trotted about in his richest manner, unconscious of threats and imprecations. Suddenly, a terrible voice was heard above the music, crying, 'Stop!' Dead silence, and we became aware of Jove in the boxes. 'Hatchway,' cried Jove to the director, ' who is that man ? Show me that man.' Hereupon Hatchway (who had a wooden leg), vigorously apostrophising the defaulter as an ' old beast,' stumped straight up to the body-guard now in line before the castle, and taking the radiant countenance by the nose, lifted it up as if it were a saucepan-lid, and disclosed below, the features of a bald, superannuated, aged person, very much in want of shaving, who looked in the forlornest way at the spectators, while the large face aslant on the top of his head mocked him. 'What ! It's *you*, is it ?' said Hatchway, with dire contempt. ' I thought it was you.' ' I knew it was that man !' cried Jove. ' I told you yesterday, Hatchway, he was not fit for it. Take him away, and bring another !' He was ejected with every mark of ignominy, and the inconstant mask was just as funny on another man's shoulders immediately afterwards. To the present

11

day, I never see a very comic pantomime-mask but I wonder whether this wretched old man can possibly have got behind it; and I never think of him as dead and buried (which is far more likely), but I make that absurd countenance a part of his mortality, and picture it to myself as gone the way of all the winks in the world.

Five-and-thirty more Fairies, and let them be good ones. I saw them next day. They ranged from an anxious woman of ten, learned in the prices of victual and fuel, up to a conceited young lady of five times that age, who always persisted in standing on one leg longer than was necessary, with the determination (as I was informed), 'to make a Part of it.' This Fairy was of long theatrical descent—centuries, I believe—and had never had an ancestor who was entrusted to communicate one word to a British audience. Yet, the whole race had lived and died with the fixed idea of 'making a Part of it'; and she, the last of the line, was still unchangeably resolved to go down on one leg to posterity. Her father had fallen a victim to the family ambition; having become in course of time so extremely difficult to 'get off,' as a villager, sea-man, smuggler, or what not, that it was at length considered unsafe to allow him to 'go on.' Consequently, those neat confidences with the public in which he had displayed the very acmé of his art—usually consisting of an explanatory tear, or an arch hint in dumb show of his own personal determination to perish in the attempt then on foot—were regarded as superfluous, and came to be dispensed with, exactly at the crisis when he himself foresaw that he would 'be put into Parts' shortly. I had the pleasure of recognising in the character of an Evil Spirit of the Marsh, overcome by this lady with one (as I should else have considered purposeless) poke of a javelin, an actor whom I had formerly encountered in the provinces under circumstances that had fixed him agreeably in my remembrance. The play represented to a nautical audience, was *Hamlet*; and this gentle-man having been killed with much credit as Polonius, reappeared in the part of Osric: provided against recognition by the removal of his white wig, and the adjustment round his waist of an extremely broad belt and buckle. He was instantly recognised, notwithstanding these artful precautions, and a solemn impression was made upon the spectators for which I could not account, until a sailor in the Pit drew a long breath, said to himself in a deep voice, ' Blowed if here an't another Ghost!' and composed himself to listen to a

12

GASLIGHT FAIRIES

second communication from the tomb. Another personage whom I recognised as taking refuge under the wings of Pantomime (she was not a Fairy, to be sure, but she kept the cottage to which the Fairies came, and lived in a neat upper bedroom, with her legs obviously behind the street door), was a country manager's wife—a most estimable woman of about fifteen stone, with a larger family than I had ever been able to count: whom I had last seen in Lincolnshire, playing Juliet, while her four youngest children (and nobody else) were in the boxes—hanging out of window, as it were, to trace with their forefingers the pattern on the front, and making all Verona uneasy by their imminent peril of falling into the Pit. Indeed, I had seen this excellent woman in the whole round of Shakesperian beauties, and had much admired her way of getting through the text. If anybody made any remark to her, in reference to which any sort of answer occurred to her mind, she made that answer ; otherwise, as a character in the drama, she preserved an impressive silence, and, as an individual, was heard to murmur to the unseen person next in order of appearance, ' Come on ! ' I found her, now, on good motherly terms with the Fairies, and kindly disposed to chafe and warm the fingers of the younger of that race. Out of Fairy-land, I suppose that so many shawls and bonnets of a peculiar limpness were never assembled together. And, as to shoes and boots, I heartily wished that ' the good people' were better shod, or were as little liable to take cold as in the sunny days when they were received at Court as Godmothers to Princesses.

Twice a-year, upon an average, these gaslight Fairies appear to us ; but, who knows what becomes of them at other times ? You are sure to see them at Christmas, and they may be looked for hopefully at Easter; but, where are they through the eight or nine long intervening months ? They cannot find shelter under mush-rooms, they cannot live upon dew ; unable to array themselves in supernatural green, they must even look to Manchester for cotton stuffs to wear. When they become visible, you find them a traditionary people, with a certain conventional monotony in their proceedings which prevents their surprising you very much, save now and then when they appear in company with Mr. Beverley. In a general way, they have been sliding out of the clouds, for some years, like barrels of beer delivering at a public-house. They sit in the same little rattling stars, with glorious corkscrews twirling about

13

them and never drawing anything, through a good many successive seasons. They come up in the same shells out of the same three rows of gauze water (the little ones lying down in front, with their heads diverse ways); and you resign yourself to what must infallibly take place when you see them armed with garlands. You know all you have to expect of them by moonlight. In the glowing day, you are morally certain that the gentleman with the muscular legs and the short tunic (like the Bust at the Hairdresser's, completely carried out), is coming, when you see them ' getting over ' to one side, while the surprising phenomenon is presented on the landscape of a vast mortal shadow in a hat of the present period, violently directing them so to do. You are acquainted with all these peculiarities of the gaslight Fairies, and you know by heart everything that they will do with their arms and legs, and when they will do it. But, as to the same good people in their invisible condition, it is a hundred to one that you know nothing, and never think of them.

I began this paper with, perhaps, the most curious trait, after all, in the history of the race. They are certain to be found when wanted. Order Mr. Vernon to lay on a hundred and fifty gaslight Fairies next Monday morning, and they will flow into the establishment like so many feet of gas. Every Fairy can bring other Fairies ; her sister Jane, her friend Matilda, her friend Matilda's friend, her brother's young family, her mother—if Mr. Vernon will allow that respectable person to pass muster. Summon the Fairies, and Drury Lane, Soho, Somers' Town, and the neighbourhood of the obelisk in St. George's Fields, will become alike prolific in them. Poor, good-humoured, patient, fond of a little self-display, perhaps, (sometimes, but far from always), they will come trudging through the mud, leading brother and sister lesser Fairies by the hand, and will hover about in the dark stage-entrances, shivering and chattering in their shrill way, and earning their little money hard, idlers and vagabonds though we may be pleased to think them. I wish, myself, that we were not so often pleased to think ill of those who minister to our amusement. I am far from having satisfied my heart that either we or they are a bit the better for it.

Nothing is easier than for any one of us to get into a pulpit, or upon a tub, or a stump, or a platform, and blight (so far as with our bilious and complacent breath we can), any class of small people we may choose to select. But, it by no means follows that because it is easy and safe, it is right. Even these very gaslight Fairies, now. Why should I be bitter on them because they are shabby personages, tawdrily dressed for the passing hour, and then to be shabby again? I have known very shabby personages indeed—the shabbiest I ever heard of—tawdrily dressed for public performances of other kinds, and performing marvellously ill too, though transcendently rewarded: yet whom none disparaged! In even-handed justice, let me render these little people their due.

Ladies and Gentlemen. Whatever you may hear to the contrary (and may sometimes have a strange satisfaction in believing), there is no lack of virtue and modesty among the Fairies. All things considered, I doubt if they be much below our own high level. In respect of constant acknowledgment of the claims of kindred, I assert for the Fairies, that they yield to no grade of humanity. Sad as it is to say, I have known Fairies even to fall, through this fidelity of theirs. As to young children, sick mothers, dissipated brothers, fathers unfortunate and fathers undeserving, Heaven and Earth, how many of these have I seen clinging to the spangled skirts, and contesting for the nightly shilling or two, of one little lop-sided, weak-legged Fairy!

Let me, before I ring the curtain down on this short piece, take a single Fairy, as Sterne took his Captive, and sketch the Family-Picture. I select Miss Fairy, aged three-and-twenty, lodging within cannon range of Waterloo Bridge, London—not alone, but with her mother, Mrs. Fairy, disabled by chronic rheumatism in the knees; and with her father, Mr. Fairy, principally employed in lurking about a public-house, and waylaying the theatrical profession for twopence wherewith to purchase a glass of old ale, that he may have something warming on his stomach (which has been cold for fifteen years); and with Miss Rosina Fairy, Miss Angelica Fairy, and Master Edmund Fairy, aged respectively, fourteen, ten, and eight. Miss Fairy has an engagement of twelve shillings a week—sole means of preventing the Fairy family from coming to a dead lock. To be sure, at this time of year the three young Fairies have a nightly engagement to come out of a Pumpkin as French soldiers; but, its advantage to the housekeeping is rendered nominal, by that dreadful old Mr. Fairy's making it a legal formality to draw the money himself every Saturday—and never coming home until his stomach is warmed, and the money gone. Miss Fairy is pretty too, makes up very pretty. This is a trying life at the best, but very trying at the worst. And the worst is, that that always beery old Fairy, the father, hovers about the stage-door four or five nights a week, and gets his cronies among the carpenters and footmen to carry in messages to his daughter (he is not admitted himself), representing the urgent coldness of his stomach and his parental demand for twopence; failing compliance with which, he creates disturbances; and getting which, he becomes maudlin and waits for the manager, to whom he represents with tears that his darling child and pupil, the pride of his soul, is 'kept down in the Theatre.' A hard life this for Miss Fairy, I say, and a dangerous! And it is good to see her, in the midst of it, so watchful of Rosina Fairy, who otherwise might come to harm one day. A hard life this, I say again, even if John Kemble Fairy, the brother, who sings a good song, and when he gets an engagement always disappears about the second week or so and is seen no more, had not a miraculous property of turning up on a Saturday without any heels to his boots, firmly purposing to commit suicide, unless bought off with half-a-crown. And yet—so curious is the gaslighted atmosphere in which these Fairies dwell!— through all the narrow ways of such an existence, Miss Fairy never relinquishes the belief that that incorrigible old Fairy, the father, is a wonderful man! She is immovably convinced that nobody ever can, or ever could, approach him in Rolla. She has grown up in this conviction, will never correct it, will die in it. If, through any wonderful turn of fortune, she were to arrive at the emolument and dignity of a Free Benefit to-morrow, she would 'put up' old Fairy, red nosed, stammering and imbecile—with delirium tremens shaking his very buttons off—as the noble Peruvian, and would play Cora herself, with a profound belief in his taking the town by storm at last.

GONE TO THE DOGS

[March 10, 1855]

WE all know what treasures Posterity will inherit, in the fulness of time. We all know what handsome legacies are bequeathed to it every day, what long luggage-trains of Sonnets it will be the better for, what patriots and statesmen it will discover to have existed in this age whom we have no idea of, how very wide awake it will be, and how stone blind the Time is. We know what multitudes of disinterested persons are always going down to it, laden, like processions of genii, with inexhaustible and incalculable wealth. We have frequent experience of the generosity with which the profoundest wits, the subtlest politicians, unerring inventors, and lavish benefactors of mankind, take beneficent aim at it with a longer range than Captain Warner's, and blow it up to the very heaven of heavens, one hundred years after date. We all defer to it as the great capitalist in expectation, the world's residuary legatee in respect of all the fortunes that are not just now convertible, the heir of a long and fruitful minority, the fortunate creature on whom all the true riches of the earth are firmly entailed. When Posterity does come into its own at last, what a coming of age there will be!

It seems to me that Posterity, as the subject of so many handsome settlements, has only one competitor. I find the Dogs to be every day enriched with a vast amount of valuable property.

What has become—to begin like Charity at home—what has become, I demand, of the inheritance I myself entered on, at nineteen years of age! A shining castle (in the air) with young Love looking out of window, perfect contentment and repose of spirit standing with ethereal aspect in the porch, visions surrounding it by night and day with an atmosphere of pure gold. This was my only inheritance, and I never squandered it. I hoarded it like a miser. Say, bright-eyed Araminta (with the obdurate parents), thou who wast sole lady of the castle, did I not? Down the flowing river by the walls, called Time, how blest we sailed together, treasuring our happiness unto death, and never knowing change, or weariness, or separation! Where is that castle now, with all

17

MISCELLANEOUS PAPERS

its magic furniture? Gone to the Dogs. Canine possession was taken of the whole of that estate, my youthful Araminta, about a quarter of a century ago.

Come back, friend of my youth. Come back from the glooms and shadows that have gathered round thee, and let us sit down once more, side by side, upon the rough, notched form at school! Idle is Bob Tample, given to shirking his work and getting me to do it for him, inkier than a well-regulated mind in connection with a well-regulated body is usually observed to be, always compounding with his creditors on pocket-money days, frequently selling off pen-knives by auction, and disposing of his sister's birthday presents at an enormous sacrifice. Yet, a rosy, cheerful, thoughtless fellow is Bob Tample, borrowing with an easy mind, sixpences of Dick Sage the prudent, to pay eighteenpences after the holidays, and freely standing treat to all comers. Musical is Bob Tample. Able to sing and whistle anything. Learns the piano (in the parlour), and once plays a duet with the musical professor, Mr. Goavus of the Royal Italian Opera (occasional-deputy-assistant-copyist in that establishment, I have since seen reason to believe), whom Bob's friends and supporters, I foremost in the throng, consider tripped up in the first half-dozen bars. Not without bright expectations is Bob Tample, being an orphan with a guardian near the Bank, and destined for the army. I boast of Bob at home that his name is 'down at the Horse Guards,' and that his father left it in his will that 'a pair of colours' (I like the expression without particularly knowing what it means) should be purchased for him. I go with Bob on one occasion to look at the building where his name is down. We wonder in which of the rooms it is down, and whether the two horse soldiers on duty know it. I also accompany Bob to see his sister at Miss Maggiggs's boarding establishment at Hammersmith, and it is unnecessary to add that I think his sister beautiful and love her. She will be independent, Bob says. I relate at home that Mr. Tample left it in his will that his daughter was to be independent. I put Mr. Tample, entirely of my own accord and invention, into the army; and I perplex my family circle by relating feats of valour achieved by that lamented officer at the Battle of Waterloo, where I leave him dead, with the British flag (which he wouldn't give up to the last) wound tightly round his left arm. So we go on, until Bob leaves for Sandhurst. *I* leave in course of time—everybody leaves.

18

GONE TO THE DOGS

Years have gone by, when I twice or thrice meet a gentleman with a moustache, driving a lady in a very gay bonnet, whose face recalls the boarding establishment of Miss Maggiggs at Hammersmith, though it does not look so happy as it did under Miss Maggiggs, iron-handed despot as I believed that accomplished woman to be. This leads me to the discovery that the gentleman with the moustache is Bob; and one day Bob pulls up, and talks, and asks me to dinner; but, on subsequently ascertaining that I don't play billiards, hardly seems to care as much about me as I had expected. I ask Bob at this period, if he is in the service still? Bob answers no my boy, he got bored and sold out; which induces me to think (for I am growing worldly), either that Bob must be very independent indeed, or must be going to the Dogs. More years elapse, and having quite lost sight and sound of Bob meanwhile, I say on an average twice a week during three entire twelvemonths, that I really will call at the guardian's near the Bank, and ask about Bob. At length I do so. Clerks, on being apprised of my errand, became disrespectful. Guardian, with bald head highly flushed, bursts out of inner office, remarks that he hasn't the honour of my acquaintance, and bursts in again, without exhibiting the least desire to improve the opportunity of knowing me. I now begin sincerely to believe that Bob is going to the Dogs. More years go by, and as they pass Bob sometimes goes by me too, but never twice in the same aspect—always tending lower and lower. No redeeming trace of better things would hang about him now, were he not always accompanied by the sister. Gay bonnet gone; exchanged for something limp and veiled, that might be a mere porter's knot of the feminine gender, to carry a load of misery on —shabby, even slipshod. I, by some vague means or other, come to the knowledge of the fact that she entrusted that independence to Bob, and that Bob—in short, that it has all gone to the Dogs. One summer day, I descry Bob idling in the sun, outside a public-house near Drury Lane; she, in a shawl that clings to her, as only the robes of poverty do cling to their wearers when all things else have fallen away, waiting for him at the street corner; he, with a stale, accustomed air, picking his teeth and pondering; two boys watchful of him, not unadmiringly. Curious to know more of this, I go round that way another day, look at a concert-bill in the public-house window, and have not a doubt that Bob is

19

Mr. Berkeley, the celebrated bacchanalian vocalist, who presides at the piano. From time to time, rumours float by me afterwards, I can't say how, or where they come from—from the expectant and insatiate Dogs for anything I know—touching hushed-up pawnings of sheets from poor furnished lodgings, begging letters to old Miss Maggiggs at Hammersmith, and the clearing away of all Miss Maggiggs's umbrellas and clogs, by the gentleman who called for an answer on a certain foggy evening after dark. Thus downward, until the faithful sister begins to beg of *me*, whereupon I moralise as to the use of giving her any money (for I have grown quite worldly now), and look furtively out of my window as she goes away by night with that half-sovereign of mine, and think, contemptuous of myself, can I ever have admired the crouching figure plashing through the rain, in a long round crop of curls at Miss Maggiggs's! Oftentimes she comes back with bedridden lines from the brother, who is always nearly dead and never quite, until he does tardily make an end of it, and at last this Actæon reversed has rung the Dogs wholly down and betaken himself to them finally. More years have passed, when I dine at Withers's at Brighton on a day, to drink 'Forty-one claret; and there, Spithers, the new Attorney-General, says to me across the table, 'Weren't you a Mithers's boy?' To which I say, 'To be sure I was!' To which he retorts, 'And don't you remember me?' To which I retort, 'To be sure I do'—which I never did until that instant—and then he says how the fellows have all dispersed, and he has never seen one of them since, and have I? To which I, finding that my learned friend has a pleasant remembrance of Bob from having given him a black eye on his fifteenth birthday in assertion of his right to 'smug' a pen-wiper forwarded to said Bob by his sister on said occasion, make response by generalising the story I have now completed, and adding that I have heard that, after Bob's death, Miss Maggiggs, though deuced poor through the decay of her school, took the sister home to live with her. My learned friend says, upon his word it does Miss Whatshername credit, and all old Mitherses ought to subscribe a trifle for her. Not seeing the necessity of that, I praise the wine, and we send it round, the way of the world (which world I am told is getting nearer to the Sun every year of its existence), and we bury Bob's memory with the epitaph that he went to the Dogs.

GONE TO THE DOGS

Sometimes, whole streets, inanimate streets of brick and mortar houses, go to the Dogs. Why, it is impossible to say, otherwise than that the Dogs bewitch them, fascinate them, magnetise them, summon them and they must go. I know of such a street at the present writing. It was a stately street in its own grim way, and the houses held together like the last surviving members of an aristocratic family, and, as a general rule, were—still not unlike them—very tall and very dull. How long the Dogs may have had their eyes of temptation upon this street is unknown to me, but they called to it, and it went. The biggest house—it was a corner one—went first. An ancient gentleman died in it; and the undertaker put up a gaudy hatchment that looked like a very bad transparency, not intended to be seen by day, and only meant to be illuminated at night; and the attorney put up a bill about the lease, and put in an old woman (apparently with nothing to live upon but a cough), who crept away into a corner like a scared old dormouse, and rolled herself up in a blanket. The mysterious influence of the Dogs was on the house, and it immediately began to tumble down. Why the infection should pass over fourteen houses to seize upon the fifteenth, I don't know; but, fifteen doors off next began to be fatally dim in the windows; and after a short decay, its eyes were closed by brokers, and its end was desolation. The best house opposite, unable to bear these sights of woe, got out a black board with all despatch, respecting unexpired remainder of term, and cards to view; and the family fled, and a bricklayer's wife and children came in to 'mind' the place, and dried their little weekly wash on lines hung across the dining-room. Black boards, like the doors of so many hearses taken off the hinges, now became abundant. Only one speculator, without suspicion of the Dogs upon his soul, responded. He repaired and stuccoed number twenty-four, got up an ornamented parapet and balconies, took away the knockers, and put in plate glass, found too late that all the steam power on earth could never have kept the street from the Dogs when it was once influenced to go, and drowned himself in a water butt. Within a year, the house he had renewed became the worst of all; the stucco decomposing like a Stilton cheese, and the ornamented parapet coming down in fragments like the sugar of a broken twelfth cake. Expiring efforts were then made by a few of the black boards to hint at the eligibility of these commodious

21

mansions for public institutions, and suites of chambers. It was useless. The thing was done. The whole street may now be bought for a mere song. But, nobody will hear of it, for who dares dispute possession of it with the Dogs!

Sometimes, it would seem as if the least yelp of these dreadful animals, did the business at once. Which of us does not remember that eminent person—with indefinite resources in the City, tantamount to a gold mine—who had the delightful house near town, the famous gardens and gardener, the beautiful plantations, the smooth green lawns, the pineries, the stabling for five-and-twenty horses, and the standing for half a dozen carriages, the billiard-room, the music-room, the picture gallery, the accomplished daughters and aspiring sons, all the pride pomp and circumstance of riches? Which of us does not recall how we knew him through the good offices of our esteemed friend Swallowfly, who was ambassador on the occasion? Which of us cannot still hear the gloating roundness of tone with which Swallowfly informed us that our new friend was worth five hun-dred thou-sand pounds, sir, if he was worth a penny? How we dined there with all the Arts and Graces ministering to us, and how we came away reflecting that wealth after all was a desirable delight, I need not say. Neither need I tell, how we every one of us met Swallowfly within six little months of that same day, when Swallowfly observed, with such surprise, 'You haven't heard? Lord bless me! Ruined—Channel Islands—gone to the Dogs!'

Sometimes again, it would seem as though in exceptional cases here and there, the Dogs relented, or lost their power over the imperilled man in an inscrutable way. There was my own cousin— he is dead now, therefore I have no objection to mention his name— Tom Flowers. He was a bachelor (fortunately), and, among other ways he had of increasing his income and improving his prospects, betted pretty high. He did all sorts of things that he ought not to have done, and he did everything at a great pace, so it was clearly seen by all who knew him that nothing would keep him from the Dogs; that he was running them down hard, and was bent on getting into the very midst of the pack with all possible speed. Well! He was as near them, I suppose, as ever man was, when he suddenly stopped short, looked them full in their jowls, and never stirred another inch onward, to the day of his death. He walked about for seventeen years, a very neat little figure, with a capital umbrella, an excellent neckcloth, and a pure white shirt, and he had not got a hair's-breadth nearer to the horrible animals at the end of that time than he had when he stopped. How he lived, our family could never make out—whether the Dogs can have allowed him anything will always be a mystery to me—but, he disappointed all of us in the matter of the canine epitaph with which we had expected to dismiss him, and merely enabled us to remark that poor Tom Flowers was gone at sixty-seven.

It is overwhelming to think of the Treasury of the Dogs. There are no such fortunes embarked in all the enterprises of life, as have gone their way. They have a capital Drama, for their amusement and instruction. They have got hold of all the People's holidays for the refreshment of weary frames, and the renewal of weary spirits. They have left the People little else in that way but a Fast now and then for the ignorances and imbecilities of their rulers. Perhaps those days will go next. To say the plain truth very seriously, I shouldn't be surprised.

Consider the last possessions that have gone to the Dogs. Consider, friends and countrymen, how the Dogs have been enriched, by your despoilment at the hands of your own blessed governors—to whom be honour and renown, stars and garters, for ever and ever!—on the shores of a certain obscure spot called Balaklava, where Britannia rules the waves in such an admirable manner, that she slays her children (who never never never will be slaves, but very very very often will be dupes), by the thousand, with every movement of her glorious trident! When shall there be added to the possessions of the Dogs, those columns of talk, which, let the columns of British soldiers vanish as they may, still defile before us wearily, wearily, leading to nothing, doing nothing, for the most part even saying nothing, only enshrouding us in a mist of idle breath that obscures the events which are forming themselves— not into playful shapes, believe me—beyond. If the Dogs, lately so gorged, still so voracious and strong, could and would deliver a most gracious bark, I have a strong impression that their warning would run thus:

' My Lords and Gentlemen. We are open-mouthed and eager. Either you must send suitable provender to us without delay, or you must come to us yourselves. There is no avoidance of the alternative. Talk never softened the three-headed dog that kept the passage to the Shades; less will it appease us. No jocular old gentleman throwing sommersaults on stilts because his great-grandmother is not worshipped in Nineveh, is a sop to us for a moment; no hearing, cheering, sealing-waxing, tapeing, fire-eating, vote-eating, or other popular Club-performance, at all imports us. We are the Dogs. We are known to you just now, as the Dogs of War. We crouched at your feet for employment, as William Shakespeare, plebeian, saw us crouching at the feet of the Fifth Harry—and you gave it us; crying Havoc! in good English, and letting us slip (quite by accident), on good Englishmen. With our appetites so whetted, we are hungry. We are sharp of scent and quick of sight, and we see and smell a great deal coming to us rather rapidly. Will you give us such old rubbish as must be ours in any case? My Lords and Gentlemen, make haste! Something must go to the Dogs in earnest. Shall it be you, or something else?'

FAST AND LOOSE

[MARCH 24, 1855]

IF the Directors of any great joint-stock commercial undertaking —say a Railway Company—were to get themselves made Directors principally in virtue of some blind superstition declaring every man of the name of Bolter to be a man of business, every man of the name of Jolter to be a mathematician, and every man of the name of Polter to possess a minute acquaintance with the construction of locomotive steam-engines; and if those ignorant Directors so managed the affairs of the body corporate, as that the trains never started at the right times, began at their right beginnings, or got to their right ends, but always devoted their steam to bringing themselves into violent collision with one another; and if by such means those incapable Directors destroyed thousands of lives, wasted millions of money, and hopelessly bewildered and conglomerated themselves and everybody else; what would the shareholding body say, if those brazen-faced Directors called them together in the midst of the wreck and ruin they had made, and with an audacious piety addressed them thus : ' Lo, ye miserable sinners, the hand of

FAST AND LOOSE

Providence is heavy on you! Attire yourselves in sackcloth, throw ashes on your heads, fast, and hear us condescend to make discourses to you on the wrong you have done!'

Or, if Mr. Matthew Marshall of the Bank of England, were to be superseded by Bolter; if the whole Bank parlour were to be cleared for Jolter; and the engraving of bank-notes were to be given as a snug thing to Polter; and if Bolter Jolter and Polter, with a short pull and a weak pull and a pull no two of them together, should tear the Money Market to pieces, and rend the whole mercantile system and credit of the country to shreds; what kind of reception would Bolter Jolter and Polter get from Baring Brothers, Rothschilds, and Lombard Street in general, if those Incapables should cry out, 'Providence has brought you all to the Gazette. Listen, wicked ones, and we will give you an improving lecture on the death of the old Lady in Threadneedle Street!'

Or, if the servants in a rich man's household were to distribute their duties exactly as the fancy took them; if the housemaid were to undertake the kennel of hounds, and the dairymaid were to mount the coachbox, and the cook were to pounce upon the secretaryship, and the groom were to dress the dinner, and the gamekeeper were to make the beds, while the gardener gave the young ladies lessons on the piano, and the stable-helper took the baby out for an airing; would the rich man, soon very poor, be much improved in his mind when the whole incompetent establishment, surrounding him, exclaimed, 'You have brought yourself to a pretty pass, sir. You had better see what fasting and humiliation will do to get you out of this. We will trouble you to pay us, keep us, and try!'

A very fine gentleman, very daintily dressed, once took an uncouth creature under his protection—a wild thing, half man and half brute. And they travelled along together.

The wild man was ignorant; but, he had some desire for knowledge too, and at times he even fell into strange fits of thought, wherein he had gleams of reason and flashes of a quick sagacity. There was also veneration in his breast, for the Maker of all the wondrous universe about him. It has even been supposed that these seeds were sown within him by a greater and wiser hand than the hand of the very fine gentleman very daintily dressed.

It was necessary that they should get on quickly to avoid a

25

storm, and the first thing that happened was, that the wild man's feet became crippled.

Now, the very fine gentleman had made the wild man put on a tight pair of boots which were altogether unsuited to him, so the wild man said:

'It's the boots.'

'It's a Rebuke,' said the very fine gentleman.

'A WHAT?' roared the wild man.

'It's Providence,' said the very fine gentleman.

The wild man cast his eyes on the earth around him, and up at the sky, and then at the very fine gentleman, and was mightily displeased to hear that great word so readily in the mouth of such an interpreter on such an occasion; but, he hobbled on as well as he could without saying a syllable, until they had gone a very long way, and he was hungry.

There was abundance of wholesome fruits and herbs by the wayside, which the wild man tried to reach by springing at them, but could not.

'I am starving,' the wild man complained.

'It's a Rebuke,' said the very fine gentleman.

'It's the handcuffs,' said the wild man. For, he had submitted to be handcuffed before he came out.

However, his companion wouldn't hear of that (he said it was not official, and was unparliamentary), so they went on and on, a weary journey; and the wild man got nothing, because he was handcuffed, and because the very fine gentleman couldn't reach the fruit for him on account of his stays; and the very fine gentleman got what he had in his pocket.

By and by, they came to a house on fire, where the wild man's brother was being burnt to death, because he couldn't get out at the door: which door had been locked seven years before, by the very fine gentleman, who had taken away the key.

'Produce the key,' exclaimed the wild man, in an agony, 'and let my brother out.'

'I meant it to have been here the day before yesterday,' returned the very fine gentleman, in his leisurely way, 'and I had it put aboard ship to be brought here; but, the fact is, the ship has gone round the world instead of coming here, and I doubt if we shall ever hear any more about it.'

26

FAST AND LOOSE

'It's Murder!' cried the wild man.

But, the very fine gentleman was uncommonly high with him, for not knowing better than that: so the brother was burnt to death, and they proceeded on their journey.

At last, they came to a fine palace by a river, where a gentleman of a thriving appearance was rolling out at the gate in a very neat chariot, drawn by a pair of blood horses, with two servants up behind in fine purple liveries.

'Bless my soul!' cried this gentleman, checking his coachman, and looking hard at the wild man, 'what monster have we here!'

Then the very fine gentleman explained that it was a hardened creature with whom Providence was very much incensed; in proof of which, here he was, rebuked, crippled, handcuffed, starved, with his brother burnt to death in a locked-up house, and the key of the house going round the world.

'Are *you* Providence?' asked the wild man, faintly.

'Hold your tongue, sir,' said the very fine gentleman.

'Are *you*?' asked the wild man of the gentleman of the palace.

The gentleman of the palace made no reply; but, coming out of his carriage in a brisk business-like manner, immediately put the wild man into a strait-waistcoat, and said to the very fine gentleman, 'He shall fast for his sins.'

'I have already done that,' the wild man protested weakly.

'He shall do it again,' said the gentleman of the palace.

'I have fasted from work too, through divers causes—you know I speak the truth—until I am miserably poor,' said the wild man.

'He shall do it again,' said the gentleman of the palace.

'A day's work just now, is the breath of my life,' said the wild man.

'He shall do without the breath of his life,' said the gentleman of the palace.

Therewith, they carried him off to a hard bench, and sat him down, and discoursed to him ding-dong, through and through the dictionary, about all manner of businesses except the business that concerned him. And when they saw his thoughts, red-eyed and angry though he was, escape from them up to the true Providence far away, and when they saw that he confusedly humbled and quieted his mind before Heaven, in his innate desire to approach it and learn from it, and know better how to bear these things and set

27

them right, they said ' He is listening to us, he is doing as we would have him, he would never be troublesome.'

What that wild man really had before him in his thoughts, at that time of being so misconstrued and so practised on, History shall tell—not the narrator of this story, though he knows full well. Enough for us, and for the present purpose, that this tale can have no application—how were that possible !—to the year one thousand eight hundred and fifty-five.

THE THOUSAND AND ONE HUMBUGS

I

[APRIL 21, 1855]

EVERYBODY is acquainted with that enchanting collection of stories, the Thousand and One Nights, better known in England as the *Arabian Nights Entertainments.* Most people know that these wonderful fancies are unquestionably of genuine Eastern origin, and are to be found in Arabic manuscripts now existing in the Vatican, in Paris, in London, and in Oxford ; the last-named city being particularly distinguished in this connection, as possessing, in the library of Christchurch, a manuscript of the never-to-be-forgotten Voyages of Sinbad the Sailor.

The civilised world is indebted to France for a vast amount of its possessions, and among the rest for the first opening to Europe of this gorgeous storehouse of Eastern riches. So well did M. Galland, the original translator, perform his task, that when Mr. Wortley Montague brought home the manuscript now in the Bodleian Library, there was found (poetical quotations excepted), to be very little, and that of a very inferior kind, to add to what M. Galland had already made perfectly familiar to France and England.

Thus much as to the Thousand and One Nights, we recall, by way of introduction to the discovery we are about to announce.

There has lately fallen into our hands, a manuscript in the Arabic Character (with which we are perfectly acquainted), containing a variety of stories extremely similar in structure and incident

28

THE THOUSAND AND ONE HUMBUGS

to the Thousand and One Nights; but presenting the strange
feature that although they are evidently of ancient origin, they
have a curious accidental bearing on the present time. Allowing
for the difference of manners and customs, it would often seem—
were it not for the manifest impossibility of such prophetic knowledge in any mere man or men—that they were written expressly
with an eye to events of the current age. We have referred the
manuscript (which may be seen at our office on the first day of
April in every year, at precisely four o'clock in the morning), to
the profoundest Oriental Scholars of England and France, who are
no less sensible than we are ourselves of this remarkable coincidence,
and are equally at a loss to account for it. They are agreed, we
may observe, on the propriety of our rendering the title in the
words, The Thousand and One Humbugs. For, although the
Eastern story-tellers do not appear to have possessed any word, or
combination of parts of words, precisely answering to the modern
English Humbug (which, indeed, they expressed by the figurative
phrase, A Camel made of sand), there is no doubt that they were
conversant with so common a thing, and further that the thing was
expressly meant to be designated in the general title of the Arabic
manuscript now before us. Dispensing with further explanation,
we at once commence the specimens we shall occasionally present,
of this literary curiosity.

INTRODUCTORY CHAPTER

Among the ancient Kings of Persia who extended their glorious
conquests into the Indies, and far beyond the famous River Ganges,
even to the limits of China, Taxedtaurus (or Fleeced Bull) was in-
comparably the most renowned. He was so rich that he scorned to
undertake the humblest enterprise without inaugurating it by ordering his Treasurers to throw several millions of pieces of gold into
the dirt. For the same reason he attached no value to his foreign
possessions, but merely used them as playthings for a little while,
and then always threw them away or lost them.

This wise Sultan, though blessed with innumerable sources of
happiness, was afflicted with one fruitful cause of discontent. He
had been married many scores of times, yet had never found a
wife to suit him. Although he had raised to the dignity of

MISCELLANEOUS PAPERS

Howsa Kummauns[1] (or Peerless Chatterer), a great variety of beautiful creatures, not only of the lineage of the high nobles of his court, but also selected from other classes of his subjects, the result had uniformly been the same. They proved unfaithful, brazen, talkative, idle, extravagant, inefficient, and boastful. Thus it naturally happened that a Howsa Kummauns very rarely died a natural death, but was generally cut short in some violent manner.

At length, the young and lovely Reefawm (that is to say Light of Reason), the youngest and fairest of all the Sultan's wives, and to whom he had looked with hope to recompense him for his many disappointments, made as bad a Howsa Kummauns as any of the rest. The unfortunate Taxedtaurus took this so much to heart that he fell into a profound melancholy, secluded himself from observation, and for some time was so seldom seen or heard of that many of his great officers of state supposed him to be dead.

Shall I never, said the unhappy Monarch, beating his breast in his retirement in the Pavilion of Failure, and giving vent to his tears, find a Howsa Kummauns, who will be true to me! He then quoted from the Poet, certain verses importing, Every Howsa Kummauns has deceived me, Every Howsa Kummauns is a Humbug, I must slay the present Howsa Kummauns as I have slain so many others, I am brought to shame and mortification, I am despised by the world. After which his grief so overpowered him, that he fainted away.

It happened that on recovering his senses he heard the voice of the last-made Howsa Kummauns, in the Divan adjoining. Applying his ear to the lattice, and finding that that shameless Princess was vaunting her loyalty and virtue, and denying a host of facts—which she always did, all night—the Sultan drew his scimetar in a fury, resolved to put an end to her existence.

But, the Grand Vizier Parmarstoon (or Twirling Weathercock), who was at that moment watching his incensed master from behind the silken curtains of the Pavilion of Failure, hurried forward and prostrated himself, trembling on the ground. This Vizier had newly succeeded to Abaddeen (or the Addled), who had for his misdeeds been strangled with a garter.

The breath of the slave, said the Vizier, is in the hands of his Lord, but the Lion will sometimes deign to listen to the croaking of

[1] Sounded like House o' Commons.

THE THOUSAND AND ONE HUMBUGS

the frog. I swear to thee, Vizier, replied the Sultan, that I have borne too much already and will bear no more. Thou and the Howsa Kummauns are in one story, and by the might of Allah and the beard of the Prophet, I have a mind to destroy ye both!

When the Vizier heard the Sultan thus menace him with destruction, his heart drooped within him. But, being a brisk and ready man, though stricken in years, he quoted certain lines from the Poet, implying that the thunder-cloud often spares the leaf or there would be no fruit, and touched the ground with his forehead in token of submission. What wouldst thou say? demanded the generous Prince, I give thee leave to speak. Thou art not unaccustomed to public speaking; speak glibly! Sire, returned the Vizier, but for the dread of the might of my Lord, I would reply in the words addressed by the ignorant man to the Genie. And what were those words? demanded the Sultan. Repeat them! Parmarstoon replied, To hear is to obey:

THE STORY OF THE IGNORANT MAN AND THE GENIE

Sire, on the barbarous confines of the kingdom of the Tartars, there dwelt an ignorant man, who was obliged to make a journey through the Great Desert of Desolation; which, as your Majesty knows, is sometimes a journey of upwards of three score and ten years. He bade adieu to his mother very early in the morning, and departed without a guide, ragged, barefoot, and alone. He found the way surprisingly steep and rugged, and beset by vile serpents and strange unintelligible creatures of horrible shapes. It was likewise full of black bogs and pits, into which he not only fell himself, but often had the misfortune to drag other travellers whom he encountered, and who got out no more, but were miserably stifled.

Sire, on the fourteenth day of the journey of the ignorant man of the kingdom of the Tartars, he sat down to rest by the side of a foul well (being unable to find a better), and there cracked for a repast, as he best could, a very hard nut, which was all he had about him. He threw the shell anywhere as he stripped it off, and having made an end of his meal arose to wander on again, when suddenly the air was darkened, he heard a frightful cry, and saw a monstrous Genie, of gigantic stature, who brandished a mighty scimetar in a hand of iron, advancing towards him. Rise, ignorant beast, said the monster, as he drew nigh, that I, Law, may kill thee for having affronted my ward. Alas, my lord, returned the ignorant man, how can I have affronted thy ward whom I never saw? He is invisible to thee, returned the Genie, because thou art a benighted barbarian; but if thou hadst ever learnt any good thing thou wouldst have seen him plainly, and wouldst have respected him. Lord of my life, pleaded the traveller, how could I learn where there were none to teach me, and how affront thy ward whom I have not the power to see? I tell thee, returned the Genie, that with thy pernicious refuse thou hast struck my ward, Prince Socieetee, in the apple of the eye; and because thou hast done this, I will be thy ruin. I maim and kill the like of thee by thousands every year, for no other crime. And shall I spare *thee*? Kneel and receive the blow.

Your Majesty will believe (continued the Grand Vizier) that the ignorant man of the kingdom of the Tartars, gave himself up for lost when he heard those cruel words. Without so much as repeating the formula of our faith—There is but one Allah, from him we come, to him we must return, and who shall resist his will (for he was too ignorant even to have heard it)—he bent his neck to receive the fatal stroke. His head rolled off as he finished saying these words: Dread Law, if thou hadst taken half the pains to teach me to discern thy ward that thou hast taken to avenge him, thou hadst been spared the great account to which I summon thee!

Taxedtaurus the Sultan of Persia listened attentively to this recital on the part of his Grand Vizier, and when it was concluded said, with a threatening brow, Expound to me, O nephew of a dog! the points of resemblance between the Tiger and the Nightingale, and what thy ignorant man of the accursed kingdom of the Tartars has to do with the false Howsa Kummauns and the glib Vizier Parmarstoon? While speaking he again raised his glittering scimetar. Let not my master sully the sole of his foot by crushing an insect, returned the Vizier, kissing the ground seven times, I meant but to offer up a petition from the dust, that the Light of the eyes of the Faithful would, before striking, deign to hear my daughter. What of thy daughter? said the Sultan impatiently, and why should I hear thy daughter any more than the daughter of the dirtiest of the dustmen? Sire, returned the Vizier, I am dirtier than the dirtiest of the dustmen in your Majesty's sight, but my daughter is deeply read in the history of every Howsa Kummauns who has aspired to

THE THOUSAND AND ONE HUMBUGS

your Majesty's favour during many years, and if your Majesty would condescend to hear some of the Legends she has to relate, they might —— What dost thou call thy daughter? demanded the Sultan, interrupting. Hansardadade, replied the Vizier. Go, said the Sultan, bring her hither. I spare thy life until thou shalt return.

The Grand Vizier Parmarstoon, on receiving the injunction to bring his daughter Hansardadade into the royal presence, lost no time in repairing to his palace which was but across the Sultan's gardens, and going straight to the women's apartments, found Hansardadade surrounded by a number of old women who were all consulting her at once. In truth, this affable Princess was perpetually being referred to, by all manner of old women. Hastily causing her attendants, when she heard her father's errand, to attire her in her finest dress which outsparkled the sun; and bidding her young sister, Brothartoon (or Chamber Candlestick), to make similar preparations and accompany her; the daughter of the Grand Vizier soon covered herself with a rich veil, and said to her father, with a low obeisance, Sir, I am ready to attend you, to my Lord, the Commander of the Faithful.

The Grand Vizier, and his daughter Hansardadade, and her young sister Brothartoon, preceded by Mistaspeeka, a black mute, the Chief of the officers of the royal Seraglio, went across the Sultan's gardens by the way the Vizier had come, and arriving at the Sultan's palace, found that monarch on his throne surrounded by his principal counsellors and officers of state. They all four prostrated themselves at a distance, and waited the Sultan's pleasure. That gracious prince was troubled in his mind when he commanded the fair Hansardadade (who, on the whole, was very fair indeed), to approach, for he had sworn an oath in the Vizier's absence from which he could not depart. Nevertheless, as it must be kept, he proceeded to announce it before the assembly. Vizier, said he, thou hast brought thy daughter here, as possessing a large stock of Howsa Kummauns experience, in the hope of her relating something that may soften me under my accumulated wrongs. Know that I have solemnly sworn that if her stories fail—as I believe they will—to mitigate my wrath, I will have her burned and her ashes cast to the winds! Also, I will strangle thee and the present Howsa Kummauns, and will take a new one every day and strangle

33

her as soon as taken, until I find a good and true one. Parmarstoon replied, To hear is to obey.

Hansardadade then took a one-stringed lute, and sang a lengthened song in prose. Its purport was, I am the recorder of brilliant eloquence, I am the chronicler of patriotism, I am the pride of sages, and the joy of nations. The continued salvation of the country is owing to what I preserve, and without it there would be no business done. Sweet are the voices of the crow and chough, and Persia never never never can have words enough. At the conclusion of this delightful strain, the Sultan and the whole divan were so faint with rapture that they remained in a comatose state for seven hours.

Would your Majesty, said Hansardadade, when all were at length recovered, prefer first to hear the story of the Wonderful Camp, or the story of the Talkative Barber, or the story of Scarli Tapa and the Forty Thieves? I would have thee commence, replied the Sultan, with the story of the Forty Thieves.

Hansardadade began, Sire, there was once a poor relation — when Brothartoon interposed. Dear sister, cried Brothartoon, it is now past midnight, it will be shortly daybreak, and if you are not asleep, you ought to be. I pray you, dear sister, by all means to hold your tongue to-night, and if my Lord the Sultan will suffer you to live another day, you can talk to-morrow. The Sultan arose with a clouded face, but went out without giving any orders for the execution.

II

[APRIL 28, 1855]

THE STORY OF SCARLI TAPA AND THE FORTY THIEVES

ACCOMPANIED by the Grand Vizier Parmarstoon, and the black mute Mistaspeeka the chief of the Seraglio, Hansardadade again repaired next day to the august presence, and, after making the usual prostrations before the Sultan, began thus:

Sire, there was once a poor relation who lived in a town in the dominions of the Sultan of the Indies, and whose name was Scarli Tapa. He was the youngest son of a Dowajah—which, as your Majesty knows, is a female spirit of voracious appetites, and generally with a wig and a carmine complexion, who prowls about old houses

THE THOUSAND AND ONE HUMBUGS

and preys upon mankind. This Dowajah had attained an immense age, in consequence of having been put by an evil Genie on the PENSHUNLIST, or talisman to secure long life; but, at length she very reluctantly died towards the close of a quarter, after making the most affecting struggles to live into the half-year.

Scarli Tapa had a rich elder brother named Cashim, who had married the daughter of a prosperous merchant, and lived magnificently. Scarli Tapa, on the other hand, could barely support his wife and family by lounging about the town and going out to dinner with his utmost powers of perseverance, betting on horse-races, playing at billiards, and running into debt with everybody who would trust him—the last being his principal means of obtaining an honest livelihood.

One day, when Scarli Tapa had strolled for some time along the banks of a great river of liquid filth which ornamented that agreeable country and rendered it salubrious, he found himself in the neighbourhood of the Woods and Forests. Lifting up his eyes, he observed in the distance a great cloud of dust. He was not surprised to see it, knowing those parts to be famous for casting prodigious quantities of dust into the eyes of the Faithful; but, as it rapidly advanced towards him, he climbed into a tree, the better to observe it without being seen himself.

As the cloud of dust approached, Scarli Tapa perceived it from his hiding-place to be occasioned by forty mounted robbers, each bestriding a severely-goaded and heavily-laden Bull. The whole troop came to a halt at the foot of the tree, and all the robbers dismounted. Every robber then tethered his hack to the most convenient shrub, gave it a full meal of very bad chaff, and hung over his arm the empty sack which had contained the same. Then the Captain of the Robbers, advancing to a door in an antediluvian rock, which Scarli Tapa had not observed before, and on which were the enchanted letters O. F. F. I. C. E., said, Debrett's Peerage. Open Sesame! As soon as the Captain of the Robbers had uttered these words, the door, obedient to the charm, flew open, and all the robbers went in. The captain went in last, and the door shut of itself.

The robbers stayed so long within the rock that Scarli Tapa more than once felt tempted to descend the tree and make off. Fearful, however, that they might reappear and catch him before he

35

could escape, he remained hidden by the leaves, as patiently as he could. At last the door opened, and the forty robbers came out. As the captain had gone in last, he came out first, and stood to see the whole troop pass him. When they had all done so, he said, Debrett's Peerage. Shut Sesame! The door immediately closed again as before! Every robber then mounted his Bull, adjusting before him his sack well filled with gold, silver, and jewels. When the captain saw that they were all ready, he put himself at their head, and they rode off by the way they had come.

Scarli Tapa remained in the tree until the receding cloud of dust occasioned by the troop of robbers with their captain at their head, was no longer visible, and then came softly down and approached the door. Making use of the words that he had heard pronounced by the Captain of the Robbers, he said, after first piously strengthening himself with the remembrance of his deceased mother the Dowajah, Debrett's Peerage. Open Sesame! The door instantly flew wide open.

Scarli Tapa, who had expected to see a dull place, was surprised to find himself in an exceedingly agreeable vista of rooms, where everything was as light as possible, and where vast quantities of the finest wheaten loaves, and the richest gold and silver fishes, and all kinds of valuable possessions, were to be got for the laying hold of. Quickly loading himself with as much spoil as he could move under, he opened and closed the door as the Captain of the Robbers had done, and hurried away with his treasure to his poor home.

When the wife of Scarli Tapa saw her husband enter their dwelling after it was dark, and proceed to pile upon the floor a heap of wealth, she cried, Alas! husband, whom have you taken in, now? Be not alarmed, wife, returned Scarli Tapa, no one suffers but the public. And then told her how he, a poor relation, had made his way into Office by the magic words and had enriched himself.

There being more money and more loaves and fishes than they knew what to do with at the moment, the wife of Scarli Tapa, transported with joy, ran off to her sister-in-law, the wife of Cashim Tapa, who lived hard by, to borrow a Measure by means of which their property could be got into some order. The wife of Cashim Tapa looking into the measure when it was brought back, found at the bottom of it, several of the crumbs of fine loaves and of the scales of gold and silver fishes; upon which, flying into an envious rage, she thus addressed her husband : Wretched Cashim, you know you are of high birth as the eldest son of a Dowajah, and you think you are rich, but your despised younger brother, Scarli Tapa, is infinitely richer and more powerful than you. Judge of his wealth from these tokens. At the same time she showed him the measure.

Cashim, who since his marriage to the merchant's widow, had treated his brother coolly and held him at a distance, was at once fired with a burning desire to know how he had become rich. He was unable to sleep all night, and at the first streak of day, before the summons to morning prayers was heard from the minarets of the mosques, arose and went to his brother's house. Dear Scarli Tapa, said he, pretending to be very fraternal, what loaves and fishes are these that thou hast in thy possession? Scarli Tapa perceiving from this discourse that he could no longer keep his secret, communicated his discovery to his brother, who lost no time in providing all things necessary for the stowage of riches, and in repairing alone to the mysterious door near the Woods and Forests.

When night came, and Cashim Tapa did not return, his relatives became uneasy. His absence being prolonged for several days and nights, Scarli Tapa at length proceeded to the enchanted door in search of him. Opening it by the infallible means, what were his emotions to find that the robbers had encountered his brother within, and had quartered him upon the spot for ever!

Commander of the Faithful, when Scarli Tapa beheld the dismal spectacle of his brother everlastingly quartered upon Office for having merely uttered the magic words, Debrett's Peerage. Open Sesame! he was greatly troubled in his mind. Feeling the necessity of hushing the matter up, and putting the best face upon it for the family credit, he at once devised a plan to attain that object.

There was, in the House where his brother had sat himself down on his marriage with the merchant's daughter, a discreet slave whose name was Jobbiana. Though a kind of under secretary in the treasury department, she was very useful in the dirty work of the establishment, and had also some knowledge of the stables, and could assist the whippers-in at a pinch. Scarli Tapa, going home and taking the discreet slave aside, related to her how her master was quartered, and how it was now their business to disguise the fact, and deceive the neighbours. Jobbiana replied, To hear is to obey.

Accordingly, before day—for she always avoided daylight—the

discreet slave went to a certain cobbler whom she knew, and found him sitting in his stall in the public street. Good morrow, friend, said she, putting a bribe into his hand, will you bring the tools of your trade and come to a House with me? Willingly, but what to do? replied the cobbler, who was a merry fellow. Nothing against my patriotism and conscience, I hope? (at which he laughed heartily). Not in the least, returned Jobbiana, giving him another bribe. But, you must go into the House blindfold and with your hands tied; you don't mind that for a job? I don't mind anything for a job, returned the cobbler with vivacity; I like a job. It is my business to job; only make it worth my while, and I am ready for any job you may please to name. At the same time he arose briskly. Jobbiana then imparted to him the quartering that had taken place, and that he was wanted to cobble the subject up and hide what had been done. Is that all? If it is no more than that, returned the cobbler, blind my eyes and tie my hands, and let us cobble away as long as you like!

Sire, the discreet slave blindfolded the cobbler, and tied his hands, and took him to the House; where he cobbled the subject up with so much skill, that she rewarded him munificently. We must now return to the Captain of the Robbers, whose name was Yawyawah, and whose soul was filled with perplexities and anxieties, when he visited the cave and found, from the state of the wheaten loaves and the gold and silver fishes, that there was yet another person who possessed the secret of the magic door.

Your majesty must know that Yawyawah, Captain of the Robbers (most of whose forefathers had been rebellious Genii, who never had had anything whatever to do with Solomon), sauntering through the city, in a highly disconsolate and languid state, chanced to come before daylight upon the cobbler working in his stall. Good morrow, honourable friend, said he, you job early. My Lord, returned the cobbler, I job early and late. You do well, observed the Captain of the Robbers; but, have you light enough? The less light the better, said the cobbler, for *my* work. Ay! returned Yawyawah; why so? Why so! repeated the cobbler, winking, because I can cobble certain businesses, best, in the dark. When the Captain of the Robbers heard him say this, he quickly understood the hint. He blindfolded him, and tied his hands, as the discreet slave had done, turned his coat, and led him away until he stopped at the House. This is the House that was concerned in the quartering and cobbling, said he. The captain set a mark upon it. But, Jobbiana coming by soon afterwards, and seeing what had been done, set exactly the same mark upon twenty other Houses in the same row. So that in truth they were all precisely alike, and one was marked by Jobbiana exactly as another was, and there was not a pin to choose between them.

Thus discomfited, the Captain of the Robbers called his troop together and addressed them. My noble, right honourable, honourable and gallant, honourable and learned, and simply honourable, friends, said he, it is apparent that we, the old band who for so many years have possessed the command of the magic door, are in danger of being superseded. In a word, it is clear that there are now two bands of robbers, and that we must overcome the opposition, or be ourselves vanquished. All the robbers applauded this sentiment. Therefore, said the captain, I will disguise myself as a trader—in the patriotic line of business—and will endeavour to prevail by stratagem. The robbers as with one voice approved of this design.

The Captain of the Robbers accordingly disguised himself as a trader of that sort which is called at the bazaars a patriot, and, having again had recourse to the cobbler, and having carefully observed the House, arranged his plans without delay. Feigning to be a dealer in soft-soap, he concealed his men in nine-and-thirty jars of that commodity, a man in every jar; and, loading a number of mules with this pretended merchandise, appeared at the head of his caravan one evening at the House, where Scarli Tapa was sitting on a bench in his usual place, taking it (as he generally did in the House) very coolly. My Lord, said the pretended trader, I am a stranger here, and know not where to bestow my merchandise for the night. Suffer me then, I beseech you, to warehouse it here. Scarli Tapa rose up, showed the pretended merchant where to put his goods, and instructed Jobbiana to prepare an entertainment for his guest. Also a bath for himself; his hands being very far from clean.

The discreet slave, in obedience to her orders, proceeded to prepare the entertainment and the bath; but was vexed to discover, when it was late and the shops of the dealers were all shut, that there was no soft-soap in the House—which was the more unexpected, as there was generally more than enough. Remembering, however, that the pretended trader had brought a large stock with him, she went to one of the jars to get a little. As she drew near to it, the impatient robber within, supposing it to be his leader, said in a low voice,—Is it time for our party to come in? Jobbiana, instantly comprehending the danger, replied, Not yet, but presently. She went in this manner to all the jars, receiving the same question, and giving the same answer.

The discreet slave returned into the kitchen, with her presence of mind not at all disturbed, and there prepared a lukewarm mess of soothing syrup, worn-out wigs, weak milk and water, poppy-heads, empty nut-shells, froth, and other similar ingredients. When it was sufficiently mawkish, she returned to the jars, bearing a large kettle filled with this mixture, poured some of it upon every robber, and threw the whole troop into a state of insensibility or submission. She then returned to the House, served up the entertainment, cleared away the fragments, and attired herself in a rich dress to dance before her master and his disguised visitor.

In the course of her dances, which were performed in the slowest time, and during which she blew both her own and the family trumpet with extraordinary pertinacity, Jobbiana took care always to approach nearer and still nearer to the Captain of the Robbers. At length she seized him by the sleeve of his disguise, disclosed him in his own dress to her master, and related where his men were, and how they had asked Was it time to come in? Scarli Tapa, so far from being angry with the pretended trader, fell upon his neck and addressed him in these friendly expressions : Since our object is the same and no great difference exists between us, O my brother, let us form a Coalition. Debrett's Peerage will open Sesame to the Scarli Tapas and the Yawyawahs equally, and will shut out the rest of mankind. Let it be so. There is plunder enough in the cave. So that it is never restored to the original owners and never gets into other hands but ours, why should we quarrel overmuch! The Captain made a suitable reply and embraced his entertainer. Jobbiana, shedding tears of joy, embraced them both.

Shortly afterwards, Scarli Tapa in gratitude to the wise Jobbiana, caused her to be invested with the freedom of the City—where she had been very much beloved for many years—and gave her in marriage to his own son. They had a large family and a powerful number of relations, who all inherited, by right of relationship, the power of opening Sesame and shutting it tight. The Yawyawahs became a very numerous tribe also, and exercised the same privilege. This, Commander of the Faithful, is the reason why, in that distant part of the dominions of the Sultan of the Indies, all true believers kiss the ground seven hundred and seventy-seven times on hearing the magic words, Debrett's Peerage—why the talisman of Office is always possessed in common by the three great races of the Scarli Tapas, the Yawyawahs, and the Jobbianas—why the public affairs, great and small, and all the national enterprises both by land and sea are conducted on a system which is the highest peak of the mountain of justice, and which always succeeds—why the people of that country are serenely satisfied with themselves and things in general, are unquestionably the envy of surrounding nations, and cannot fail in the inevitable order of events to flourish to the end of the world—why all these great truths are incontrovertible, and why all who dispute them receive the bastinado as atheists and rebels.

Here, Hansardadade concluded the story of the Forty Thieves, and said, If my Lord the Sultan will deign to hear another narrative from the lips of the lowest of his servants, I have adventures yet more surprising than these to relate : adventures that are worthy to be written in letters of gold. By Allah ! exclaimed the Sultan, whose hand had been upon his scimetar several times during the previous recital, and whose eyes had menaced Parmarstoon until the soul of that Vizier had turned to water, what thou hast told but now, deserves to be recorded in letters of Brass !

Hansardadade was proceeding, Sire, in the great plain at the feet of the mountains of Casgar, which is seven weeks' journey across— when Brothartoon interrupted her: Sister, it is nearly daybreak, and if you are not asleep you ought to be. I pray you, dear sister, tell us at present no more of those stories that you know so well, but hold your tongue and go to bed. Hansardadade was silent, and the Sultan arose in a very indifferent humour and gloomily walked out —in great doubt whether he would let her live, on any consideration, over another day.

MISCELLANEOUS PAPERS

III

[MAY 5, 1855]

On the following night, Hansardadade proceeded with:

THE STORY OF THE TALKATIVE BARBER

In the great plain which lies at the feet of the mountains of Casgar, and which is seven weeks' journey across, there is a city where a lame young man was once invited, with other guests, to an entertainment. Upon his entrance, the company already assembled rose up to do him honour, and the host taking him by the hand invited him to sit down with the rest upon the estrade. At the same time the master of the house greeted his visitor with the salutation, Allah is Allah, there is no Allah but Allah, may his name be praised, and may Allah be with you!

Sire, the lame young man, who had the appearance of one that had suffered much, was about to comply with the invitation of the master of the house to seat himself upon the estrade with the rest of the company, when he suddenly perceived among them, a Barber. He instantly flew back with every token of abhorrence, and made towards the door. The master of the house, amazed at this behaviour, stopped him. Sir, exclaimed the young man, I adjure you by Mecca, do not stop me, let me go. I cannot without horror look upon that abominable Barber. Upon him and upon the whole of his relations be the curse of Allah, in return for all I have endured from his intolerable levity, and from his talk never being to the point or purpose! With these words, the lame young man again made violently towards the door. The guests were astonished at this behaviour, and began to have a very bad opinion of the Barber.

The master of the house so courteously entreated the lame young man to recount to the company the causes of this strong dislike, that at length he could not refuse. Averting his head so that he might not see the Barber, he proceeded. Gentlemen, you must know that this accursed Barber is the cause of my being crippled, and is the occasion of all my misfortunes. I became acquainted with him in the following manner.

42

THE THOUSAND AND ONE HUMBUGS

I am called Publeek, or The Many Headed. I am one of a large family, who have undergone an infinite variety of adventures and afflictions. One day, I chanced to sit down to rest on a seat in a narrow lane, when a lattice over against me opened, and I obtained a glimpse of the most ravishing Beauty in the world. After watering a pot of budding flowers which stood in the window, she perceived me and modestly withdrew; but, not before she had directed towards me a glance so full of charms, that I screamed aloud with love and became insensible for a considerable time.

When I came to myself, I directed a favourite slave to make enquiries among the neighbours, and, on pain of death, to bring me an exact account of the young lady's family and condition. The slave acquitted himself so well, that he informed me within an hour that the young lady's name was Fair Guvawnment, and that she was the daughter of the chief Cadi. The violence of my passion became so great that I took to my bed that evening, fell into a fever, and was reduced to the brink of death, when an old lady of my acquaintance came to see me. Son, said she, after observing me attentively, I perceive that your disease is love. Inform me who is the object of your affections, and rely upon me to bring you together. This address of the good old lady's had such an effect upon me, that I immediately arose quite restored in health, and began to dress myself.

In a word (continued the lame young man, addressing the company assembled in the house of the citizen of the plain at the feet of the mountains of Casgar, and always keeping his head in such a position as that he could not see the Barber), the old lady exerted herself in my behalf with such effect, that on the very next day she returned, commissioned by the enchantress of my soul to appoint a meeting between us. I arranged to attire myself in my richest clothes, and dispatched the same favourite slave with instructions to fetch a Barber, who knew his business, and who could skilfully prepare me for the interview I was to have, for the first time in all my life, with Fair Guvawnment. Gentlemen, the slave returned with the wretch whom you see here.

Sir, began this accursed Barber whom a malignant destiny thus inflicted on me, how do you do, I hope you are pretty well. I do not wish to praise myself, but you are lucky to have sent for me. My name is Praymiah. In me you behold an accomplished diplomatist, a first-rate statesman, a frisky speaker, an easy shaver, a touch-and-go joker, a giver of the go-by to all complainers, and above all a member of the aristocracy of Barbers. Sir, I am a lineal descendant of the Prophet, and consequently a born Barber. All my relations, friends, acquaintances, connexions, and associates, are likewise lineal descendants of the Prophet, and consequently born Barbers every one. As I said, but the other day, to Layardeen, or the Troublesome, the aristocracy—May Allah confound thy aristocracy and thee! cried I, will you begin to shave me?

Gentlemen (proceeded the lame young man), the Barber had brought a showy case with him, and he consumed such an immense time in pretending to open it, that I was well nigh fretted to death. I will not be shaved at all, said I. Sir, returned the unabashed Barber, you sent for me to shave you, and with your pardon I will do it, whether you like it or not. Ah, Sir! you have not so good an opinion of me as your father had. I knew your father, and he appreciated me. I said a thousand pleasant things to him, and rendered him a thousand services, and he adored me. Just Heaven, he would exclaim, you are an inexhaustible fountain of wisdom, no man can plumb the depth of your profundity! My dear Sir, I would reply, you do me more honour than I deserve. Still, as a lineal descendant of the Prophet, and one of the aristocracy of born Barbers, I will, with the help of Allah, shave you pretty close before I have done with you.

You may guess, gentlemen, in my state of expectancy, with my heart set on Fair Guvawnment, and the precious time running by, how I cursed this impertinent chattering on the part of the Barber. Barber of mischief, Barber of sin, Barber of false pretence, Barber of froth and bubble, said I, stamping my foot upon the ground, will you begin to do your work? Fair and softly, Sir, said he, let me count you out first. With that, he counted from one up to thirty-eight with great deliberation, and then laughed heartily and went out to look at the weather.

When the Barber returned, he went on prattling as before. You are in high feather, Sir, said he. I am glad to see you look so well. But, how can you be otherwise than flourishing, after having sent for *me*! I am called the Careless. I am not like Dizzee, who draws blood; nor like Darbee, who claps on blisters; nor like Johnnee, who works with the square and rule; I am the easy shaver, and I care for nobody, I can do anything. Shall I dance the dance of Mistapit to please you, or shall I sing the song of Mistafoks, or joke the joke of Jomillah? Honour me with your attention while I do all three.

The Barber (continued the lame young man, with a groan), danced the dance of Mistapit, and sang the song of Mistafoks, and joked the joke of Jomillah, and then began with fresh impertinences. Sir, said he, with a lofty flourish, when Britteen first at Heaven's command, arose from out the azure main, this was the charter of the land, and guardian angels sang this strain: Singing, as First Lord was a wallerking the Office-garding around, no end of born Barbers he picked up and found, Says he I will load them with silvier and gold, for the country's a donkey, and as such is sold.— At this point I could bear his insolence no longer, but starting up, cried, Barber of hollowness, by what consideration am I restrained from falling upon and strangling thee? Calmly, Sir, said he, let me count you out first. He then played his former game of counting from one to under forty, and again laughed heartily, and went out to take the height of the sun, and make a calculation of the state of the wind, that he might know whether it was an auspicious time to begin to shave me.

I took the opportunity (said the young man) of flying from my house so darkened by the fatal presence of this detestable Barber, and of repairing with my utmost speed to the house of the Cadi. But, the appointed hour was long past, and Fair Guvawnment had withdrawn no one knew whither. As I stood in the street cursing my evil destiny and execrating this intolerable Barber, I heard a hue and cry. Looking in the direction whence it came, I saw the diabolical Barber, attended by an immense troop of his relations and friends, the lineal descendants of the Prophet and aristocracy of born Barbers, all offering a reward to any one who would stop me, and all proclaiming the unhappy Publeek to be their natural prey and rightful property. I turned and fled. They jostled and bruised me cruelly among them, and I became maimed, as you see. I utterly detest, abominate, and abjure this Barber, and ever since and ever-more I totally renounce him. With these concluding words, the lame young man arose in a sullen way that had something very threatening in it, and left the company.

Commander of the Faithful, when the lame young man was gone, the guests, turning to the Barber, who wore his turban very much on one side and smiled complacently, asked him what he had to say for himself? The Barber immediately danced the dance of Mistapit, and sang the song of Mistafoks, and joked the joke of Jomillah. Gentlemen, said he, not at all out of breath after these performances, it is true that I am called the Careless; permit me to recount to you, as a lively diversion, what happened to a twin-brother of that young man who has so undeservedly abused me, in connexion with a near relation of mine. No one objecting, the Barber related :

THE STORY OF THE BARMECIDE FEAST

The young man's twin-brother, Guld Publeek, was in very poor circumstances and hardly knew how to live. In his reduced condition he was fain to go about to great men, begging them to take him in—and to do them justice, they did it extensively.

One day in the course of his poverty-stricken wanderings, he came to a large house with two high towers, a spacious hall, and abundance of fine gilding, statuary, and painting. Although the house was far from finished, he could see enough to assure him that enormous sums of money must be lavished upon it. He inquired who was the master of this wealthy mansion, and received for information that he was a certain Barmecide. (The Barmecide, gentlemen, is my near relation, and, like myself, a lineal descendant of the Prophet, and a born Barber.)

The young man's twin brother passed through the gateway, and crept submissively onward, until he came into a spacious apartment, where he descried the Barmecide sitting at the upper end in the post of honour. The Barmecide asked the young man's brother what he wanted? My Lord, replied he, in a pitiful tone, I am sore distressed, and have none but high and mighty nobles like yourself, to help me. That much at least is true, returned the Barmecide, there is no help save in high and mighty nobles, it is the appointment of Allah. But, what is your distress? My Lord, said the young man's brother, I am fasting from all the nourishment I want, and—whatever you may please to think—am in a dangerous extremity. A very little more at any moment, and you would be astonished at the figure I should make. Is it so, indeed? inquired the Barmecide. Sir, returned the young man's brother, I swear by Heaven and Earth that it is so, and Heaven and Earth are every

46

hour drawing nearer to the discovery that it is so. Alas, poor man! replied the Barmecide, pretending to have an interest in him. Ho, boy! Bring us of the best here, and let us not spare our liberal measures. This poor man shall make good cheer without delay.

Though no boy appeared, gentlemen, and though there was no sign of the liberal measures of which the Barmecide spoke so ostentatiously, the young man's brother, Guld Publeek, endeavoured to fall in with the Barmecide's humour. Come! cried the Barmecide, feigning to pour water on his hands, let us begin fair and fresh. How do you like this purity? Ah, my Lord, returned Guld Publeek, imitating the Barmecide's action, this is indeed purity: this is in truth a delicious beginning. Then let us proceed, said the Barmecide, seeming to dry his hands, with this smoking dish of Reefawm. How do you like it? Fat? At the same time he pretended to hand choice morsels to the young man's brother. Take your fill of it, exclaimed the Barmecide, there is plenty here, do not spare it, it was cooked for you. May Allah prolong your life, my Lord, said Guld Publeek, you are liberal indeed!

The Barmecide having boasted in this pleasant way of his smoking dish of Reefawm, which had no existence, affected to call for another dish. Ho! cried he, clapping his hands, bring in those Educational Kabobs. Then, he imitated the action of putting some upon the plate of the young man's brother, and went on. How do you like these Educational Kabobs? The cook who made them is a treasure. Are they not justly seasoned? Are they not so honestly made, as to be adapted to all digestions? You want them very much, I know, and have wanted them this long time. Do you enjoy them? And here is a delicious mess, called Foreen Leejun. Eat of it also, for I pride myself upon it, and expect it to bring me great respect and much friendship from distant lands. And this pillau of Church-endowments-and-duties, which you see so beautifully divided, pray how do you approve of this pillau? It was invented on your account, and no expense has been spared to render it to your taste. Ho, boy, bring in that ragout! Now here, my friend, is a ragout, called Law-of-Partnership. It is expressly made for poor men's eating, and I particularly pride myself upon it. This is indeed a dish at which you may cut and come again. And boy! hasten to set before my good friend, Guld Publeek, the rare stew of colonial spices, minced crime, hashed poverty, swollen liver of ignorance, stale confusion, rotten tape, and chopped-up bombast, steeped in official sauce, and garnished with a great deal of tongue and a very little brains—the crowning dish, of which my dear friend never can have enough, and upon which he thrives so well! But, you don't eat with an appetite, my brother, said the Barmecide. I fear the repast is hardly to your liking? Pardon me, my benefactor, returned the guest, whose jaws ached with pretending to eat, I am full almost to the throat.

Well then, said the Barmecide, since you have dined so well, try the dessert. Here are apples of discord from the Horse Guards and Admiralty, here is abundance of the famous fruit from the Dead Sea that turns to ashes on the lips, here are dates from the Peninsula in great profusion, and here is a fig for the nation. Eat and be happy! My Lord, replied the object of his merriment, I am quite worn out by your liberality, and can bear no more.

Gentlemen (continued the loquacious Barber), when the humorous Barmecide, my near relation lineally descended from the Prophet, had brought his guest to this pass, he clapped his hands three times to summon around him his slaves, and instructed them to force in reality the vile stew of which he had spoken down the throat of the hungry Guld Publeek, together with a nauseous mess called DUBLIN-CUMTAX, and to put bitters in his drink, strew dust on his head, blacken his face, shave his eyebrows, pluck away his beard, insult him and make merry with him. He then caused him to be attired in a shameful dress and set upon an ass with his face to the tail, and in this state to be publicly exposed with the inscription round his neck, This is the punishment of Guld Publeek who asked for nourishment and said he wanted it. Such is the present droll condition of this person; while my near relation, the Barmecide, sits in the post of honour with his turban very much on one side, enjoying the joke. Which I think you will all admit is an excellent one.

Hansardadade having made an end of the discourse of the loquacious Barber, would have instantly begun another story, had not Brothartoon shut her up with, Dear Sister, it will be shortly daybreak. Get to bed and be quiet.

THE TOADY TREE

[May 26, 1855]

It is not a new remark, that any real and true change for the public benefit, must derive its vitality from the practice of consistent people. Whatever may be accepted as the meaning of the adage, Charity begins at home—which for the most part has very little meaning that I could ever discover—it is pretty clear that Reform begins at home. If I had the lungs of Hercules and the eloquence of Cicero, and devoted them at any number of monster-meetings to a cause which I deserted in my daily life whensoever the opportunity of desertion was presented to me (say on an average fifty times a day), I had far better keep my lungs and my eloquence to myself, and at all times and seasons leave that cause alone.

The humble opinion of the present age, is, that no privileged class should have an inheritance in the administration of the public affairs, and that a system which fails to enlist in the service of the country, the greatest fitness and merit that the country produces, must have in it something inherently wrong. It might be supposed, the year One having been for some time in the calendar of the past, that this is on the whole a moderate and reasonable opinion—not very far in advance of the period, or of any period, and involving no particularly unchristian revenge for a great national breakdown. Yet, to the governing class in the main, the sentiment is altogether so novel and extraordinary, that we may observe it to be received as an incomprehensible and incredible thing. I have been seriously asking myself, whose fault is this? I have come to the conclusion that it is the fault of the over-cultivation of the great Toady Tree; the tree of many branches, which grows to an immense height in England, and which overshadows all the land.

My name is Cobbs. Why do I, Cobbs, love to sit like a Patri-arch, in the shade of my Toady Tree! What have I to do with it? What comfort do I derive from it, what fruit of self-respect does it yield to me, what beauty is there in it? To lure me to a Public Dinner, why must I have a Lord in the chair? To gain me to a Subscription-list, why do I need fifty Barons, Marquises, Viscounts, Dukes, and Baronets, at the head of it, in larger type and longer lines than the commonalty? If I don't want to be perpetually decorated with these boughs from the Toady Tree—if it be my friend Dobbs, and not I, Cobbs, in whose ready button-hole such appliances are always stuck—why don't I myself quietly and good-humouredly renounce them? Why not! Because I *will* be always gardening, more or less, at the foot of the Toady Tree.

Take Dobbs. Dobbs is a well-read man, an earnest man, a man of strong and sincere convictions, a man who would be deeply wounded if I told him he was not a true Administrative Reformer in the best sense of the word. When Dobbs talks to me about the House of Commons, (and lets off upon me those little revolvers of special official intelligence which he always carries, ready loaded and capped), why does he adopt the Lobby slang: with which he has as much to do as with any dialect in the heart of Africa? Why must he speak of Mr. Fizmaili as 'Fizzy,' and of Lord Gambaroon as 'Gam'? How comes it that he is acquainted with the intentions of the Cabinet six weeks beforehand—often, indeed, so long before-hand that I shall infallibly die before there is the least sign of their having ever existed? Dobbs is perfectly clear in his generation that men are to be deferred to for their capacity for what they undertake, for their talents and worth, and for nothing else. Aye, aye, I know he is. But, I have seen Dobbs dive and double about that Royal Academy Exhibition, in pursuit of a nobleman, in a marvellously small way. I have stood with Dobbs examining a picture, when the Marquis has entered, and I have known of the Marquis's entrance without lifting my eyes or turning my head, solely by the increased gentility in the audible tones of Dobbs's critical observations. And then, the Marquis approaching, Dobbs has talked to me as his lay figure, at and for the Marquis, until the Marquis has said, 'Ha, Dobbs?' and Dobbs, with his face folded into creases of deference, has piloted that illustrious nobleman away, to the contemplation of some pictorial subtleties of his own discovery. Now, Dobbs has been troubled and abashed in all this; Dobbs's voice, face, and manner, with a stubbornness far beyond his control, have revealed his uneasiness; Dobbs, leading the noble Marquis away, has shown me in the expression of his very shoulders that he knew I laughed at him, and that he knew he deserved it; and yet Dobbs could not for his life resist the shadow of the Toady Tree, and come out into the natural air!

THE TOADY TREE

The other day, walking down Piccadilly from Hyde Park Corner, I overtook Hobbs. Hobbs had two relations starved to death with needless hunger and cold before Sebastopol, and one killed by mistake in the hospital at Scutari. Hobbs himself had the misfortune, about fifteen years ago, to invent a very ingenious piece of mechanism highly important to dockyards, which has detained him unavailingly in the waiting-rooms of public offices ever since, and which was invented last month by somebody else in France, and immediately adopted there. Hobbs had been one of the public at Mr. Roebuck's committee, the very day I overtook him, and was burning with indignation at what he had heard. 'This Gordian knot of red tape,' said Hobbs, 'must be cut. All things considered, there never was a people so abused as the English at this time, and there never was a country brought to such a pass. It will not bear thinking of— (Lord Joddle).' The parenthesis referred to a passing carriage, which Hobbs turned and looked after with the greatest interest. 'The system,' he continued, 'must be totally changed. We must have the right man in the right place (Duke of Twaddleton on horseback), and only capability and not family connexions placed in office (brother-in-law of the Bishop of Gorhambury). We must not put our trust in mere idols (how do you do!—Lady Coldveal— little too highly painted, but fine woman for her years), and we must get rid as a nation of our ruinous gentility and deference to mere rank. (Thank you, Lord Edward, I am quite well. Very glad indeed to have the honour and pleasure of seeing you. I hope Lady Edward is well. Delighted, I am sure.)' Pending the last parenthesis, he stopped to shake hands with a dim old gentleman in a flaxen wig, whose eye he had been exceedingly solicitous to catch, and, when we went on again, seemed so refreshed and braced by the interview that I believe him to have been for the time actually taller. This in Hobbs, whom I knew to be miserably poor, whom I saw with my eyes to be prematurely grey, the best part of whose life had been changed into a wretched dream from which he could never awake now, who was in mourning without and in mourning within, and all through causes that any half-dozen shopkeepers taken at random from the London Directory and shot into Downing Street out of sacks could have turned aside—this, I say, in Hobbs, of all men, gave me so much to think about, that I took little or no heed of his further conversation until I found we

51

had come to Burlington House. 'A little sketch,' he was saying then, 'by a little child, and two hundred and fifty pounds already bid for it! Well, it's very gratifying, isn't it? Really, it's very gratifying! Won't you come in? Do come in!' I excused myself, and Hobbs went in without me: a drop in a swollen current of the general public. I looked into the courtyard as I went by, and thought I perceived a remarkably fine specimen of the Toady Tree in full growth there.

There is my friend Nobbs. A man of sufficient merit, one would suppose, to be calmly self-reliant, and to preserve that manly equilibrium which as little needs to assert itself overmuch, as to derive a sickly reflected light from any one else. I declare in the face of day, that I believe Nobbs to be morally and physically unable to sit at a table and hear a man of title mentioned, whom he knows, without putting in his claim to the acquaintance. I have observed Nobbs under these circumstances, a thousand times, and have never found him able to hold his peace. I have seen him fidget, and worry himself, and try to get himself away from the Toady Tree, and say to himself as plainly as he could have said aloud, 'Nobbs, Nobbs, is not this base in you, and what can it possibly matter to these people present, whether you know this man, or not?' Yet, there has been a compulsion upon him to say, 'Lord Dash Blank?' 'Oh, yes! I know him very well; very well, indeed. I have known Dash Blank—let me see—really I am afraid to say how long I have known Dash Blank. It must be a dozen years. A very good fellow, Dash Blank!' And, like my friend Hobbs, he has been positively taller for some moments afterwards. I assert of Nobbs, as I have already in effect asserted of Dobbs, that if I could be brought blindfold into a room full of company, of whom he made one, I could tell in a moment, by his manner of speaking, not to say by his mere breathing, whether there were a title present. The ancient Egyptians in their palmiest days, had not an enchanter among them who could have wrought such a magical change in Nobbs, as the incarnation of one line from the book of the Peerage can effect in one minute.

Pobbs is as bad, though in a different way. Pobbs affects to despise these distinctions. He speaks of his titled acquaintances, in a light and easy vein, as 'the swells.' According as his humour varies, he will tell you that the swells are, after all, the best people a man can have to do with, or that he is weary of the swells and has had enough of them. But, note, that to the best of my knowledge, information, and belief, Pobbs would die of chagrin, if the swells left off asking him to dinner. That he would rather exchange nods in the Park with a semi-idiotic Dowager, than fraternise with another Shakespeare. That he would rather have his sister, Miss Pobbs (he is greatly attached to her, and is a most excellent brother), received on sufferance by the swells, than hold her far happier place in the outer darkness of the untitled, and be loved and married by some good fellow, who could daff the world of swells aside, and bid it pass. Yet, O, Pobbs, Pobbs! if for once—only for once—you could hear the magnificent patronage of some of those Duchesses of yours, casually making mention of Miss Pobbs, as 'a rather pretty person!'

I say nothing of Robbs, Sobbs, Tobbs, and so on to Zobbs, whose servility has no thin coating of disguise or shame upon it, who grovel on their waistcoats with a sacred joy, and who turn and roll titles in their mouths as if they were exquisite sweetmeats. I say nothing of Mayors and such like ;—to lay on adulation with a whitewashing brush and have it laid on in return, is the function of such people, and verily they have their reward. I say nothing of County families, and provincial neighbourhoods, and lists of Stewards and Lady Patronesses, and electioneering, and racing, and flower-showing, and demarcations and counter-demarcations in visiting, and all the forms in which the Toady Tree is cultivated in and about cathedral towns and rural districts. What I wish to remark in conclusion is not that, but this :

If, at a momentous crisis in the history and progress of the country we all love, we, the bulk of the people, fairly embodying the general moderation and sense, are so mistaken by a class, undoubtedly of great intelligence and public and private worth, as that, either they cannot by any means comprehend our resolution to live henceforth under a Government, instead of a Hustlement and Shufflement; or, comprehending it, can think to put it away by cocking their hats in our faces (which is the official exposition of policy conceded to us on all occasions by our chief minister of State); the fault is our own. As the fault is our own, so is the remedy. We do not present ourselves to these personages as we really are, and we have no reason for surprise or complaint, if they take us for what we are at so much pains to appear. Let every man, therefore, apply his own axe to his own branch of the Toady Tree. Let him begin the essential Reform with himself, and he need have no fear of its ending there. We require no ghost to tell us that many inequalities of condition and distinction there must always be. Every step at present to be counted in the great social staircase would be still there, though the shadow of the Toady Tree were cleared away. More than this, the whole of the steps would be safer and stronger; for, the Toady Tree is a tree infected with rottenness, and its droppings wear away what they fall upon.

CHEAP PATRIOTISM

[June 9, 1855]

When the writer of this paper states that he has retired from the civil service on a superannuation fund to which he contributed during forty years, he trusts that the prejudice likely to be engendered by the admission that he has been a Government-clerk, will not be violently strong against him.

In short, to express myself in the first person at once—for, to that complexion I feel I must come, in consequence of the great difficulty of sustaining the third—I beg to make it known that I have no longer any connexion with Somerset House. I am a witness without bias, and will relate my experience in an equitable manner.

Of my official career as an individual clerk, I may soon dispose. I went into the office at eighteen (my father having recently 'plumped for Grobus,' who, under the less familiar designation of The Right Honourable Sir Gilpin Grobus Grobus, Bart., one of His Majesty's Most Honourable Privy Council, retired into remote space and unapproachable grandeur immediately after his election), and began at ninety pounds a-year. I did all the usual things. I wasted as much writing-paper as I possibly could. I set up all my younger brothers with public penknives. I took to modelling in sealing-wax (being hopeless of getting through the quantity I was expected to consume by any other means), and I copied a large amount of flute music into a ponderous vellum-covered book with an anchor outside (supposed to be devoted to the service of the Royal Navy), on every page of which there was a neat water-mark, representing Britannia with a sprig in her hand, seated in an oval.

54

CHEAP PATRIOTISM

I lunched at the office every day, when I stayed till lunch time which was two o'clock, at an average expense of about sixty pounds per annum. My dress cost me (or cost somebody—I really at this distance of time cannot say whom), about a hundred more; and I spent the remainder of my salary in general amusements.

We had the usual kind of juniors in the office, when I was a junior. We had young O'Killamollybore, nephew of the Member, and son of the extensive Irish Proprietor who had killed the other extensive Irish Proprietor in the famous duel arising out of the famous quarrel at the famous assembly about dancing with the famous Beauty—with the whole particulars of which events, mankind was acquainted. O'Killamollybore represented himself to have been educated at every seat of learning in the empire—and I dare say had been ; but, he had not come out of the ordeal, in an orthographical point of view, with the efficiency that might have been expected. He also represented himself as a great artist, and used to put such capital imitations of the marks they make at the shops, on the backs of his pencil-drawings, that they had all the appearance of having been purchased. We had young Percival Fitz-Legionite, of the great Fitz-Legionite family, who, ' took the quarterly pocket-money,' as he told us, for the sake of having something to do (he never did it), and who went to all the parties in the morning papers, and used to be always opening soda-water all over the desks. We had Meltonbury, another nob and our great light, who had been in a crack regiment, and had betted and sold out, and had got his mother, old Lady Meltonbury, to 'stump up,' on condition of his coming into our office, and playing at hockey with the coals. We had Scrivens (just of age), who dressed at the Prince Regent ; and we had Baber, who represented the Turf in our department, and made a book, and wore a speckled blue cravat and top-boots. Finally, we had one extra clerk at five shillings a-day, who had three children, and did all the work, and was much looked down upon by the messengers.

As to our ways of getting through the time, we used to stand before the fire, warming ourselves behind, until we made ourselves faint ; and we used to read the papers ; and, in hot weather, we used to make lemonade and drink it. We used to yawn a good deal, and ring the bell a good deal, and chat and lounge a good deal, and go out a good deal, and come back a little. We used to compare notes

55

as to the precious slavery it was, and as to the salary not being enough for bread and cheese, and as to the manner in which we were screwed by the public—and we used to take our revenge on the public by keeping it waiting and giving it short answers, whenever it came into our office. It has been matter of continuous astonishment to me, during many years, that the public never took me, when I was a junior, by the nape of my neck, and dropped me over the banisters down three stories into the hall.

However, Time was good enough without any assistance on my part, to remove me from the juniors and to hoist me upward. I shed some of my impertinences as I grew older (which is the custom of most men), and did what I had to do, reasonably well. It did not require the head of a Chief Justice, or a Lord Chancellor, and I may even say that in general I believe I did it very well. There is a considerable flourish just now, about examining candidates for clerkships, as if they wanted to take high degrees in learned professions. I don't myself think that Chief Justices and Lord Chancellors are to be got for twenty-two pound ten a quarter, with a final prospect of some five or six hundred a year in the ripe fulness of futurity—and even if they were, I doubt if their abilities could come out very strongly in the usual work of a government office.

This brings me to that part of my experience which I wish to put forth. It is surprising what I have, in my time, seen done in our Department in the reforming way—but always beginning at the wrong end—always stopping at the small men—always showing the public virtue of Two thousand a year M.P. at the expense of that wicked little victim, Two hundred a year. I will recall a few instances.

The head of our Department came in and went out with the Ministry. The place was a favourite place, being universally known among place-people as a snug thing. Soon after I became a Chief in the office, there was a change of Ministry, and we got Lord Stumpington. Down came Lord Stumpington on a certain day, and I had notice to be in readiness to attend him. I found him a very free and pleasant nobleman (he had lately had great losses on the turf, or he wouldn't have accepted any public office), and he had his nephew the Honourable Charles Random with him, whom he had appointed as his official private secretary.

CHEAP PATRIOTISM

'Mr. Tapenham, I believe?' said His Lordship, with his hands under his coat-tails before the fire. I bowed and repeated, 'Mr. Tapenham.' 'Well, Mr. Tapenham,' said His Lordship, 'how are we getting on in this Department?' I said that I hoped we were getting on pretty well. 'At what time do your fellows come in the morning, now?' said His Lordship. 'Half-past ten, my Lord.' 'The devil they do!' said His Lordship. 'Do *you* come at half-past ten?' 'At half-past ten, my Lord.' 'Can't imagine how you do it,' said His Lordship. 'Surprising! Well, Mr. Tapenham, we must do something here, or the opposition will be down upon us and we shall get floored. *What* can we do? What do your fellows work at? Do they do sums, or do they write, or what are they usually up to?' I explained the general duties of our Department, which seemed to stagger His Lordship exceedingly. ''Pon my soul,' he said, turning to his private secretary, 'I am afraid from Mr. Tapenham's account this is a horrible bore, Charley. However, we must do something, Mr. Tapenham, or we shall have those fellows down upon us and get floored. Isn't there any Class (you spoke of the various Classes in the Department just now), that we could cut down a bit? Couldn't we clear off some salaries, or superannuate a few fellows, or blend something with something else, and make a sort of an economical fusion somewhere?' I looked doubtful, and felt perplexed. 'I tell you what we can do, Mr. Tapenham, at any rate,' said His Lordship, brightening with a happy idea. 'We can make your fellows come at ten—Charley, you must turn out in the middle of the night and come at ten. And let us have a Minute that in future the fellows must know something—say French, Charley; and be up in their arithmetic—Rule of Three, Tare and Tret, Charley, Decimals, or something or other. And Mr. Tapenham, if you will be so good as to put yourself in communication with Mr. Random, perhaps you will be able between you to knock out some idea in the economical fusion way. Charley, I am sure you will find Mr. Tapenham a most invaluable coadjutor, and I have no doubt that with such assistance, and getting the fellows here at Ten, we shall make quite a Model Department of it and do all sorts of things to promote the efficiency of the public service.' Here His Lordship, who had a very easy and captivating manner, laughed, and shook hands with me, and said that he needn't detain me any longer.

57

That Government lasted two or three years, and then we got Sir Jasper Janus, who had acquired in the House the reputation of being a remarkable man of business, through the astonishing confidence with which he explained details of which he was entirely ignorant, to an audience who knew no more of them than he did. Sir Jasper had been in office very often, and was known to be a Dragon in the recklessness of his determination to make out a case for himself. It was our Department's first experience of him, and I attended him with fear and trembling. 'Mr. Tapenham,' said Sir Jasper, 'if your memoranda are prepared, I wish to go through the whole business and system of this Department with you. I must first master it completely, and then take measures for consolidating it.' He said this with severe official gravity, and I entered on my statement; he leaning back in his chair with his feet on the fender, outwardly looking at me, and inwardly (as it appeared to me), paying no attention whatever to anything I said. ' Very good, Mr. Tapenham,' he observed, when I had done. 'Now, I gather from your exposition '—whereas I *know* he had got it out of the Court Calendar before he came—' that there are forty-seven clerks in this Department, distributed through four classes, A, B, C, and D. This Department must be consolidated, by the reduction of those forty-seven clerks to thirty-four—in other words, by the abolition of thirteen juniors—the substitution of two classes and a Remove for four—and the construction of an entirely new system of check, by double entry and countersign, on the issue at the outports of fore-top-gallant-yards and snatch-blocks to the Royal Navy. You will be so good, Mr. Tapenham, as to furnish me with the project you would recommend for carrying this consolidation into effect, the day after to-morrow, as I desire to be in a condition to explain the consolidation I propose, when the House is in committee on the Miscellaneous Estimates.' I had nothing for it but to flounder through an impracticable plan that would barely last Sir Jasper Janus's time (which I knew perfectly well, was all he cared for), and he made a speech upon it that would have set up the Ministry, if any effort could have made such a lame thing walk. I do in my conscience believe that in every single point he touched arising out of our Department, he was as far from accuracy as mortal man could possibly be; yet he was inaccurate with such an air, that I almost doubted my own knowledge of the facts as I sat below the bar and

CHEAP PATRIOTISM

heard him. I myself observed three admirals cheering vigorously when the fore-top-gallant-yards and snatch-blocks came into play; and though the effect of that part of the consolidation was, that no ship in the Navy could under any conceivable circumstances of emergency have got rigged while it lasted, it became so strong a card in Sir Jasper's favour that within a fortnight after the coming-in of the opposition, he gave notice of his intention to ask his successor 'Whether Her Majesty's Government had abandoned the system of check by double-entry and countersign, on the issue at the outports of fore-top-gallant-yards and snatch-blocks,' amidst vehement cheering.

The next man of mark we got, was the Right Honourable Mr. Gritts, the member for Sordust. Mr. Gritts came to our Department with a Principle; and the principle was, that no man in a clerkship ought to have more than a hundred a-year. Mr. Gritts held that more did such a man no good; that he didn't want it; that he was not a producer—for he grew nothing; or a manufacturer—for he changed the form of nothing; and that there was some first principle in figures which limited the income of a man who grew nothing and changed the form of nothing, to a maximum of exactly one hundred pounds a-year. Mr. Gritts had acquired a reputation for unspeakable practical sagacity, entirely on the strength of this discovery. I believe it is not too much to say, that he had destroyed two Chancellors of the Exchequer by hammering them on the head with it, night and day. Now, I have seen a little jobbery in forty years; but, such a jobber as Mr. Gritts of Sordust never entered our Department. He brought a former book-keeper of his with him as his private secretary, and I am absolutely certain, to begin with, that he pocketed one-half of that unfortunate man's public salary, and made it an exalted piece of patronage to let him have the other. Of all the many underfed, melancholy men whom Mr. Gritts appointed, I doubt if there were one who was not appointed corruptly. We had consolidations of clerkships to provide for his brother-in-law, we had consolidations of clerkships to provide for his cousin, we had amalgamations to increase his own salary, we had immolations of juniors on the altar of the country every day—but I never knew the country to require the immolation of a Gritts. Add to this, that it became the pervading characteristic of our Department to do everything with intense meanness; to alienate

59

everybody with whom it had to deal; to shuffle, and chaffer, and equivocate; and be shabby, suspicious, and huckstering; and the Gritts administration is faithfully described. Naturally enough, we soon got round to Lord Stumpington again, and then we came to Sir Jasper Janus again; and so we have been ringing the changes on the Stumpingtons and Januses, and each of them has been undoing the doings of the other, ever since.

I am in a disinterested position, and wish to give the public a caution. They will never get any good out of those virtuous changes that are severely virtuous upon the juniors. Such changes originate in the cheapest patriotism in the world, and the commonest. The official system is upside down, and the roots are at the top. Begin there, and the little branches will soon come right.

SMUGGLED RELATIONS

[June 23, 1855]

WHEN I was a child, I remember to have had my ears boxed for informing a lady-visitor who made a morning call at our house, that a certain ornamental object on the table, which was covered with marbled-paper, 'wasn't marble.' Years of reflection upon this injury have fully satisfied me that the honest object in question never imposed upon anybody; further, that my honoured parents, though both of a sanguine temperament, never can have conceived it possible that it might, could, should, would, or did, impose upon anybody. Yet, I have no doubt that I had my ears boxed for violating a tacit compact in the family and among the family visitors, to blink the stubborn fact of the marbled paper, and agree upon a fiction of real marble.

Long after this, when my ears had been past boxing for a quarter of a century, I knew a man with a cork leg. That he had a cork leg—or, at all events, that he was at immense pains to take about with him a leg which was not his own leg, or a real leg—was so plain and obvious a circumstance, that the whole universe might have made affidavit of it. Still, it was always understood that this cork leg was to be regarded as a leg of flesh and blood, and even that the very subject of cork in the abstract was to be avoided in the wearer's society.

I have had my share of going about the world; wherever I have been, I have found the marbled paper and the cork leg. I have found them in many forms; but, of all their Protean shapes, at once the commonest and strangest has been—Smuggled Relations.

I was on intimate terms for many, many years, with my late lamented friend, Cogsford, of the great Greek house of Cogsford Brothers and Cogsford. I was his executor. I believe he had no secrets from me but one—his mother. That the agreeable old lady who kept his house for him *was* his mother, must be his mother, couldn't possibly be anybody but his mother, was evident: not to me alone, but to everybody who knew him. She was not a refugee, she was not proscribed, she was not in hiding, there was no price put upon her venerable head; she was invariably liked and respected as a good-humoured, sensible, cheerful old soul. Then why did Cogsford smuggle his mother all the days of his life? I have not the slightest idea why. I cannot so much as say whether she had ever contracted a second marriage, and her name was really Mrs. Bean: or whether that name was bestowed upon her as a part of the smuggling transaction. I only know that there she used to sit at one end of the hospitable table, the living image in a cap of Cogsford at the other end, and that Cogsford knew that I knew who she was. Yet, if I had been a Custom-house officer at Folkestone, and Mrs. Bean a French clock that Cogsford was furtively bringing from Paris in a hat-box, he could not have made her the subject of a more determined and deliberate pretence. It was prolonged for years upon years. It survived the good old lady herself. One day, I received an agitated note from Cogsford, entreating me to go to him immediately; I went, and found him weeping, and in the greatest affliction, 'My dear friend,' said he, pressing my hand, 'I have lost Mrs. Bean. She is no more.' I went to the funeral with him. He was in the deepest grief. He spoke of Mrs. Bean, on the way back, as the best of women. But, even then he never hinted that Mrs. Bean was his mother; and the first and last acknowledgment of the fact that I ever had from him was in his last will, wherein he entreated 'his said dear friend and executor' to observe that he requested to be buried beside his mother—whom he didn't even name, he was so perfectly confident that I had detected Mrs. Bean.

I was once acquainted with another man who smuggled a brother. This contraband relative made mysterious appearances and disappearances, and knew strange things. He was called John—simply John. I have got into a habit of believing that he must have been under a penalty to forfeit some weekly allowance if he ever claimed a surname. He came to light in this way;—I wanted some information respecting the remotest of the Himalaya range of mountains, and I applied to my friend Benting (a member of the Geographical Society, and learned on such points), to advise me. After some consideration, Benting said, in a half reluctant and constrained way, very unlike his usual frank manner, that he 'thought he knew a man' who could tell me, of his own experience, what I wanted to learn. An appointment was made for a certain evening at Benting's house. I arrived first, and had not observed for more than five minutes that Benting was under a curious cloud, when his servant announced—in a hushed, and I may say unearthly manner—'Mr. John.' A rather stiff and shabby person appeared, who called Benting by no name whatever (a singularity that I always observed whenever I saw them together afterwards), and whose manner was curiously divided between familiarity and distance. I found this man to have been all over the Indies, and to possess an extraordinary fund of traveller's experience. It came from him drily at first; but he warmed, and it flowed freely until he happened to meet Benting's eye. Then, he subsided again, and (it appeared to me), felt himself, for some unknown reason, in danger of losing that weekly allowance. This happened a dozen times in a couple of hours, and not the least curious part of the matter was, that Benting himself was always as much disconcerted as the other man. It did not occur to me that night, that this was Benting's brother, for I had known him very well indeed for years, and had always understood him to have none. Neither can I now recall, nor, if I could, would it matter, by what degrees and stages I arrived at the knowledge. However this may be, I knew it, and Benting knew that I knew it. But, we always preserved the fiction that I could have no suspicion that there was any sort of kindred or affinity between them. He went to Mexico, this John—and he went to Australia—and he went to China—and he died somewhere in Persia—and one day, when we went down to dinner at Benting's, I would find him in the dining-room, already seated (as if he had just been counting the allowance on the tablecloth), and another day I would hear of him as being among scarlet parrots in the tropics; but, I never knew whether he had ever done anything wrong, or whether he had ever done anything right, or why he went about the world, or how. As I have already signified, I get into habits of believing; and I have got into a habit of believing that Mr. John had something to do with the dip of the magnetic needle—he is all vague and shadowy to me, however, and I only know him for certain to have been a smuggled relation.

Other people, again, put these contraband commodities entirely away from the light, as smugglers of wine and brandy bury tubs. I have heard of a man who never imparted, to his most intimate friend, the terrific secret that he had a relation in the world, except when he lost one by death; and then he would be weighed down by the greatness of the calamity, and would refer to his bereavement as if he had lost the very shadow of himself, from whom he had never been separated since the days of infancy. Within my own experience, I have observed smuggled relations to possess a wonderful quality of coming out when they die. My own dear Tom, who married my fourth sister, and who is a great Smuggler, never fails to speak to me of one of his relations newly deceased, as though, instead of never having in the remotest way alluded to that relative's existence before, he had been perpetually discoursing of it. 'My poor, dear, darling Emmy,' he said to me, within these six months, 'she is gone—I have lost her.' Never until that moment had Tom breathed one syllable to me of the existence of any Emmy whomsoever on the face of this earth, in whom he had the smallest interest. He had scarcely allowed me to understand, very distantly and generally, that he had some relations—'my people,' he called them— down in Yorkshire. 'My own dear, darling Emmy,' says Tom notwithstanding, 'she has left me for a better world.' (Tom must have left her for his own world, at least fifteen years). I repeated, feeling my way, 'Emmy, Tom?' 'My favourite niece,' said Tom, in a reproachful tone, 'Emmy, you know. I was her godfather, you remember. Darling, fair-haired Emmy! Precious, blue-eyed child!' Tom burst into tears, and we both understood that henceforth the fiction was established between us that I had been quite familiar with Emmy by reputation, through a series of years.

Occasionally, smuggled relations are discovered by accident: just as those tubs may be, to which I have referred. My other half

—I mean, of course, my wife—once discovered a large cargo in this way, which had been long concealed. In the next street to us, lived an acquaintance of ours, who was a Commissioner of something or other, and kept a handsome establishment. We used to exchange dinners, and I have frequently heard him at his own table mention his father as a 'poor dear good old boy,' who had been dead for any indefinite period. He was rather fond of telling anecdotes of his very early days, and from them it appeared that he had been an only child. One summer afternoon, my other half, walking in our immediate neighbourhood, happened to perceive Mrs. Commissioner's last year's bonnet (to every inch of which, it is unnecessary to add, she could have sworn), going along before her on somebody else's head. Having heard generally of the swell mob, my good lady's first impression was, that the wearer of this bonnet belonged to that fraternity, had just abstracted the bonnet from its place of repose, was in every sense of the term walking off with it, and ought to be given into the custody of the nearest policeman. Fortunately, however, my Susannah, who is not distinguished by closeness of reasoning or presence of mind, reflected, as it were by a flash if inspiration, that the bonnet might have been given away. Curious to see to whom, she quickened her steps, and descried beneath it, an ancient lady of an iron-bound presence, in whom (for my Susannah has an eye), she instantly recognised the lineaments of the Commissioner! Eagerly pursuing this discovery, she, that very afternoon, tracked down an ancient gentleman in one of the Commissioner's hats. Next day she came upon the trail of four stony maidens, decorated with artificial flowers out of the Commissioner's epergne ; and thus we dug up the Commissioner's father and mother and four sisters, who had been for some years secreted in lodgings round the corner and never entered the Commissioner's house save in the dawn of morning and the shades of evening. From that time forth, whenever my Susannah made a call at the Commissioner's, she always listened on the doorstep for any slight preliminary scuffling in the hall, and, hearing it, was delighted to remark, 'The family are here, and they are hiding them ! '

I have never been personally acquainted with any gentleman who kept his mother-in-law in the kitchen, in the useful capacity of Cook ; but I have heard of such a case on good authority. I once lodged in the house of a genteel lady claiming to be a widow, who had four pretty children, and might be occasionally overheard coercing an obscure man in a sleeved waistcoat, who appeared to be confined in some Pit below the foundations of the house, where he was condemned to be always cleaning knives. One day, the smallest of the children crept into my room, and said, pointing downward with a little chubby finger, 'Don't tell! It's Pa!' and vanished on tiptoe.

One other branch of the smuggling trade demands a word of mention before I conclude. My friend of friends in my bachelor days, became the friend of the house when I got married. He is our Amelia's godfather; Amelia being the eldest of our cherubs. Through upwards of ten years he was backwards and forwards at our house three or four times a week, and always found his knife and fork ready for him. What was my astonishment on coming home one day to find Susannah sunk upon the oil-cloth in the hall, holding her brow with both hands, and meeting my gaze, when I admitted myself with my latch-key, in a distracted manner! 'Susannah,' I exclaimed, 'what has happened?' She merely ejaculated, 'Larver'—that being the name of the friend in question. 'Susannah!' said I, 'what of Larver? Speak! Has he met with any accident? Is he ill?' Susannah replied faintly, 'Married— married before we were!' and would have gone into hysterics but that I make a rule of never permitting that disorder under my roof.

For upwards of ten years, my bosom friend Larver, in close communication with me every day, had smuggled a wife! He had at last confided the truth to Susannah, and had presented Mrs. Larver. There was no kind of reason for this, that we could ever find out. Even Susannah had not a doubt of things being all correct. He had 'run' Mrs. Larver into a little cottage in Hertfordshire, and nobody ever knew why, or ever will know. In fact, I believe there was no why in it.

The most astonishing part of the matter is, that I have known other men do exactly the same thing. I could give the names of a dozen in a footnote, if I thought it right.

THE GREAT BABY

[August 4, 1855]

Has it occurred to any of our readers that that is surely an unsatisfactory state of society which presents, in the year eighteen hundred and fifty-five, the spectacle of a committee of the People's representatives, pompously and publicly inquiring how the People shall be trusted with the liberty of refreshing themselves in humble taverns and tea-gardens on their day of rest? Does it appear to any one whom we now address, and who will pause here to reflect for a moment on the question we put, that there is anything at all humiliating and incongruous in the existence of such a body, and pursuit of such an enquiry, in this country, at this time of day?

For ourselves, we will answer the question without hesitation. We feel indignantly ashamed of the thing as a national scandal. It would be merely contemptible, if it were not raised into importance by its slanderous aspersions of a hard-worked, heavily-taxed, but good-humoured and most patient people, who have long deserved far better treatment. In this green midsummer, here is a committee virtually enquiring whether the English can be regarded in any other light, and domestically ruled in any other manner, than as a gang of drunkards and disorderlies on a Police charge-sheet! O my Lords and Gentlemen, my Lords and Gentlemen, have we got so very near Utopia after our long travelling together over the dark and murderous road of English history, that we have nothing else left to say and do to the people but this? Is there nothing abroad, nothing at home, nothing seen by us, nothing hidden from us, which points to higher and more generous things?

There are two public bodies remarkable for knowing nothing of the people, and for perpetually interfering to put them right. The one is the House of Commons; the other the Monomaniacs. Between the Members and the Monomaniacs, the devoted People, quite unheard, get harried and worried to the last extremity. Everybody of ordinary sense, possessing common sympathies with necessities not their own, and common means of observation — Members and Monomaniacs are of course excepted—has perceived for months past, that it was manifestly impossible that the People

THE GREAT BABY

could or would endure the inconveniences and deprivations, sought to be imposed upon them by the latest Sunday restrictions. We who write this, have again and again by word of mouth forewarned many scores both of Members and Monomaniacs, as we have heard others forewarn them, that what they were in the densest ignorance allowing to be done, could not be borne. Members and Monomaniacs knew better, or cared nothing about it; and we all know the rest—to this time.

Now, the Monomaniacs, being by their disease impelled to clamber upon platforms, and there squint horribly under the strong possession of an unbalanced idea, will of course be out of reason and go wrong. But, why the Members should yield to the Monomaniacs is another question. And why do they? Is it because the People is altogether an abstraction to them; a Great Baby, to be coaxed and chucked under the chin at elections, and frowned upon at quarter sessions, and stood in the corner on Sundays, and taken out to stare at the Queen's coach on holidays, and kept in school under the rod, generally speaking, from Monday morning to Saturday night? Is it because they have no other idea of the People than a big-headed Baby, now to be flattered and now to be scolded, now to be sung to and now to be denounced to old Boguey, now to be kissed and now to be whipped, but always to be kept in long clothes, and never under any circumstances to feel its legs and go about of itself? We take the liberty of replying, Yes.

And do the Members and Monomaniacs suppose that this is *our* discovery? Do they live in the shady belief that the object of their capricious dandling and punishing does not resentfully perceive that it is made a Great Baby of, and may not begin to kick thereat with legs that may do mischief?

In the first month of the existence of this Journal, we called attention to a detachment of the Monomaniacs, who, under the name of jail-chaplains, had taken possession of the prisons, and were clearly offering premiums to vice, promoting hypocrisy, and making models of dangerous scoundrels.[1] They had their way, and the Members backed them; and now their Pets recruit the very worst class of criminals known. The Great Baby, to whom this copy was set as a moral lesson, is supposed to be perfectly unimpressed by the real facts, and to be entirely ignorant of them. So,

[1] See previous article entitled *Pet Prisoners*.

67

down at Westminster, night after night, the Right Honourable Gentleman the Member for Somewhere, and the Honourable Gentleman the Member for Somewherelse, badger one another, to the infinite delight of their adherents in the cockpit; and when the Prime Minister has released his noble bosom of its personal injuries, and has made his jokes and retorts for the evening, and has said little and done less, he winds up with a standard form of words respecting the vigorous prosecution of the war, and a just and honourable peace, which are especially let off upon the Great Baby; which Baby is always supposed never to have heard before; and which it is understood to be a part of Baby's catechism to be powerfully affected by. And the Member for Somewhere, and the Member for Somewherelse, and the Noble Lord, and all the rest of that Honourable House, go home to bed, really persuaded that the Great Baby has been talked to sleep!

Let us see how the unfortunate Baby is addressed and dealt with, in the inquiry concerning his Sunday eatings and drinkings— as wild as a nursery rhyme, and as inconclusive as Bedlam.

The Great Baby is put upon his trial. A mighty noise of creaking boots is heard in an outer passage. O good gracious, here's an official personage! Here's a solemn witness! Mr. Gamp, we believe you have been a dry-nurse to the Great Baby for some years? Yes, I have.—Intimately acquainted with his character? Intimately acquainted—As a police magistrate, Mr. Gamp? As a police magistrate. (Sensation.)—Pray, Mr. Gamp, would you allow a working man, a small tradesman, clerk, or the like, to go to Hampstead or to Hampton Court at his own convenience on a Sunday, with his family, and there to be at liberty to regale himself and them, in a tavern where he could buy a pot of beer and a glass of gin-and-water? I would on no account concede that permission to any person.—Will you be so kind as to state why, Mr. Gamp? Willingly. Because I have presided for many years at the Bo-Peep police office, and have seen a great deal of drunkenness there. A large majority of the Bo-Peep charges are charges against persons of the lowest class, of having been found drunk and incapable of taking care of themselves.—Will you instance a case, Mr. Gamp? I will instance the case of Sloggins.[1]—Was that a man with a broken nose, a black eye, and a bull-dog? Precisely so.—Was Sloggins frequently

[1] See previous article entitled *It is not Generally Known.*

the subject of such a charge? Continually. I may say, constantly.
—Especially on Monday? Just so. Especially on Monday.—And
therefore you would shut the public-houses, and particularly the
suburban public-houses, against the free access of working-people on
Sunday? Most decidedly so. (Mr. Gamp retires, much complimented.)

Naughty Baby, attend to the Reverend Single Swallow! Mr.
Swallow, you have been much in the confidence of thieves and
miscellaneous miscreants? I have the happiness to believe that
they have made me the unworthy depository of their unbounded
confidence.—Have they usually confessed to you that they have
been in the habit of getting drunk? Not drunk; upon that point
I wish to explain. Their ingenuous expression has generally been,
'lushy.'—But those are convertible terms? I apprehend they are;
still, as gushing freely from a penitent breast, I am weak enough to
wish to stipulate for lushy; I pray you bear with me.—Have you
reason, Mr. Swallow, to believe that excessive indulgence in 'lush'
has been the cause of these men's crimes? O yes indeed. O yes!—
Do you trace their offences to nothing else? They have always
told me, that they themselves traced them to nothing else worth
mentioning.—Are you acquainted with a man named Sloggins? O
yes! I have the truest affection for Sloggins.—Has he made any
confidence to you that you feel justified in disclosing, bearing on this
subject of becoming lushy? Sloggins, when in solitary confinement,
informed me, every morning for eight months, always with tears in
his eyes, and uniformly at five minutes past eleven o'clock, that he
attributed his imprisonment to his having partaken of rum-and-
water at a licensed house of entertainment, called (I use his own
words) The Wiry Tarrier. He never ceased to recommend that the
landlord, landlady, young family, potboy, and the whole of the
frequenters of that establishment, should be taken up.—Did you
recommend Sloggins for a commutation of his term, on a ticket of
leave? I did.—Where is he now? I believe he is in Newgate now.—
Do you know what for? Not of my own knowledge, but I have heard
that he got into trouble through having been weakly tempted into the
folly of garotting a market gardener.—Where was he taken for this
last offence? At The Wiry Tarrier, on a Sunday.—It is unnecessary
to ask you, Mr. Single Swallow, whether you therefore recommend
the closing of all public-houses on a Sunday? Quite unnecessary.

Bad Baby, fold your hands and listen to the Reverend Temple

69

MISCELLANEOUS PAPERS

Pharisee, who will step out of his carriage at the Committee Door, to give you a character that will rather astonish you. Mr. Temple Pharisee, you are the incumbent of the extensive rectory of Camel-cum-Needle's-eye? I am.—Will you be so good as to state your experience of that district on a Sunday? Nothing can be worse. That part of the Rectory of Camel-cum-Needle's-eye in which my principal church is situated, abuts upon the fields. As I stand in the pulpit, I can actually see the people, through the side windows of the building (when the heat of the weather renders it necessary to have them open), walking. I have, on some occasions, heard them laughing. Whistling has reached my curate's ears (he is an industrious and well-meaning young man); but I cannot say I have heard it myself.—Is your church well frequented? No. I have no reason to complain of the Pew-portion of my flock, who are eminently respectable; but, the Free Seats are comparatively deserted: which is the more emphatically deplorable, as there are not many of them.—Is there a Railway near the church? I regret to state that there is, and that I hear the rush of the trains, even while I am preaching.—Do you mean to say that they do not slacken speed for your preaching? Not in the least.—Is there anything else near the church, to which you would call the Committee's attention? At the distance of a mile and a half and three rods (for my clerk has measured it by my direction), there is a common public-house with tea-gardens, called The Glimpse of Green. In fine weather these gardens are filled with people on a Sunday evening. Frightful scenes take place there. Pipes are smoked; liquors mixed with hot water are drunk; shrimps are eaten; cockles are consumed; tea is swilled; ginger-beer is loudly exploded. Young women with their young men; young men with their young women; married people with their children; baskets, bundles, little chaises, wickerwork perambulators, every species of low abomination, is to be observed there. As the evening closes in, they all come straggling home together through the fields; and the vague sounds of merry conversation which then strike upon the ear, even at the further end of my dining-room (eight-and-thirty feet by twenty-seven), are most distressing. I consider The Glimpse of Green irreconcileable with public morality.—Have you heard of pickpockets resorting to this place? I have. My clerk informed me that his uncle's brother-in-law, a marine store-dealer who went there to observe the depravity

70

THE GREAT BABY

of the people, missed his pocket-handkerchief when he reached home. Local ribaldry has represented him to be one of the persons who had their pockets picked at St. Paul's Cathedral on the last occasion when the Bishop of London preached there. I beg to deny this; I know those individuals very well, and they were people of condition.—Do the mass of the inhabitants of your district work hard all the week? I believe they do.—Early and late? My curate reports so.—Are their houses close and crowded? I believe they are.—Abolishing The Glimpse of Green, where would you recommend them to go on a Sunday? I should say to church.—Where after church? Really, that is their affair; not mine.

Adamantine-hearted Baby, dissolve into scalding tears at sight of the next witness, hanging his head and beating his breast. He was one of the greatest drunkards in the world, he tells you. When he was drunk, he was a very demon—and he never was sober. He never takes any strong drink now, and is as an angel of light. And because this man never could use without abuse; and because he imitated the Hyæna or other obscene animal, in not knowing, in the ferocity of his appetites, what Moderation was; therefore, O Big-headed Baby, you perceive that he must become as a standard for you; and for his backslidings you shall be put in the corner evermore.

Ghost of John Bunyan, it is surely thou who usherest into the Committee Room, the volunteer testifier, Mr. Monomaniacal Patriarch! Baby, a finger in each eye, and ashes from the nearest dustbin on your wretched head, for it is all over with you now. Mr. Monomaniacal Patriarch, have you paid great attention to drunkenness? Immense attention, unspeakable attention.—For how many years? Seventy years.—Mr. Monomaniacal Patriarch, have you ever been in Whitechapel? Millions of times.—Did you ever shed tears over the scenes you have witnessed there? Oceans of tears.—Mr. Monomaniacal Patriarch, will you proceed with your testimony? Yes; I am the only man to be heard on the subject; I am the only man who knows anything about it. No connexion with any other establishment; all others are impostors; I am the real original. Other men are said to have looked into these places, and to have worked to raise them out of the Slough of Despond. Don't believe it. Nothing is genuine unless signed by me. I am the original fly with the little eye. Nobody ever mourned over the

71

miseries and vices of the lowest of the low, but I. Nobody has ever been haunted by them, waking and sleeping, but I. Nobody would raise up the sunken wretches, but I. Nobody understands how to do it, but I.—Do you think the People ever really want any beer or liquor to drink? Certainly not. I know all about it, and I know they don't.—Do you think they ever ought to have any beer or liquor to drink? Certainly not. I know all about it, and I know they oughtn't.—Do you think they could suffer any inconvenience from having their beer and liquor entirely denied them? Certainly not. I know all about it, and I know they couldn't.

Thus, the Great Baby is dealt with from the beginning to the end of the chapter. It is supposed equally by the Members and by the Monomaniacs to be incapable of putting This and That together, and of detecting the arbitrary nonsense of these monstrous deductions. That a whole people,—a domestic, reasonable, considerate people, whose good-nature and good sense are the admiration of intelligent foreigners, and who are no less certain to secure the affectionate esteem of such of their own countrymen as will have the manhood to be open with them, and to trust them,—that a whole people should be judged by, and made to answer and suffer for, the most degraded and most miserable among them, is a principle so shocking in its injustice, and so lunatic in its absurdity, that to entertain it for a moment is to exhibit profound ignorance of the English mind and character. In Monomaniacs this may be of no great significance, but in Members it is alarming; for, if they cannot be brought to understand the People for whom they make laws, and if they so grievously under-rate them, how is it to be hoped that they, and the laws, and the People, being such a bundle of anomalies, can possibly thrive together?

It is not necessary for us, or for any decent person, to go to Westminster, or anywhere else, to make a flourish against intemperance. We abhor it; would have no drunkard about us, on any consideration; would thankfully see the child of our heart, dead in his baby beauty, rather than he should live and grow with the shadow of such a horror upon him. In the name of Heaven, let drunkards and ruffians restrain themselves and be restrained by all conceivable means—but, not govern, bind, and defame, the temperance, the industry, the rational wants and decent enjoyments of a whole toiling nation! We oppose those virtuous Malays who run amuck out of the House of Peers or Exeter Hall, as much as those vicious Malays who run amuck out of Sailors' lodging-houses in Rotherhithe. We have a constitutional objection in both cases to being stabbed in the back, and we claim that the one kind of Monomaniac has no more right than the other to gash and disfigure honest people going their peaceable way. Lastly, we humbly beg to assert and protest with all the vigour that is in us, that the People is, in sober truth and reality, something very considerably more than a Great Baby; that it has come to an age when it can distinguish sound from sense; that mere jingle, will not do for it; in a word, that the Great Baby is growing up, and had best be measured accordingly.

THE WORTHY MAGISTRATE

[August 25, 1855]

UNDER this stereotyped title expressive of deference to the police-bench, we take the earliest opportunity afforded us by our manner of preparing this publication, of calling upon every Englishman who reads these pages to take notice what he is. The circulation of this journal comprising a wide diversity of classes, we use it to disseminate the information that every Englishman is a drunkard. Drunkenness is the national characteristic. Whereas the German people (when uncontaminated by the English), are always sober, the English, setting at nought the bright example of the pure Germans domiciled among them, are always drunk. The authority for this polite and faithful exposition of the English character, is a modern Solomon, whose temple rears its head near Drury Lane; the wise Mr. Hall, Chief Police Magistrate, sitting at Bow Street, Covent Garden, in the County of Middlesex, Barrister-at-Law.

As we hope to keep this household word of Drunkard, affixed to the Englishman by the awful Mr. Hall from whom there is no appeal, pretty steadily before our readers, we present the very pearl discovered in that magisterial oyster. On Thursday, the ninth of this present month of August, the following sublime passage evoked the virtuous laughter of the thief-takers of Bow Street:

Mr. HALL.—Were you sober, Sir?

Prosecutor.—Yes, certainly.

Mr. HALL.—You must be a foreigner, then?

Prosecutor.—I am a German.

Mr. HALL.—Ah, that accounts for it. If you had been an Englishman, you would have been drunk, for a certainty.

Prosecutor (smiling).—The Germans get drunk sometimes, I fear.

Mr. HALL.—Yes, after they have resided any time in this country. They acquire our English habits.

In reproducing these noble expressions, equally honourable to the Sage who uttered them, and to the Country that endures them, we will correct half a dozen vulgar errors which, within our observation, have been rather prevalent since the great occasion on which the Oracle at Bow Street spake.

1. It is altogether a mistake to suppose that if a magistrate wilfully deliver himself of a slanderous aspersion, knowing it to be unjust, he is unfit for his post.

2. It is altogether a mistake to suppose that if a magistrate, in a fit of bile brought on by recent disregard of some very absurd evidence of his, so yield to his ill-temper as to deliver himself, in a sort of mad exasperation, of such slanderous aspersion as aforesaid, he is unfit for his post.

3. It is altogether a mistake to suppose it to be very questionable whether, even in degraded Naples at this time, a magistrate could from the official bench insult and traduce the whole people, without being made to suffer for it.

4. It is altogether a mistake to suppose that it would be becoming in some one individual out of between six and seven hundred national representatives, to be so far jealous of the honour of his country, as indignantly to protest against its being thus grossly stigmatised.

5. It is altogether a mistake to suppose that the Home Office has any association whatever with the general credit, the general self-respect, the general feeling in behalf of decent utterance, or the general resentment when the same is most discreditably violated. The Home Office is merely an ornamental institution supported out of the general pocket.

6. It is altogether a mistake to suppose that Mr. Hall is any-

body's business, or that we, the mere bone and sinew, tag rag and bobtail of England, have anything to do with him, but to pay him his salary, accept his Justice, and meekly bow our heads to his high and mighty reproof.

A SLIGHT DEPRECIATION OF THE CURRENCY

[November 3, 1855]

It was said by the wise and witty Sydney Smith, that many Englishmen appear to have a remarkable satisfaction in even speaking of large sums of money ; and that when men of this stamp say of Mr. So-and-So, 'I am told he is worth Two Hun-dred Thou-sand pounds,' there is a relish in their emphasis, an unctuous appetite and zest in their open-mouthed enunciation, which nothing but the one inspiring theme, Money, develops in them.

That this is an accurate piece of observation, few who observe at all will dispute. Its application is limited to no class of society, and it is even more generally true of the genteel than of the vulgar. The last famous golden calf that disfigured this country, was set up for worship in the highest places, and was pampered to its face and made a standing-jest of behind its back throughout Belgravia, with an intensity of meanness never surpassed in Seven Dials.

But I am not going to write a homily upon that ancient text, the general deification of Money. The few words that I wish to note down here, bear reference to one particular misuse of Money, and exaggeration of its power, which presents itself to my mind as a curious rottenness appertaining to this age.

Let us suppose, to begin with, that there was once upon a time a Baron, who governed his estate not wisely nor too well, and whose dependants sustained in consequence many preventible hardships. Let us suppose that the Baron was of a highly generous disposition, and that when he found a vassal to have been oppressed or mal-treated by a hard or foolish steward, who had strained against him some preposterous point of the discordant system on which the estate was administered, he immediately gave that vassal Money.

Let us suppose that such munificent action set the noble Baron's mind completely at rest, and that, having performed it, he felt quite satisfied with himself and everybody else ; considered his duty done, and never dreamed of so adjusting that point for the future as that the thing could not recur. Let us suppose the Baron to have been continually doing this from day to day and from year to year—to have been perpetually patching broken heads with Money, and repairing moral wrongs with Money, yet leaving the causes of the broken heads and the moral wrongs in unchecked operation. Agreed upon these suppositions, we shall probably agree in the conclusion that the Baron's estate was not in a promising way ; that the Baron was a lazy Baron, who would have done far better to be just than generous ; and that the Baron, in this easy satisfaction of his noble conscience, showed a false idea of the powers and uses of Money.

Is it possible that we, in England, at the present time, bear any resemblance to the supposititious and misguided Baron ? Let us inquire.

A year or so ago, there was a court-martial held at Windsor, which attracted the public attention in an unusual manner ; not so much because it was conducted in a spirit hardly reconcileable with the popular prejudice in favour of fair play, as because it suggested very grave defects in our military system, and exhibited us, as to the training of our officers, in very disadvantageous contrast with other countries. The result at which that court-martial arrived, was widely regarded as absurd and unjust. What were we who held that opinion, moved by our honest conviction, to do ? To bestir ourselves to amend the system thus exposed ? To apply ourselves to reminding our countrymen that it was fraught with enormous dangers to us and to our children, and that, in suffering any authorities whatsoever to maintain it, or in allowing ourselves to be either bullied or cajoled about it, we were imperilling the institutions under which we live, the national liberty of which we boast, and the very existence of England in her place among the nations ? Did we go to work to point out to the unthinking, what our valiant forefathers did for us, what their resolute spirit won for us, what their earnestness secured to us, and what we, by allowing work to degenerate into play, were relaxing our grasp of, every hour ? Did numbers of us unite into a phalanx of steady purpose, bent upon

76

impressing these truths upon those who accept the responsibility of government, and on having them enforced, in stern and steady practice, through all the vital functions of Great Britain? No. Not quite that. We were highly indignant, we were a little alarmed; between the two emotions we were made, for the moment, exceedingly uncomfortable; so we relieved our uneasy souls by — giving the subject of the court-martial, Money. In putting our hands into our pockets and pulling out our five-pound notes, we discharged, as to that matter, the whole duty of man. The thing was set right, the country had nothing further to do with it. The subscription amounted, sir, to upwards of Two THOU-sand POUNDS.

Now, I will assume that the cash could not have been better laid out. I will assume that the recipient in every such case is none the worse for the gift, but is all the more independent, high-spirited, and self-reliant. Still I take the liberty of questioning whether I have any right to be satisfied with my part in that subscription; whether it is the least discharge of my duty as a citizen; whether it is not an easy shirking of my difficult task in that capacity; whether it is not a miserable compromise leading to the substitution of sand for rock in the foundations of this kingdom; whether it does not exhibit my sordid appreciation of Money, and the low belief I have within me that it can do anything.

Take another case. Two labouring men leave their work for half a day (having given notice of their intention before-hand, and having risen betimes to make amends), and go to see a review : which review is commended to their fellows and neighbours as a highly patriotic and loyal sight. Under a foolish old act of Parliament which nobody but a country justice would have the kindred foolishness to enforce, the men are haled before country justices, and committed by those Brobdingnagian donkeys to jail—illegally, by the bye; but never mind that. An unconstitutional person in the neighbourhood, making this Bedlamite cruelty known, there arises a growl of wonder and dissatisfaction from all the other unconstitutional persons in the country. We try the Home Secretary, but he 'sees no reason' to reverse the decision—and how can we expect that he should; knowing that he never sees any reason, hears any reason, or utters any reason, for anything? What do we then? Do we get together and say, 'We really must not in these times allow the labouring men to live under the impression that this is the spirit of our Law towards them. We positively must not, cannot, will not, put such a weapon in the hands of those who tamper with them constantly. These justices have made it necessary for us to insist on their dismissal from the bench, as an assurance to the order so ridiculously oppressed in the persons of these two men, that the common sense of the country revolts from the outrage. Furthermore, we must now exert ourselves to prevent other such justices from being intrusted with like powers, and to take new securities for their moderate and reasonable exercise.' Is this our course? Why no. What is our course? We give the two men Money—and there an end of it.

Try again. A countryman has a little field of wheat which he reaps upon a Sunday; foreseeing that he will otherwise have his tiny harvest spoiled. For this black offence he, too, is had before a country justice of the vast Shallow family, and is punished by fine. It is to be presumed that, with this new stimulant upon us, we are roused into an attitude against the Shallows, which has some faint approach to determination in it, and that we become resolved to take our laws and our people out of their hands. But, no. This would occasion us trouble, and we all have our business to attend to, and have a languid objection to being bored. We put our hands into our pockets again, and let the obsolete acts of Parliament and the evergreen Shallows drift us where they may.

It was remarked in these pages, some time ago, that the raising of a shout of triumph over the enactment of a wretched little law for the protection of women,[1] punishing the greatest brutes on the earth with six months' imprisonment, surely suggested that our legislative civilisation must be very imperfect and bad. The insufficiency of this puny law, and the frequency of the offence against which it is directed, are matter of public notoriety. Do we take this subject into our own hands, then; declare that we will have the severity of the Law increased; examine the social condition laid bare in such cases, and plainly avow that we find great numbers of the people sunk in horrible debasement, and that they must be got out of it by (among other means), having more humanising pleasures provided for them, and better escapes than gin-shops afforded them from the wretchedness of their existence? That they even stand in need of cheerful relief without the Cant

[1] See previous article entitled *Things that Cannot be Done.*

78

of instruction, and that Marlborough House itself, may be but a solemn nightmare to legions who, nevertheless, pay taxes, and have souls to be saved? Do we leave off blinking the real question, and manfully say, 'We find the existence of these people—men, women, and children, all alike—to be most deplorable, and, as matters stand, we really do not know what it is made easy for them to do when they are not at work, but to lurk, and sot, and quarrel, and fight?' All of us who know anything of the facts know this to be God's truth; but, instead of asserting it, we send five shillings' worth of postage stamps to the police magistrate for the relief of the last unhappy woman who has been half-murdered; and go to church next Sunday with the adhesive plaster of those sixty queen's heads, binding up our rickety consciences.

Neither is it we alone, the body of the people, who have this base recourse to Money as a healing balm on all occasions. The leaders who carry the banners we engage to follow, set us the example, and do the same. The last Thanksgiving Day was not so long ago but that we may all remember the advertising columns of the newspapers about that time, and the desirable opportunities they offered for devout investment. It was clear to the originators of those advertisements, manifest to the whole tribe of Moses (and Sons) who published those decorous appeals—that we must coin our thankful feelings into Money. If we wanted another victory, we could not hope to get it for nothing, or on credit, but must come down with our ready Money. There was not a church-organ unpaid for, not a beadle's cocked hat and blushing breeches for which church-wardens were responsible, not a chapel painting and glazing job, on any painters' and glaziers' books, but we were called upon to liquidate that obligation, and get a ticket in return, entitling us to the other side of Sebastopol. And we paid the money and took the ticket. Hosts of us did so. We paid the balance due upon that organ, we settled the bill for the cocked hat and blushing breeches, we settled the account of the painter and glazier, and we felt, in the vulgar phrase, that we had gone and been and done it.

So many of us parted with our small change to clear off these scores, because we found it much easier to pay the fine than undertake the service. The service required of us was severe. Paralysis had disclosed itself in the heart and brain of our administration of affairs; favour and dull routine were all in all, merit and exigency were nothing. A class had got possession of our strength, and made it weakness; and three-quarters of the globe stood looking on with a rather keen interest in the wonderful sight. The service demanded of us by the crisis, was the recovery of our strength through steadfastness in what was plainly right, and overthrow of what was plainly wrong. The service was difficult, ungentlemanly, unpopular in good society; and we paid the fine with pleasure.

But if every man drawn in a conscription paid a fine instead of going for a soldier, the country in which that happened would have no defenders. There are fights not fought by soldiers, O my countrymen, and they are no less necessary to the defence of a country, and the conscription for that war is on every one of us. Money is great, but it is not omnipotent. All the Money that could be piled up between this and the moon would not fill the place of one little grain of duty.

INSULARITIES

[JANUARY 19, 1856]

IT is more or less the habit of every country—more or less commendable in every case—to exalt itself and its institutions above every other country, and be vain-glorious. Out of the partialities thus engendered and maintained, there has arisen a great deal of patriotism, and a great deal of public spirit. On the other hand, it is of paramount importance to every nation that its boastfulness should not generate prejudice, conventionality, and a cherishing of unreasonable ways of acting and thinking, which have nothing in them deserving of respect, but are ridiculous or wrong.

We English people, owing in a great degree to our insular position, and in a small degree to the facility with which we have permitted electioneering lords and gentlemen to pretend to think for us, and to represent our weaknesses to us as our strength, have been in particular danger of contracting habits which we will call for our present purpose, Insularities. Our object in this paper, is to string together a few examples.

On the continent of Europe, generally, people dress according to their personal convenience and inclinations. In that capital which is supposed to set the fashion in affairs of dress, there is an especial independence in this regard. If a man in Paris have an idiosyncrasy on the subject of any article of attire between his hat and his boots, he gratifies it without the least idea that it can be anybody's affair but his; nor does anybody else make it his affair. If, indeed, there be anything obviously convenient or tasteful in the peculiarity, then it soon ceases to be a peculiarity, and is adopted by others. If not, it is let alone. In the meantime, the commonest man in the streets does not consider it at all essential to his character as a true French-man, that he should howl, stare, jeer, or otherwise make himself offensive to the author of the innovation. That word has ceased to be Old Boguey to him since he ceased to be a serf, and he leaves the particular sample of innovation to come in or go out upon its merits.

Our strong English prejudice against anything of this kind that is new to the eye, forms one of our decided insularities. It is dis-appearing before the extended knowledge of other countries conse-quent upon steam and electricity, but it is not gone yet. The hermetically-sealed, black, stiff, chimney-pot, a foot and a half high, which we call a hat, is generally admitted to be neither convenient nor graceful; but, there are very few middle-aged gentlemen within two hours' reach of the Royal Exchange, who would bestow their daughters on wide-awakes, however estimable the wearers. Smith Payne and Smith, or Ransom and Co., would probably consider a run upon the house not at all unlikely, in the event of their clerks coming to business in caps, or with such felt-fashions on their heads as didn't give them the headache, and as they could wear comfort-ably and cheaply. During the dirt and wet of at least half the year in London, it would be a great comfort and a great saving of expense to a large class of persons, to wear the trousers gathered up about the leg, as a Zouave does, with a long gaiter below—to shift which, is to shift the whole mud-incumbered part of the dress, and to be dry, and clean directly. To such clerks, and others with much out-door work to do, as could afford it, Jack-boots, a much more costly article, would, for similar reasons, be excellent wear. But what would Griggs and Bodger say to Jack-boots? They would say, 'This sort of thing, sir, is not the sort of thing the house has been accustomed to, you will bring the house into the Gazette, you must ravel out four inches of trousers daily, sir, or you must go.'

81

MISCELLANEOUS PAPERS

Some years ago, we, the writer, not being in Griggs and Bodger's, took the liberty of buying a great-coat which we saw exposed for sale in the Burlington Arcade, London, and which appeared to be in our eyes the most sensible great-coat we had ever seen. Taking the further liberty to wear this great-coat after we had bought it, we became a sort of Spectre, eliciting the wonder and terror of our fellow creatures as we flitted along the streets. We accompanied the coat to Switzerland for six months; and, although it was perfectly new there, we found it was not regarded as a portent ot the least importance. We accompanied it to Paris for another six months; and, although it was perfectly new there too, nobody minded it. This coat so intolerable to Britain, was nothing more nor less than the loose wide-sleeved mantle, easy to put on, easy to put off, and crushing nothing beneath it, which everybody now wears.

During hundreds of years, it was the custom in England to wear beards. It became, in course of time, one of our Insularities to shave close. Whereas, in almost all the other countries of Europe, more or less of moustache and beard was habitually worn, it came to be established in this speck of an island, as an Insularity from which there was no appeal, that an Englishman, whether he liked it or not, must hew, hack, and rasp his chin and upper lip daily. The inconvenience of this infallible test of British respectability was so widely felt, that fortunes were made by razors, razor-strops, hones, pastes, shaving-soaps, emollients for the soothing of the tortured skin, all sorts of contrivances to lessen the misery of the shaving process and diminish the amount of time it occupied. This particular Insularity even went some miles further on the broad highway of Nonsense than other Insularities; for it not only tabooed unshorn civilians, but claimed for one particular and very limited military class the sole right to dispense with razors as to their upper lips. We ventured to suggest in this journal that the prohibition was ridiculous, and to show some reasons why it was ridiculous. The Insularity having no sense in it, has since been losing ground every day.

One of our most remarkable Insularities is a tendency to be firmly persuaded that what is not English is not natural. In the Fine Arts department of the French Exhibition, recently closed, we repeatedly heard, even from the more educated and reflective of our

INSULARITIES

countrymen, that certain pictures which appeared to possess great merit—of which not the lowest item was, that they possessed the merit of a vigorous and bold Idea—were all very well, but were 'theatrical.' Conceiving the difference between a dramatic picture and a theatrical picture, to be, that in the former case a story is strikingly told, without apparent consciousness of a spectator, and that in the latter case the groups are obtrusively conscious of a spectator, and are obviously dressed up, and doing (or not doing) certain things with an eye to the spectator, and not for the sake of the story; we sought in vain for this defect. Taking further pains then, to find out what was meant by the term theatrical, we found that the actions and gestures of the figures were not English. That is to say,—the figures expressing themselves in the vivacious manner natural in a greater or less degree to the whole great continent of Europe, were overcharged and out of the truth, because they did not express themselves in the manner of our little Island—which is so very exceptional, that it always places an Englishman at a disadvantage, out of his own country, until his fine sterling qualities shine through his external formality and constraint. Surely nothing can be more unreasonable, say, than that we should require a Frenchman of the days of Robespierre, to be taken out of his jail to the guillotine with the calmness of Clapham or the respectability of Richmond Hill, after a trial at the Central Criminal Court in eighteen hundred and fifty-six. And yet this exactly illustrates the requirement of the particular Insularity under consideration.

When shall we get rid of the Insularity of being afraid to make the most of small resources, and the best of scanty means of enjoyment? In Paris (as in innumerable other places and countries) a man who has six square feet of yard, or six square feet of housetop, adorns it in his own poor way, and sits there in the fine weather because he likes to do it, because he chooses to do it, because he has got nothing better of his own, and has never been laughed out of the enjoyment of what he has got. Equally, he will sit at his door, or in his balcony, or out on the pavement, because it is cheerful and pleasant and he likes to see the life of the city. For the last seventy years his family have not been tormenting their lives with continual enquiries and speculations whether other families, above and below, to the right and to the left, over the way and round the corner, would consider these recreations genteel, or would do the like, or would not do the like. That abominable old Tyrant, Madame Grundy, has never been of his acquaintance. The result is, that, with a very small income and in a very dear city, he has more innocent pleasure than fifty Englishmen of the same condition ; and is distinctly, in spite of our persuasion to the contrary (another Insularity !) a more domestic man than the Englishman, in regard of his simple pleasures being, to a much greater extent, divided with his wife and children. It is a natural consequence of their being easy and cheap, and profoundly independent of Madame Grundy.

But, this Insularity rests, not to the credit of England, on a more palpable foundation than perhaps any other. The old school of Tory writers did so pertinaciously labour to cover all easily available recreations and cheap reliefs from the monotony of common life, with ridicule and contempt, that great numbers of the English people got scared into being dull, and are only now beginning to recover their courage. The object of these writers, when they had any object beyond an insolent disparagement of the life-blood of the nation, was to jeer the weaker members of the middle class into making themselves a poor fringe on the skirts of the class above them, instead of occupying their own honest, honourable, independent place. Unfortunately they succeeded only too well, and to this grievous source may be traced many of our present political ills. In no country but England have the only means and scenes of relaxation within the reach of some million or two of people been systematically lampooned and derided. This disgraceful Insularity exists no longer. Still, some weak traces of its contemptuous spirit may occasionally be found, even in very unlikely places. The accomplished Mr. Macaulay, in the third volume of his brilliant History, writes loftily about 'the thousands of clerks and milliners who are now thrown into raptures by the sight of Loch Katrine and Loch Lomond.' No such responsible gentleman, in France or Germany, writing history—writing anything—would think it fine to sneer at any inoffensive and useful class of his fellow subjects. If the clerks and milliners—who pair off arm in arm, by thousands, for Loch Katrine and Loch Lomond, to celebrate the Early Closing Movement, we presume—will only imagine their presence poisoning those waters to the majestic historian as he roves along the banks, looking for Whig Members of Parliament to sympathise with him in admiration of the beauties of Nature, we think they will be amply avenged in the absurdity of the picture.

Not one of our Insularities is so astonishing in the eyes of an intelligent foreigner, as the Court Newsman. He is one of the absurd little obstructions perpetually in the way of our being understood abroad. The quiet greatness and independence of the national character seems so irreconcileable with its having any satisfaction in the dull slipslop about the slopes and the gardens, and about the Prince Consort's going a-hunting and coming back to lunch, and about Mr. Gibbs and the ponies, and about the Royal Highnesses on horseback and the Royal infants taking carriage exercise, and about the slopes and the gardens again, and the Prince Consort again, and Mr. Gibbs and the ponies again, and the Royal Highnesses on horseback again, and the Royal infants taking carriage exercise again, and so on for every day in the week and every week in the year, that in questions of importance the English as a people, really miss their just recognition. Similar small beer is chronicled with the greatest care about the nobility in their country-houses. It is in vain to represent that the English people don't care about these insignificant details, and don't want them ; that aggravates the misunderstanding If they don't want them, why do they have them ? If they feel the effect of them to be ridiculous, why do they consent to be made ridiculous ? If they can't help it, why, then the bewildered foreigner submits that he was right at first, and that it is not the English people that is the power, but Lord Aberdeen, or Lord Palmerston, or Lord Aldborough, or Lord Knowswhom.

It is an Insularity well worth general consideration and correction, that the English people are wanting in self-respect. It would be difficult to bear higher testimony to the merits of the English aristocracy than they themselves afford in not being very arrogant or intolerant, with so large a public always ready to abase themselves before titles. On all occasions, public and private, where the opportunity is afforded, this readiness is to be observed. So long as it obtains so widely, it is impossible that we should be justly appreciated and comprehended, by those who have the greatest part in ruling us. And thus it happens that now we are facetiously pooh-poohed by our Premier in the English capital, and now the accredited representatives of our arts and sciences are disdainfully slighted by our Ambassador in the French capital, and we wonder to find ourselves in such curious and disadvantageous comparison with the people of other countries. Those people may, through many causes, be less fortunate and less free ; but, they have more social self-respect : and that self-respect must, through all their changes, be deferred to, and will assert itself. We apprehend that few persons are disposed to contend that Rank does not receive its due share of homage on the continent of Europe ; but, between the homage it receives there, and the homage it receives in our island, there is an immense difference. Half a dozen dukes and lords, at an English county ball, or public dinner, or any tolerably miscellaneous gathering, are painful and disagreeable company ; not because they have any disposition unduly to exalt themselves, or are generally otherwise than cultivated and polite gentlemen, but, because too many of us are prone to twist ourselves out of shape before them, into contortions of servility and adulation. Elsewhere, Self-respect usually steps in to prevent this ; there is much less toadying and tuft-hunting ; and the intercourse between the two orders is infinitely more agreeable to both, and far more edifying to both.

It is one of our Insularities, if we have a royal or titled visitor among us, to use expressions of slavish adulation in our public addresses that have no response in the heart of any breathing creature, and to encourage the diffusion of details respecting such visitor's devout behaviour at church, courtly behaviour in reception-rooms, decent behaviour at dinner-tables, implying previous acquaintance with the uses of knife, fork, spoon, and wine-glass,—which would really seem to denote that we had expected Orson. These doubtful compliments are paid nowhere else, and would not be paid by us if we had a little more self-respect. Through our intercourse with other nations, we cannot too soon import some. And when we have left off representing, fifty times a day, to the King of Brentford and the Chief Tailor of Tooley Street, that their smiles are necessary to our existence, those two magnificent persons will begin to doubt whether they really are so, and we shall have begun to get rid of another Insularity.

A NIGHTLY SCENE IN LONDON

[JANUARY 26, 1856]

On the fifth of last November, I, the Conductor of this journal, accompanied by a friend well-known to the public, accidentally strayed into Whitechapel. It was a miserable evening; very dark, very muddy, and raining hard.

There are many woful sights in that part of London, and it has been well-known to me in most of its aspects for many years. We had forgotten the mud and rain in slowly walking along and looking about us, when we found ourselves, at eight o'clock, before the Workhouse.

Crouched against the wall of the Workhouse, in the dark street, on the muddy pavement-stones, with the rain raining upon them, were five bundles of rags. They were motionless, and had no resemblance to the human form. Five great beehives, covered with rags—five dead bodies taken out of graves, tied neck and heels, and covered with rags—would have looked like those five bundles upon which the rain rained down in the public street.

'What is this!' said my companion. 'What *is* this!'

'Some miserable people shut out of the Casual Ward, I think,' said I.

We had stopped before the five ragged mounds, and were quite rooted to the spot by their horrible appearance. Five awful Sphinxes by the wayside, crying to every passer-by, 'Stop and guess! What is to be the end of a state of society that leaves us here!'

As we stood looking at them, a decent working-man, having the appearance of a stone-mason, touched me on the shoulder.

'This is an awful sight, sir,' said he, 'in a Christian country!'

'God knows it is, my friend,' said I.

'I have often seen it much worse than this, as I have been going home from my work. I have counted fifteen, twenty, five-and-twenty, many a time. It's a shocking thing to see.'

'A shocking thing, indeed,' said I and my companion together.

The man lingered near us a little while, wished us good-night, and went on.

We should have felt it brutal in us who had a better chance of being heard than the working-man, to leave the thing as it was, so we knocked at the Workhouse Gate. I undertook to be spokesman. The moment the gate was opened by an old pauper, I went in, followed close by my companion. I lost no time in passing the old porter, for I saw in his watery eye a disposition to shut us out.

'Be so good as to give that card to the master of the Workhouse, and say I shall be glad to speak to him for a moment.'

We were in a kind of covered gateway, and the old porter went across it with the card. Before he had got to a door on our left, a man in a cloak and hat bounced out of it very sharply, as if he were in the nightly habit of being bullied and of returning the compliment.

'Now, gentlemen,' said he in a loud voice, 'what do you want here?'

'First,' said I, 'will you do me the favour to look at that card in your hand. Perhaps you may know my name.'

'Yes,' says he, looking at it. 'I know this name.'

'Good. I only want to ask you a plain question in a civil manner, and there is not the least occasion for either of us to be angry. It would be very foolish in me to blame you, and I don't blame you. I may find fault with the system you administer, but pray understand that I know you are here to do a duty pointed out to you, and that I have no doubt you do it. Now, I hope you won't object to tell me what I want to know.'

'No,' said he, quite mollified, and very reasonable, 'not at all. What is it?'

'Do you know that there are five wretched creatures outside?'

'I haven't seen them, but I dare say there are.'

'Do you doubt that there are?'

'No, not at all. There might be many more.'

'Are they men? Or women?'

'Women, I suppose. Very likely one or two of them were there last night, and the night before last.'

'There all night, do you mean?'

'Very likely.'

My companion and I looked at one another, and the master of

A NIGHTLY SCENE IN LONDON

the Workhouse added quickly, 'Why, Lord bless my soul, what am I to do? What can I do? The place is full. The place is always full—every night. I must give the preference to women with children, mustn't I? You wouldn't have me not do that?'

'Surely not,' said I. 'It is a very humane principle, and quite right; and I am glad to hear of it. Don't forget that I don't blame *you*.'

'Well!' said he. And subdued himself again.

'What I want to ask you,' I went on, 'is whether you know anything against those five miserable beings outside?'

'Don't know anything about them,' said he, with a wave of his arm.

'I ask, for this reason: that we mean to give them a trifle to get a lodging—if they are not shelterless because they are thieves for instance.—You don't know them to be thieves?'

'I don't know anything about them,' he repeated emphatically.

'That is to say, they are shut out, solely because the Ward is full?'

'Because the Ward is full.'

'And if they got in, they would only have a roof for the night and a bit of bread in the morning, I suppose?'

'That's all. You'll use your own discretion about what you give them. Only understand that I don't know anything about them beyond what I have told you.'

'Just so. I wanted to know no more. You have answered my question civilly and readily, and I am much obliged to you. I have nothing to say against you, but quite the contrary. Good-night!'

'Good-night, gentlemen!' And out we came again.

We went to the ragged bundle nearest to the Workhouse-door, and I touched it. No movement replying, I gently shook it. The rags began to be slowly stirred within, and by little and little a head was unshrouded. The head of a young woman of three or four and twenty, as I should judge; gaunt with want, and foul with dirt; but not naturally ugly.

'Tell us,' said I, stooping down. 'Why are you lying here?'

'Because I can't get into the Workhouse.'

She spoke in a faint dull way, and had no curiosity or interest left. She looked dreamily at the black sky and the falling rain, but never looked at me or my companion.

'Were you here last night?'

'Yes. All last night. And the night afore too.'

'Do you know any of these others?'

'I know her next but one. She was here last night, and she told me she come out of Essex. I don't know no more of her.'

'You were here all last night, but you have not been here all day?'

'No. Not all day.'

'Where have you been all day?'

'About the streets.'

'What have you had to eat?'

'Nothing.'

'Come!' said I. 'Think a little. You are tired and have been asleep, and don't quite consider what you are saying to us. You have had something to eat to-day. Come! Think of it!'

'No I haven't. Nothing but such bits as I could pick up about the market. *Why, look at me!*'

She bared her neck, and I covered it up again.

'If you had a shilling to get some supper and a lodging, should you know where to get it?'

'Yes. I could do that.'

'For GOD's sake get it then!'

I put the money into her hand, and she feebly rose up and went away. She never thanked me, never looked at me—melted away into the miserable night, in the strangest manner I ever saw. I have seen many strange things, but not one that has left a deeper impression on my memory than the dull impassive way in which that worn-out heap of misery took that piece of money, and was lost.

One by one I spoke to all the five. In every one, interest and curiosity were as extinct as in the first. They were all dull and languid. No one made any sort of profession or complaint; no one cared to look at me; no one thanked me. When I came to the third, I suppose she saw that my companion and I glanced, with a new horror upon us, at the two last, who had dropped against each other in their sleep, and were lying like broken images. She said, she believed they were young sisters. These were the only words that were originated among the five.

And now let me close this terrible account with a redeeming and

A NIGHTLY SCENE IN LONDON

beautiful trait of the poorest of the poor. When we came out of the Workhouse, we had gone across the road to a public house, finding ourselves without silver, to get change for a sovereign. I held the money in my hand while I was speaking to the five apparitions. Our being so engaged, attracted the attention of many people of the very poor sort usual to that place; as we leaned over the mounds of rags, they eagerly leaned over us to see and hear; what I had in my hand, and what I said, and what I did, must have been plain to nearly all the concourse. When the last of the five had got up and faded away, the spectators opened to let us pass; and not one of them, by word, or look, or gesture, begged of us. Many of the observant faces were quick enough to know that it would have been a relief to us to have got rid of the rest of the money with any hope of doing good with it. But, there was a feeling among them all, that their necessities were not to be placed by the side of such a spectacle; and they opened a way for us in profound silence, and let us go.

My companion wrote to me, next day, that the five ragged bundles had been upon his bed all night. I debated how to add our testimony to that of many other persons who from time to time are impelled to write to the newspapers, by having come upon some shameful and shocking sight of this description. I resolved to write in these pages an exact account of what we had seen, but to wait until after Christmas, in order that there might be no heat or haste. I know that the unreasonable disciples of a reasonable school, demented disciples who push arithmetic and political economy beyond all bounds of sense (not to speak of such a weakness as humanity), and hold them to be all-sufficient for every case, can easily prove that such things ought to be, and that no man has any business to mind them. Without disparaging those indispensable sciences in their sanity, I utterly renounce and abominate them in their insanity; and I address people with a respect for the spirit of the New Testament, who do mind such things, and who think them infamous in our streets.

91

THE FRIEND OF THE LIONS

[FEBRUARY 2, 1856]

WE are in the Studio of a friend of ours, whose knowledge of all kinds of Beasts and Birds has never been surpassed, and to whose profound acquaintance with the whole Animal Kingdom, every modern picture-gallery and every print-shop, at home and abroad, bears witness. We have been wanted by our friend as a model for a Rat-catcher. We feel much honoured, and are sitting to him in that distinguished capacity, with an awful Bulldog much too near us.

Our friend is, as might be expected, the particular friend of the Lions in the Zoological Gardens, Regent's Park, London. On behalf of that Royal Family dear to his heart, he offers— standing painting away at his easel, with his own wonderful vigour and ease—a few words of friendly remonstrance to the Zoological Society.

You are an admirable society (says our friend, throwing in, now a bit of our head, and now a bit of the Bulldog's), and you have done wonders. You are a society that has established in England, a national menagerie of the most beautiful description, and that has placed it freely and in a spirit deserving of the highest commendation within the reach of the great body of the people. You are a society rendering a real service and advantage to the public, and always most sensibly and courteously represented by your excellent Mitchell.

Then why (proceeds our friend), don't you treat your Lions better?

In the earnestness of his enquiry, our friend looks harder than usual at the Bulldog. The Bulldog immediately droops and becomes embarrassed. All dogs feel that our friend knows all their secrets, and that it is utterly hopeless to attempt to take him in. The last base action committed by this Bulldog is on his conscience, the moment our friend fixes him. 'What? You did, eh?' says our friend to the Bulldog. The Bulldog licks his lips with the greatest nervousness, winks his red eyes, balances himself afresh on his bandy forelegs, and becomes a spectacle of dejection. He is as little like his vagabond self, as that remarkable breed which the French call a bouledogue.

Your birds (says our friend, resuming his work, and addressing himself again to the Zoological Society), are as happy as the day is—he was about to add, long, but glances at the light and substitutes—short. Their natural habits are perfectly understood, their structure is well-considered, and they have nothing to desire. Pass from your birds to those members of your collection whom Mr. Rogers used to call, 'our poor relations.' Of course I mean the monkeys. They have an artificial climate carefully prepared for them. They have the blessing of congenial society carefully secured to them. They are among their own tribes and connexions. They have shelves to skip upon, and pigeon-holes to creep into. Graceful ropes dangle from the upper beams of their sitting-rooms, by which they swing, for their own enjoyment, the fascination of the fair sex, and the instruction of the enquiring minds of the rising generation. Pass from our poor relations to that beast, the Hippopotamus—What do you mean?

The last enquiry is addressed, not to the Zoological Society, but to the Bulldog, who has deserted his position, and is sneaking away. Passing his brush into the left thumb on which he holds his palette, our friend leisurely walks up to the Bulldog, and slaps his face! Even we, whose faith is great, expect to see him next moment with the Bulldog hanging on to his nose; but, the Bulldog is abjectly polite, and would even wag his tail if it had not been bitten off in his infancy.

Pass, I was saying (coolly pursues our friend at his easel again), from our poor relations to that impersonation of sensuality, the Hippopotamus. How do you provide for him? Could he find, on the banks of the Nile, such a villa as you have built for him on the banks of the Regent's canal? Could he find, in his native Egypt, an appropriately furnished drawing-room, study, bath, wash-house, and spacious pleasure-ground, all *en suite*, and always ready? I think not. Now, I beseech your managing committee and your natural philosophers, to come with me and look at the Lions.

Here, our friend seizes a piece of charcoal and instantly produces, on a new canvas standing on another easel near, a noble Lion and

Lioness. The Bulldog (who deferentially resumed his position after having his face slapped), looks on in manifest uneasiness, lest this new proceeding should have something to do with him.

There! says our friend, throwing the charcoal away, there they are! The majestic King and Queen of quadrupeds. The British Lion is no longer a fictitious creature in the British coat of arms. You produce your British Lion every year from this royal couple. And how, with all the vast amount of resources, knowledge, and experience at your command, how do you treat these your great attractions? From day to day, I find the noble creatures patiently wearing out their weary lives in narrow spaces where they have hardly room to turn, and condemned to face in the roughest weather a bitter Nor'-Westerly aspect. Look at those wonderfully-constructed feet, with their exquisite machinery for alighting from springs and leaps. What do you conceive to be the kind of ground to which those feet are, in the great foresight of Nature, least adapted? Bare, smooth, hard boards, perhaps, like the deck of a ship? Yes. A strange reason why you should choose that and no other flooring for their dens!

Why, Heaven preserve us! (cries our friend, frightening the Bulldog very much) do any of you keep a cat? Will any of you do me the favour to watch a cat in a field or garden, on a bright sunshiny day—how she crouches in the mould, rolls in the sand, basks in the grass, delights to vary the surface upon which she rests, and change the form of the substance upon which she takes her ease. Compare such surfaces and substances with the one uniform, unyielding, unnatural, unelastic, inappropriate piece of human carpentry upon which these beautiful animals, with their vexed faces, pace and repace, and pass each other two hundred and fifty times an hour.

It is really incomprehensible (our friend proceeds), in you who should be so well acquainted with animals, to call these boards—or that other uncomfortable boarded object like a Mangle with the inside taken out—a Bed, for creatures with these limbs and these habits. That, a Bed for a Lion and Lioness, which does not even give them a chance of being bruised in a new place? Learn of your cat again, and see how *she* goes to bed. Did you ever find her, or any living creature, go to bed, without re-arranging to the whim and sensation of the moment, the materials of the bed itself? Don't you, the Zoological Society, punch and poke your pillows, and settle

94

THE FRIEND OF THE LIONS

into suitable places in your beds? Consider then, what the discomfort of these magnificent brutes must be, to whom you leave no diversity of choice, no power of new arrangement, and as to whose unchanging and unyielding beds you begin with a form and substance that have no parallel in their natural lives. If you doubt the pain they must endure, go to museums and colleges where the bones of lions and other animals of the feline tribe who have lived in captivity under similar circumstances, are preserved; and you will find them thickly encrusted with a granulated substance, the result of long lying upon unnatural and uncomfortable planes.

I will not be so pressing as to the feeding of my Royal Friends (pursues the Master), but even there I think you are wrong. You may rely upon it, that the best regulated families of Lions and Lionesses don't dine every day punctually at the same hour, in their natural state, and don't always keep the same kind and quantity of meat in the larder. However, I will readily waive that question of board, if you will only abandon the other.

The time of the sitting being out, our friend takes his palette from his thumb, lays it aside with his brush, ceases to address the Zoological Society, and releases the Bulldog and myself. Having occasion to look closely at the Bulldog's chest, he turns that model over as if he were made of clay (if I were to touch him with my little finger he would pin me instantly), and examines him without the smallest regard to his personal wishes or convenience. The Bulldog, having humbly submitted, is shown to the door.

'Eleven precisely, to-morrow,' says our friend, 'or it will be the worse for you.' The Bulldog respectfully slouches out. Looking out of the window, I presently see him going across the garden, accompanied by a particularly ill-looking proprietor with a black eye—my prototype I presume—again a ferocious and audacious Bulldog, who will evidently kill some other dog before he gets home.

95

WHY?

[MARCH 1, 1856]

I AM going to ask a few questions which frequently present themselves to my mind. I am not going to ask them with any expectation of getting an answer, but in the comforting hope that I shall find some thousands of sympathising readers, whose minds are constantly asking similar questions.

Why does a young woman of prepossessing appearance, glossy hair, and neat attire, taken from any station of life and put behind the counter of a Refreshment Room on an English Railroad, conceive the idea that her mission in life is to treat me with scorn? Why does she disdain my plaintive and respectful solicitations for portions of pork-pie or cups of tea? Why does she feed me like a hyæna? What have I done to incur the young lady's displeasure? Is it, that I have come there to be refreshed? It is strange that she should take that ill, because her vocation would be gone if I and my fellow-travellers did not appear before her, suing in humility to be allowed to lay out a little money. Yet I never offered her any other injury. Then, why does she wound my sensitive nature by being so dreadfully cross to me? She has relations, friends, acquaintances, with whom to quarrel. Why does she pick *me* out for her natural enemy?

When a Reviewer or other Writer has crammed himself to choking with some particularly abstruse piece of information, why does he introduce it with the casual remark, that 'every schoolboy knows' it? He didn't know it himself last week; why is it indispensable that he should let off this introductory cracker among his readers? We have a vast number of extraordinary fictions in common use, but this fiction of the schoolboy is the most unaccountable to me of all. It supposes the schoolboy to know everything. The schoolboy knows the exact distance, to an inch, from the moon to Uranus. The schoolboy knows every conceivable quotation from the Greek and Latin authors. The schoolboy is up at present, and has been these two years, in the remotest corners of the maps of Russia and Turkey; previously to which display of his geographical accomplishments he had been on the most intimate terms with the whole of the gold regions of Australia. If there were a run against the monetary system of the country to-morrow, we should find this prodigy of a schoolboy down upon us with the deepest mysteries of banking and the currency. We have nearly got rid of the Irishman who stood by us so long, and did so much public service, by enabling the narrators of facetious anecdotes to introduce them with 'As the Irishman said.' We have quite got rid of the Frenchman who was for many years in partnership with him. Are we never, on any terms, to get rid of the schoolboy?

If the Court Circular be a sacred institution for the edification of a free people, why is the most abhorred villain always invested, in right of that frightful distinction, with a Court Circular of his own? Why am I always to be told about the ruffian's pleasant manners, his easy ways, his agreeable smile, his affable talk, the profound conviction of his innocence that he blandly wafts into the soft bosoms of guileless lambs of turnkeys, the orthodox air with which he comes and goes, with his Bible and prayer-book in his hand, along the yard, that I fervently hope may have no outlet for him but the gallows? Why am I to be dosed and drenched with these nauseous particulars, in the case of every wretch sufficiently atrocious to become their subject? Why am I supposed never to know all about it beforehand, and never to have been pelted with similar mud in my life? Has not the whole detestable programme been presented to me without variation, fifty times? Am I not familiar with every line of it, from its not being generally known that Sharmer was much respected in the County of Blankshire, down to the virtuous heat of Bilkins, Sharmer's counsel, when, in his eloquent address, he cautions the jurymen about laying their heads on their pillows, and is moved to pious wrath by the wicked predisposition of human nature to object to the foulest murder that its faculties can imagine? Why, why, why, must I have the Newgate Court Circular over and over again, as if the genuine Court Circular were not enough to make me modestly independent, proud, grateful, and happy?

When I overhear my friend Blackdash inquire of my friend Asterisk whether he knows Sir Giles Scroggins, why does Asterisk reply, provisionally and with limitation, that he has met him? Asterisk knows as well as I do, that he has no acquaintance with

Sir Giles Scroggins; why does he hesitate to say so, point blank? A man may not even know Sir Giles Scroggins by sight, yet be a man for a' that. A man may distinguish himself, without the privity and aid of Sir Giles Scroggins. It is even supposed by some that a man may get to Heaven without being introduced by Sir Giles Scroggins. Then why not come out with the bold declaration, 'I really do not know Sir Giles Scroggins, and I have never found that eminent person in the least necessary to my existence?'

When I go to the Play, why must I find everything conventionally done—reference to nature discharged, and reference to stage-usage the polar star of the dramatic art? Why does the baron, or the general, or the venerable steward, or the amiable old farmer, talk about his chee-ilde? He knows of no such thing as a chee-ilde anywhere else; what business has he with a chee-ilde on the boards alone? I never knew an old gentleman to hug himself with his left arm, fall into a comic fit of delirium tremens, and say to his son, 'Damme, you dog, will you marry her?' Yet, the moment I see an old gentleman on the stage with a small cape to his coat, I know of course that this will infallibly happen. Now, why should I be under the obligation to be always entertained by this spectacle, however refreshing, and why should I never be surprised?

Why have six hundred men been trying through several generations to fold their arms? The last twenty Parliaments have directed their entire attention to this graceful art. I have heard it frequently declared by individual senators that a certain ex-senator still producible, 'folded his arms better than any man in the house.' I have seen aspirants inflamed with a lofty ambition, studying through whole sessions the folded arms on the Treasury Bench, and trying to fold their arms according to the patterns there presented. I have known neophytes far more distracted about the folding of their arms than about the enunciation of their political views, or the turning of their periods. The injury inflicted on the nation by Mr. Canning, when he folded his arms and got his portrait taken, is not to be calculated. Every member of Parliament from that hour to the present has been trying to fold his arms. It is a graceful, a refined, a decorative art; but, I doubt if its results will bear comparison with the infinite pains and charges bestowed upon its cultivation.

WHY?

Why are we so fond of talking about ourselves as 'eminently a practical people?' *Are* we eminently a practical people? In our national works, for example; our public buildings, our public places, our columns, the lines of our new streets, our monstrous statues; do we come so very practically out of all that? No, to be sure; but we have our railroads, results of private enterprise, and they are great works. Granted. Yet, is it very significant of an eminently practical people that we live under a system which wasted hundreds of thousands of pounds in law and corruption, before an inch of those roads could be made! Is it a striking proof of an eminently practical people having invested their wealth in making them, that in point of money return, in point of public accommodation, in every particular of comfort, profit, and management, they are at a heavy discount when compared with the railways on the opposite side of a sea-channel five-and twenty miles across, though those were made under all the disadvantages consequent upon unstable governments and shaken public confidence? Why do we brag so? If an inhabitant of some other sphere were to light upon our earth in the neighbourhood of Norwich, were to take a first-class ticket to London, were to attend an Eastern Counties' Railway meeting in Bishopsgate Street, were to go down from London Bridge to Dover, cross to Calais, travel from Calais to Marseilles, and be furnished with an accurate statement of the railway cost and profit on either side of the water (having compared the ease and comfort for himself), which people would he suppose to be the eminently practical one, I wonder!

Why, on the other hand, do we adopt, as a mere matter of lazy usage, charges against ourselves, that have as little foundation as some of our boasts? We are eminently a money-loving people. Are we? Well, we are bad enough; but, I have heard Money more talked of in a week under the stars and stripes, than in a year under the union-jack. In a two hours' walk in Paris, any day, you shall overhear more scraps of conversation that turn upon Money, Money, Money, Money, than in a whole day's saunter between Temple Bar and the Royal Exchange. I go into the Théâtre Français, after the rising of the curtain; fifty to one the first words I hear from the stage as I settle myself in my seat, are fifty thousand francs; she has a dowry of fifty thousand francs; he has an income of fifty thousand francs; I will bet you fifty thousand francs upon it, my

99

dear Emile; I come from winning at the Bourse, my celestial Diane, fifty thousand francs. I pass into the Boulevard theatres one by one. At the Variétés, I find an old lady who must be conciliated by two opposing nephews, because she has fifty thousand francs per annum. At the Gymnase, I find the English Prime Minister (attended by his faithful servant Tom Bob), in a fearful predicament occasioned by injudicious speculation in millions of francs. At the Porte St. Martin, I find a picturesque person with a murder on his mind, into which he has been betrayed by a pressing necessity for a box containing fifty thousand francs. At the Ambigu, I find everybody poisoning everybody else for fifty thousand francs. At the Lyrique, I find on the stage a portly old gentleman, a slender young gentleman, and a piquante little woman with sprightly eyebrows, all singing an extremely short song together about fifty thousand francs Lira lara, fifty thousand francs Ting ting! At the Impérial, I find a general with his arm in a bandage, sitting in a magnificent summer-house, relating his autobiography to his niece, and arriving at this point: ' It is to this ravishing spot then, my dearest Julie, that I, thy uncle, faithful always to his Emperor, then retired; bringing with me my adorable Georgette, this wounded arm, this cross of glory, the love of France, remembrances ever inextinguishable of the Emperor my master, and fifty thousand francs.' At this establishment the sum begins to diminish, and goes on rapidly decreasing until I finish at the Funambules and find Pierrot despoiling a friend of only one hundred francs, to the great satisfaction of the congregated blouses. Again. Will any Englishman undertake to match me that generic French old lady whom I will instantly produce against him, from the private life of any house of five floors in the French capital, and who is a mere gulf for swallowing my money, or any man's money? That generic French old lady who, whether she gives me her daughter to wife, or sits next me in a balcony at a theatre, or opposite to me in a public carriage, or lets me an apartment, or plays me a match at dominoes, or sells me an umbrella, equally absorbs my substance, calculates my resources with a fierce nicety, and is intent upon my ruin? That generic French old lady who is always in black, and always protuberant, and always complimentary, and who always eats up everything that is presented to her—almost eats her knife besides —and who has a supernatural craving after francs which fascinates

WHY?

me, and inclines me to pour out all I have at her feet, saying, 'Take them and twinkle at me with those hungry eyes no more?' *We* eminently a money-loving people! Why do we talk such nonsense with this terrible old woman to contradict us?

Why do we take conclusions into our heads for which we have no warrant, and bolt with them like mad horses, until we are brought up by stone walls? Why do we go cheering and shouting after an officer who didn't run away—as though all the rest of our brave officers did run away!—and why do we go plucking hairs out of the tail of the identical charger, and why do we follow up the identical uniform, and why do we stupidly roar ourselves hoarse with acclamation about nothing? Why don't we stop to think? Why don't we say to one another, 'What have the identical charger and the identical uniform done for us, and what have they done against us: let us look at the account.' How much better this would be than straining our throats first, and afterwards discovering that there was less than no reason for the same!

Why am I, at any given moment, in tears of triumph and joy, because Buffy and Boodle are at the head of public affairs? I freely declare that I have not the least idea what specific action Buffy and Boodle have ever in the whole course of their existence done, that has been of any appreciable advantage to my beloved country. On the other hand, I no less freely acknowledge that I have seen Buffy and Boodle (with some small appearance of trading in principles), nail their colours to every mast in the political fleet. Yet I swear to everybody—because everybody swears to me—that Buffy and Boodle are the only men for the crisis, and that none of women born, but Buffy and Boodle, could pull us through it. I would quarrel with my son for Buffy and Boodle. I almost believe that in one of my states of excitement I would die for Buffy and Boodle. I expect to be presently subscribing for statues to Buffy and Boodle. Now, I am curious to know why I go on in this way? I am profoundly in earnest; but I want to know Why?

I wonder why I feel a glow of complacency in a court of justice, when I hear the learned judges taking uncommon pains to prevent the prisoner from letting out the truth. If the object of the trial be to discover the truth, perhaps it might be as edifying to hear it, even from the prisoner, as to hear what is unquestionably not the truth from the prisoner's advocate. I wonder why I say, in a flushed

101

and rapturous manner, that it would be ' un-English ' to examine the prisoner. I suppose that with common fairness it would be next to impossible to confuse him, unless he lied ; and if he did lie, I suppose he could hardly be brought to confusion too soon. Why does that word ' un-English,' always act as a spell upon me, and why do I suffer it to settle any question ? Twelve months ago, it was un-English to abstain from throttling our soldiers. Thirty years ago, it was un-English not to hang people up by scores every Monday. Sixty years ago, it was un-English to be sober after dinner. A hundred years ago, it was un-English not to love cock-fighting, prize-fighting, dog-fighting, bull-baiting, and other savageries. Why do I submit to the word as a clincher, without asking myself whether it has any meaning ? I don't dispute that I do so, every day of my life ; but I want to know why I do so ?

On the other hand, why am I meek in regard of really non-English sentiments, if the potent bugbear of that term be not called into play ? Here is a magistrate tells me I am one of a nation of drunkards. All Englishmen are drunkards, is the judicial bray. Here is another magistrate propounding from the seat of justice the stupendous nonsense that it is desirable that every person who gives alms in the streets should be fined for that offence. This to a Christian people, and with the New Testament lying before him—as a sort of Dummy, I suppose, to swear witnesses on. Why does my so-easily-frightened nationality not take offence at such things ? My hobby shies at shadows ; why does it amble so quietly past these advertising-vans of Blockheads seeking notoriety ?

Why ? I might as well ask, Why I leave off here, when I have a long perspective of Why stretching out before me.

RAILWAY DREAMING

[May 10, 1856]

When was I last in France all the winter, deducting the many hours I passed upon the wet and windy way between France and England? In what autumn and spring was it that those Champs Elysées trees were yellow and scant of leaf when I first looked at them out of my balcony, and were a bright and tender green when I last looked at them on a beautiful May morning?

I can't make out. I am never sure of time or place upon a Railroad. I can't read, I can't think, I can't sleep—I can only dream. Rattling along in this railway carriage in a state of luxurious confusion, I take it for granted I am coming from somewhere, and going somewhere else. I seek to know no more. Why things come into my head and fly out again, whence they come and why they come, where they go and why they go, I am incapable of considering. It may be the guard's business, or the railway company's; I only know it is not mine. I know nothing about myself—for anything I know, I may be coming from the Moon.

If I am coming from the Moon, what an extraordinary people the Mooninians must be for sitting down in the open air! I have seen them wipe the hoar-frost off the seats in the public ways, on the faintest appearance of a gleam of sun, and sit down to enjoy themselves. I have seen them, two minutes after it has left off raining for the first time in eight-and-forty hours, take chairs in the midst of the mud and water, and begin to chat. I have seen them by the roadside, easily reclining on iron couches, when their beards have been all but blown off their chins by the east wind. I have seen them, with no protection from the black drizzle and dirt but a saturated canvas blind overhead, and a handful of sand underfoot, smoke and drink new beer, whole evenings. And the Mooninian babies. Heavens, what a surprising race are the Mooninian babies! Seventy-one of these innocents have I counted, with their nurses and chairs, spending the day outside the Café de la Lune, in weather that would have satisfied Herod. Thirty-nine have I beheld in that locality at once, with these eyes, partaking of their

103

natural refreshment under umbrellas. Twenty-three have I seen
engaged with skipping-ropes, in mire three inches thick. At three
years old the Mooninian babies grow up. They are by that time
familiar with coffee-houses, and used up as to truffles. They dine
at six. Soup, fish, two entrées, a vegetable, a cold dish, or paté-de-
foie-gras, a roast, a salad, a sweet, and a preserved peach or so, form
(with occasional whets of sardines, radishes, and Lyons sausage)
their frugal repast. They breakfast at eleven, on a light beefsteak
with Madeira sauce, a kidney steeped in champagne, a trifle of
sweetbread, a plate of fried potatoes, and a glass or two of wholesome Bordeaux wine. I have seen a marriageable young female aged
five, in a mature bonnet and crinoline, finish off at a public establishment with her amiable parents, on coffee that would consign a child
of any other nation to the family undertaker in one experiment. I
have dined at a friendly party, sitting next to a Mooninian baby,
who ate of nine dishes besides ice and fruit, and, wildly stimulated
by sauces, in all leisure moments flourished its spoon about its head
in the manner of a pictorial glory.

The Mooninian Exchange was a strange sight in my time. The
Mooninians of all ranks and classes were gambling at that period
(whenever it was), in the wildest manner—in a manner, which, in its
extension to all possible subjects of gambling, and in the prevalence
of the frenzy among all grades, has few parallels that I can recall.
The steps of the Mooninian Bourse were thronged every day with
a vast, hot, mad crowd, so expressive of the desperate game in
which the whole City were players, that one stood aghast. In the
Mooninian Journals I read, any day, without surprise, how such a
Porter had rushed out of such a house and flung himself into the
river, ' because of losses on the Bourse'; or how such a man had
robbed such another, with the intent of acquiring funds for speculation on the Bourse. In the great Mooninian Public Drive, every
day, there were crowds of riders on blood-horses, and crowds of riders
in dainty carriages red-velvet lined and white-leather harnessed, all
of whom had the cards and counters in their pockets; who were all
feeding the blood-horses on paper and stabling them on the board;
who were leading a grand life at a great rate and with a mighty
show; who were all profuse and prosperous while the cards could
continue to be shuffled and the deals to go round.

In the same place, I saw, nearly every day, a curious spectacle.

RAILWAY DREAMING

One pretty little child at a window, always waving his hand at, and cheering, an array of open carriages escorted by out-riders in green and gold; and no one echoing the child's acclamation. Occasional deference in carriages, occasional curiosity on foot, occasional adulation from foreigners, I noticed in that connection, in that place; but, four great streams of determined indifference I always saw flowing up and down; and I never, in six months, knew a hand or heard a voice to come in real aid of the child.

I am not a lonely man, though I was once a lonely boy; but that was long ago. The Mooninian capital, however, is the place for lonely men to dwell in. I have tried it, and have condemned myself to solitary freedom expressly for the purpose. I sometimes like to pretend to be childless and companionless, and to wonder whether, if I were really so, I should be glad to find somebody to ask me out to dinner, instead of living under a constant terror of weakly making engagements that I don't want to make. Hence, I have been into many Mooninian restaurants as a lonely man. The company have regarded me as an unfortunate person of that description. The paternal character, occupying the next table with two little boys whose legs were difficult of administration in a narrow space, as never being the right legs in the right places, has regarded me, at first, with looks of envy. When the little boys have indecorously inflated themselves out of the seltzer-water bottle, I have seen discomfiture and social shame on that Mooninian's brow. Meanwhile I have sat majestically using my tooth-pick, in silent assertion of my counterfeit superiority. And yet it has been good to see how that family Mooninian has vanquished me in the long-run. I have never got so red in the face over my meat and wine, as he. I have never warmed up into such enjoyment of my meal as he has of his. I have never forgotten the legs of the little boys, whereas from that Mooninian's soul they have quickly walked into oblivion. And when, at last, under the ripening influence of dinner, those boys have both together pulled at that Mooninian's waistcoat (imploring him, as I conceived, to take them to the play-house, next door but one), I have shrunk under the glance he has given me; so emphatically has it said, with the virtuous farmer in the English domestic comedy, 'Dang it, Squoire, can'ee doa thic!' (I may explain in a parenthesis that 'thic,' which the virtuous farmer can do and the squire can't, is to lay his hand upon his heart—a result opposed to

105

my experience in actual life, where the humbugs are always able to lay their hands upon their hearts, and do it far oftener and much better than the virtuous men.)

In my solitary character I have walked forth after eating my dinner and paying my bill—in the Mooninian capital we used to call the bill ' the addition '—to take my coffee and cigar at some separate establishment devoted to such enjoyments. And in the customs belonging to these, as in many other easy and gracious customs, the Mooninians are highly deserving of imitation among ourselves. I have never had far to go, unless I have been particularly hard to please ; a dozen houses at the utmost. A spring evening is in my mind when I sauntered from my dinner into one of these resorts, haphazard. The thoroughfare in which it stood, was not as wide as the Strand in London, by Somerset House ; the houses were no larger and no better than are to be found in that place ; the climate (we find ours a convenient scapegoat) had been, for months, quite as cold and wet, and very very often almost as dark, as the climate in the Strand. The place into which I turned, had been there all the winter just as it was then. It was like a Strand-shop, with the front altogether taken away. Within, it was sanded, prettily painted and papered, decorated with mirrors and glass chandeliers for gas ; furnished with little round stone tables, crimson stools, and crimson benches. It was made much more tasteful (at the cost of three and fourpence a week) by two elegant baskets of flowers on pedestals. An inner raised-floor, answering to the back shop in the Strand, was partitioned off with glass, for those who might prefer to read the papers and play at dominoes, in an atmosphere free from tobacco-smoke. There, in her neat little tribune, sits the Lady of the Counter, surrounded at her needlework by lump-sugar and little punch-bowls. To whom I touch my hat ; she graciously acknowledging the salute. Forth from her side comes a pleasant waiter, scrupulously clean, brisk, attentive, honest : a man to be very obliging to me, but expecting me to be obliging in return, and whom I cannot bully—which is no deprivation to me, as I don't at all want to do it. He brings me, at my request, my cup of coffee and cigar, and, of his own motion, a small decanter of brandy and a liqueur-glass. He gives me a light, and leaves me to my enjoyment. The place from which the shop-front has been taken makes a gay proscenium ; as I sit and smoke, the street becomes a stage, with an endless procession of lively actors crossing and re-crossing. Women with children, carts and coaches, men on horseback, soldiers, water-carriers with their pails, family groups, more soldiers, lounging exquisites, more family groups (coming past, flushed, a little too late for the play), stone-masons leaving work on the new buildings and playing tricks with one another as they go along, two lovers, more soldiers, wonderfully neat young women from shops, carrying flat boxes to customers; a seller of cool drink, with the drink in a crimson velvet temple at his back, and a waistcoat of tumblers on; boys, dogs, more soldiers, horse-riders strolling to the Circus in amazing shirts of private life, and yellow kid gloves; family groups; pickers-up of refuse, with baskets at their backs and hooked rods in their hands to fill them with; more neat young women, more soldiers. The gas begins to spring up in the street; and my brisk waiter lighting our gas, enshrines me, like an idol, in a sparkling temple. A family group come in: father and mother and little child. Two short-throated old ladies come in, who will pocket their spare sugar, and out of whom I foresee that the establishment will get as little profit as possible. Workman in his common frock comes in; orders his small bottle of beer, and lights his pipe. We are all amused, sitting seeing the traffic in the street, and the traffic in the street is in its turn amused by seeing us. It is surely better for me, and for the family group, and for the two old ladies, and for the workman, to have thus much of community with the city life of all degrees, than to be getting bilious in hideous black-holes, and turning cross and suspicious in solitary places! I may never say a word to any of these people in my life, nor they to me; but, we are all interchanging enjoyment frankly and openly—not fencing ourselves off and boxing ourselves up. We are forming a habit of mutual consideration and allowance; and this institution of the café (for all my entertainment and pleasure in which, I pay tenpence), is a part of the civilised system that requires the giant to fall into his own place in a crowd, and will not allow him to take the dwarf's; and which renders the commonest person as certain of retaining his or her commonest seat in any public assembly, as the marquis is of holding his stall at the Opera through the evening.

There were many things among the Mooninians that might be changed for the better, and there were many things that they might learn from us. They could teach us, for all that, how to make and keep a Park—which we have been accustomed to think ourselves rather learned in—and how to trim up our ornamental streets, a dozen times a-day, with scrubbing-brushes, and sponges, and soap, and chloride of lime. As to the question of sweetness within doors, I would rather not have put my own residence, even under the perpetual influence of peat charcoal, in competition with the cheapest model lodging-house in England. And one strange sight, which I have contemplated many a time during the last dozen years, I think is not so well arranged in the Mooninian capital as in London, even though our coroners hold their dread courts at the little public-houses —a custom which I am of course prepared to hear is, and which I know beforehand must be, one of the Bulwarks of the British Constitution.

I am thinking of the Mooninian Morgue, where the bodies of all persons discovered dead, with no clue to their identity upon them, are placed to be seen by all who choose to go and look at them. All the world knows this custom, and perhaps all the world knows that the bodies lie on inclined planes within a great glass window, as though Holbein should represent Death, in his grim Dance, keeping a shop, and displaying his goods like a Regent Street or Boulevard linen-draper. But, all the world may not have had the means of remarking perhaps, as I by chance have had from time to time, some of the accidental peculiarities of the place. The keeper seems to be fond of birds. In fair weather, there is always a cage outside his little window, and a something singing within it as such a something sang, thousands of ages ago, before ever a man died on this earth. The spot is sunny in the forenoon, and, there being a little open space there, and a market for fruit and vegetables close at hand, and a way to the Great Cathedral past the door, is a reasonably good spot for mountebanks. Accordingly, I have often found Paillasse there, balancing a knife or a straw upon his nose, with such intentness that he has almost backed himself in at the doorway. The learned owls have elicited great mirth there, within my hearing, and once the performing dog who had a wait in his part, came and peeped in, with a red jacket on, while I was alone in the contemplation of five bodies, one with a bullet through the temple. It happened, on another occasion, that a handsome youth lay in front in the centre of the window, and that a press of people behind me rendered it a difficult and slow process to get out. As I gave place to the man at my right shoulder, he slipped into the position I had occupied, with his attention so concentrated on the dead figure that he seemed unaware of the change of place. I never saw a plainer expression than that upon his features, or one that struck more enduringly into my remembrance. He was an evil-looking fellow of two or three and twenty, and had his left hand at the draggled ends of his cravat, which he had put to his mouth, and his right hand feeling in his breast. His head was a little on one side; his eyes were intently fixed upon the figure. 'Now, if I were to give that pretty young fellow, my rival, a stroke with a hatchet on the back of the head, or were to tumble him over into the river by night, he would look pretty much like that, I am thinking!' He could not have said it more plainly;—I have always an idea that he went away and did it.

It is wonderful to see the people at this place. Cheery married women, basket in hand, strolling in, on their way to or from the buying of the day's dinner; children in arms with little pointing fingers; young girls; prowling boys; comrades in working, soldiering, or what not. Ninety-nine times in a hundred, nobody about to cross the threshold, looking in the faces coming out, could form the least idea, from anything in their expression, of the nature of the sight. I have studied them attentively, and have reason for saying so.

But, I never derived so strange a sensation from this dismal establishment as on going in there once, and finding the keeper moving about among the bodies. I never saw any living creature in among them, before or since, and the wonder was that he looked so much more ghastly and intolerable than the dead, stark people. There is a strong light from above, and a general cold, clammy aspect; and I think that with the first start of seeing him must have come the impression that the bodies were all getting up! It was instantaneous; but he looked horribly incongruous there, even after it had departed. All about him was a library of mysterious books that I have often had my eyes on. From pegs and hooks and rods, hang, for a certain time, the clothes of the dead who have been buried without recognition. They mostly have been taken off people who were found in the water, and are swollen (as the people often are) out of shape and likeness. Such awful boots, with turned-up toes, and sand and gravel clinging to them, shall be seen in no other collection of dress; nor, such neckcloths, long and lank, still retaining the form of having been wrung out; nor, such slimy garments with puffed legs and arms; nor such hats and caps that have been battered against pile and bridge; nor, such dreadful rags. Whose work ornaments that decent blouse; who sewed that shirt? And the man who wore it. Did he ever stand at this window wondering, as I do, what sleepers shall be brought to these beds, and whether wonderers as to who should occupy them, have come to be laid down here themselves?

London! Please to get your tickets ready, gentlemen! I must have a coach. And that reminds me, how much better they manage coaches for the public in the capital of the Mooninians! But, it is done by Centralisation! somebody shrieks to me from some vestry's topmost height. Then, my good sir, let us have Centralisation. It is a long word, but I am not at all afraid of long words when they represent efficient things. Circumlocution is a long word, but it represents inefficiency; inefficiency in everything; inefficiency from the state coach to my hackney cab.

THE DEMEANOUR OF MURDERERS

[June 14, 1856]

The recent trial of the greatest villain[1] that ever stood in the Old Bailey dock, has produced the usual descriptions inseparable from such occasions. The public has read from day to day of the murderer's complete self-possession, of his constant coolness, of his profound composure, of his perfect equanimity. Some describers have gone so far as to represent him, occasionally rather amused than otherwise by the proceedings; and all the accounts that we have seen, concur in more or less suggesting that there is something admirable, and difficult to reconcile with guilt, in the bearing so elaborately set forth.

As whatever tends, however undesignedly, to insinuate this uneasy sense of incongruity into any mind, and to invest so abhorrent a ruffian with the slightest tinge of heroism, must be prejudicial to the general welfare, we revive the detestable subject with the hope of showing that there is nothing at all singular in such a deportment, but that it is always to be looked for and counted on, in the

[1] William Palmer.

THE DEMEANOUR OF MURDERERS

case of a very wicked murderer. The blacker the guilt, the stronger the probability of its being thus carried off.

In passing, we will express an opinion that Nature never writes a bad hand. Her writing, as it may be read in the human countenance, is invariably legible, if we come at all trained to the reading of it. Some little weighing and comparing are necessary. It is not enough in turning our eyes on the demon in the Dock, to say he has a fresh colour, or a high head, or a bluff manner, or what not, and therefore he does not look like a murderer, and we are surprised and shaken. The physiognomy and conformation of the Poisoner whose trial occasions these remarks, were exactly in accordance with his deeds; and every guilty consciousness he had gone on storing up in his mind, had set its mark upon him.

We proceed, within as short a compass as possible, to illustrate the position we have placed before our readers in the first paragraph of this paper.

The Poisoner's demeanour was considered exceedingly remarkable, because of his composure under trial, and because of the confident expectation of acquittal which he professed to the last, and under the influence of which he, at various times during his incarceration, referred to the plans he entertained for the future when he should be free again.

Can any one, reflecting on the matter for five minutes, suppose it possible—we do not say probable, but possible—that in the breast of this Poisoner there were surviving, in the days of his trial, any lingering traces of sensibility, or any wrecked fragment of the quality which we call sentiment? Can the profoundest or the simplest man alive, believe that in such a heart there could have been left, by that time, any touch of Pity? An objection to die, and a special objection to be killed, no doubt he had; and with that objection very strong within him for divers very weighty reasons, he was—*not* quite composed. Distinctly *not* quite composed, but, on the contrary, very restless. At one time, he was incessantly pulling on and pulling off his glove; at another time, his hand was constantly passing over and over his face; and the thing most instanced in proof of his composure, the perpetual writing and scattering about of little notes, which, as the verdict drew nearer and nearer, thickened from a sprinkling to a heavy shower, is in itself a proof of miserable restlessness. Beyond this

111

emotion, which any lower animal would have, with an apprehension on it of a similar fate, what was to be expected from such a creature but insensibility? I poison my friend in his drink, and I poison my friend in his bed, and I poison my wife, and I poison her memory, and do you look to ME, at the end of such a career as mine, for sensibility? I have not the power of it even in my own behalf, I have lost the manner of it, I don't know what it means, I stand contemptuously wondering at you people here when I see you moved by this affair. In the Devil's name, man, have you heard the evidence of that chambermaid, whose tea I should like to have the sweetening of? Did you hear her describe the agonies in which my friend expired? Do you know that it was my trade to be learned in poisons, and that I foresaw all that, and considered all that, and knew, when I stood at his bedside looking down upon his face turned to me for help on its road to the grave through the frightful gate then swinging on its hinges, that in so many hours or minutes all those horrors would infallibly ensue? Have you heard that, after my poisonings, I have had to face the circumstances out, with friends and enemies, doctors, undertakers, all sorts of men, and have uniformly done it; and do you wonder that I face it out with you? Why not? What right or reason can you have to expect anything else of me? Wonder! You might wonder, indeed, if you saw me moved, here now before you. If I had any natural human feeling for my face to express, do you imagine that those medicines of my prescribing and administering would ever have been taken from my hand? Why, man, my demeanour at this bar is the natural companion of my crimes, and, if it were a tittle different from what it is, you might even begin reasonably to doubt whether I had ever committed them!

The Poisoner had a confident expectation of acquittal. We doubt as little that he really had some considerable hope of it, as we do that he made a pretence of having more than he really had. Let us consider, first, if it be wonderful that he should have been rather sanguine. He had poisoned his victims according to his carefully laid plans; he had got them buried out of his way; he had murdered, and forged, and yet kept his place as a good fellow and a sporting character; he had made a capital friend of the coroner, and a serviceable traitor of the postmaster; he was a great public character, with a special Act of Parliament for his trial; the choice

THE DEMEANOUR OF MURDERERS

spirits of the Stock Exchange were offering long odds in his favour, and, to wind up all, here was a tip-top Counsellor bursting into tears for him, saying to the jury, three times over, ' You dare not, you dare not, you dare not ! ' and bolting clean out of the course to declare his belief that he was innocent. With all this to encourage him, with his own Derby-day division of mankind into knaves and fools, and with his own secret knowledge of the difficulties and mysteries with which the proof of Poison had been, in the manner of the Poisoning, surrounded, it would have been strange indeed if he were not borne up by some idea of escape. But, why should he have professed himself to have more hope of escape than he really entertained ? The answer is, because it belongs to that extremity, that the villain in it should not only declare a strong expectation of acquittal himself, but should try to infect all the people about him with it. Besides having an artful fancy (not wholly without foundation) that he disseminates by that means an impression that he is innocent ; to surround himself in his narrowed world with this fiction is, for the time being, to fill the jail with a faintly rose-coloured atmosphere, and to remove the gallows to a more agreeable distance. Hence, plans are laid for the future, communicated with an engaging candour to turnkeys, and discussed in a reliant spirit. Even sick men and women, over whom natural death is impending, constantly talk with those about them on precisely the same principle.

It may be objected that there is some slight ingenuity in our endeavours to resolve the demeanour of this Poisoner into the same features as the demeanour of every other very wicked and very hardened criminal in the same strait, but that a parallel would be better than argument. We have no difficulty in finding a parallel ; we have no difficulty in finding scores, beyond the almost insuperable difficulty of finding, in the criminal records, as deeply-dyed a murderer. To embarrass these remarks, however, with references to cases that have passed out of the general memory, or have never been widely known, would be to render the discussion very irksome. We will confine ourselves to a famous instance. We will not even ask if it be so long ago since Rush was tried, that *his* demeanour is forgotten. We will call Thurtell into court, as one of the murderers best remembered in England.

With the difference that the circumstances of Thurtell's guilt

113

are not comparable in atrocity with those of the Poisoner's, there are points of strong resemblance between the two men. Each was born in a fair station, and educated in conformity with it; each murdered a man with whom he had been on terms of intimate association, and for whom he professed a friendship at the time of the murder; both were members of that vermin-race of outer betters and blacklegs, of whom some worthy samples were presented on both trials, and of whom, as a community, mankind would be blessedly rid, if they could all be, once and for ever, knocked on the head at a blow. Thurtell's demeanour was exactly that of the Poisoner's. We have referred to the newspapers of his time, in aid of our previous knowledge of the case; and they present a complete confirmation of the simple fact for which we contend. From day to day, during his imprisonment before his trial, he is described as 'collected and resolute in his demeanour,' as 'rather mild and conciliatory in his address,' as being visited by 'friends whom he receives with cheerfulness,' as 'remaining firm and unmoved,' as 'increasing in confidence as the day which is to decide his fate draws nigh,' as 'speaking of the favourable result of the trial with his usual confidence.' On his trial, he looks 'particularly well and healthy.' His attention and composure are considered as wonderful as the Poisoner's; he writes notes as the Poisoner did; he watches the case with the same cool eye; he 'retains that firmness for which, from the moment of his apprehension, he has been distinguished'; he 'carefully assorts his papers on a desk near him'; he is (in this being singular) his own orator, and makes a speech in the manner of Edmund Kean, on the whole not very unlike that of the leading counsel for the Poisoner, concluding, as to his own innocence, with a So help me God! Before his trial, the Poisoner says he will be at the coming race for the Derby. Before his trial, Thurtell says, 'that after his acquittal he will visit his father, and will propose to him to advance the portion which he intended for him, upon which he will reside abroad.' (So Mr. Manning observed, under similar circumstances, that when all that nonsense was over, and the thing wound up, he had an idea of establishing himself in the West Indies.) When the Poisoner's trial is yet to last another day or so, he enjoys his half-pound of steak and his tea, wishes his best friends may sleep as he does, and fears the grave 'no more than his bed.' (See the Evening Hymn for a Young Child.) When Thurtell's trial is yet to

114

last another day or so, he takes his cold meat, tea, and coffee, and 'enjoys himself with great comfort'; also, on the morning of his execution, he wakes from as innocent a slumber as the Poisoner's, declaring that he has had an excellent night, and that he hasn't dreamed 'about this business.' Whether the parallel will hold to the last, as to 'feeling very well and very comfortable,' as to 'the firm step and perfect calmness,' as to 'the manliness and correctness of his general conduct,' as to 'the countenance unchanged by the awfulness of the situation'—not to say as to bowing to a friend, from the scaffold 'in a friendly but dignified manner'—our readers will know for themselves when we know too.

It is surely time that people who are not in the habit of dissecting such appearances, but who are in the habit of reading about them, should be helped to the knowledge that, in the worst examples they are the most to be expected, and the least to be wondered at. That, there is no inconsistency in them, and no fortitude in them. That, there is nothing in them but cruelty and insensibility. That, they are seen, because the man is of a piece with his misdeeds; and that it is not likely that he ever could have committed the crimes for which he is to suffer, if he had not this demeanour to present, in standing publicly to answer for them.

NOBODY, SOMEBODY, AND EVERYBODY

[AUGUST 30, 1856]

THE power of Nobody is becoming so enormous in England, and he alone is responsible for so many proceedings, both in the way of commission and omission; he has so much to answer for, and is so constantly called to account; that a few remarks upon him may not be ill-timed.

The hand which this surprising person had in the late war is amazing to consider. It was he who left the tents behind, who left the baggage behind, who chose the worst possible ground for encampments, who provided no means of transport, who killed the horses, who paralysed the commissariat, who knew nothing of the business he professed to know and monopolised, who decimated the

MISCELLANEOUS PAPERS

English army. It was Nobody who gave out the famous unroasted coffee, it was Nobody who made the hospitals more horrible than language can describe, it was Nobody who occasioned all the dire confusion of Balaklava harbour, it was even Nobody who ordered the fatal Balaklava cavalry charge. The non-relief of Kars was the work of Nobody, and Nobody has justly and severely suffered for that infamous transaction.

It is difficult for the mind to span the career of Nobody. The sphere of action opened to this wonderful person, so enlarges every day, that the limited faculties of Anybody are too weak to compass it. Yet, the nature of the last tribunal expressly appointed for the detection and punishment of Nobody may, as a part of his stupendous history, be glanced at without winking.

At the Old Bailey, when a person under strong suspicion of malpractices is tried, it is the custom (the rather as the strong suspicion has been found, by a previous enquiry, to exist), to conduct the trial on stringent principles, and to confide it to impartial hands. It has not yet become the practice of the criminal, or even of the civil courts—but they, indeed, are constituted for the punishment of Somebody—to invite the prisoner's or defendant's friends to talk the matter over with him in a cosy, tea-and-muffin sort of way, and make out a verdict together, that shall be what a deposed iron king called making things 'pleasant.' But, when Nobody was shown within these few weeks to have occasioned intolerable misery and loss in the late war, and to have incurred a vast amount of guilt in bringing to pass results which all morally sane persons can understand to be fraught with fatal consequences, far beyond present calculation, this cosy course of proceeding was the course pursued. My Lord, intent upon establishing the responsibility of Nobody, walked into court as he would walk into a ball-room; and My Lord's friends and admirers toadied and fawned upon him in court, as they would toady him and fawn upon him in the other assembly. My Lord carried his head very high, and took a mighty great tone with the common people; and there was no question as to anything My Lord did or said, and Nobody got triumphantly fixed. Ignorance enough and incompetency enough to bring any country that the world has ever seen to defeat and shame, and to lay any head that ever was in it low, were proved beyond question; but, My Lord cried, 'On Nobody's eyes be it!' and My Lord's impaneled chorus cried, 'There is no impostor but Nobody ; on him be the shame and blame !'

Surely, this is a rather wonderful state of things to be realising itself so long after the Flood, in such a country as England. Surely, it suggests to us with some force, that wherever this ubiquitous Nobody is, there mischief is and there danger is. For, it is especially to be borne in mind that wherever failure is accomplished, there Nobody lurks. With success, he has nothing to do. That is Everybody's business, and all manner of improbable people will invariably be found at the bottom of it. But, it is the great feature of the present epoch that all public disaster in the United Kingdom of Great Britain and Ireland is assuredly, and to a dead certainty, Nobody's work.

We have, it is not to be denied, punished Nobody, with exemplary rigour. We have, as a nation, allowed ourselves to be deluded by no influences or insolences of office or rank, but have dealt with Nobody in a spirit of equal and uncompromising justice that has moved the admiration of the world. I have had some opportunities of remarking, out of England, the impression made on other peoples by the stern Saxon spirit with which, the default proved and the wrong done, we have tracked down and punished the defaulter and wrong-doer. And I do here declare my solemn belief, founded on much I have seen, that the remembrance of our frightful failures within the last three years, and of our retaliation upon Nobody, will be more vivid and potent in Europe (mayhap in Asia, too, and in America) for years upon years to come than all our successes since the days of the Spanish Armada.

In civil matters we have Nobody equally active. When a civil office breaks down, the break-down is sure to be in Nobody's department. I entreat on my reader, dubious of this proposition, to wait until the next break-down (the reader is certain not to have to wait long), and to observe, whether or no, it is in Nobody's department. A dispatch of the greatest moment is sent to a minister abroad, at a most important crisis ; Nobody reads it. British subjects are affronted in a foreign territory ; Nobody interferes. Our own loyal fellow-subjects, a few thousand miles away, want to exchange political, commercial, and domestic intelligence with us ; Nobody stops the mail. The government, with all its mighty means and appliances, is invariably beaten and outstripped by private enterprise ; which we all know to be Nobody's fault. Something will be the national death of us, some day; and who can doubt that Nobody will be brought in Guilty?

Now, might it not be well, if it were only for the novelty of the experiment, to try Somebody a little? Reserving Nobody for statues, and stars and garters, and batons, and places and pensions without duties, what if we were to try Somebody for real work? More than that, what if we were to punish Somebody with a most inflexible and grim severity, when we caught him pompously undertaking in holiday-time to do work, and found him, when the working-time came, altogether unable to do it?

Where do I, as an Englishman, want Somebody? Before high Heaven, I want him everywhere! I look round the whole dull horizon, and I want Somebody to do work while the Brazen Head, already hoarse with crying 'Time is!' passes into the second warning, 'Time was!' I don't want Somebody to let off Parliamentary penny crackers against evils that need to be stormed by the thunderbolts of Jove. I don't want Somebody to sustain, for Parliamentary and Club entertainment, and by the desire of several persons of distinction, the character of a light old gentleman, or a fast old gentleman, or a debating old gentleman, or a dandy old gentleman, or a free-and-easy old gentleman, or a capital old gentleman considering his years. I want Somebody to be clever in doing the business, not clever in evading it. The more clever he is in the latter quality (which has been the making of Nobody), the worse I hold it to be for me and my children and for all men and their children. I want Somebody who shall be no fiction; but a capable, good, determined workman. For, it seems to me that from the moment when I accept Anybody in a high place, whose function in that place is to exchange winks with me instead of doing the serious deeds that belong to it, I set afloat a system of false pretence and general swindling, the taint of which soon begins to manifest itself in every department of life, from Newgate to the Court of Bankruptcy, and thence to the highest Court of Appeal. For this reason, above all others, I want to see the working Somebody in every responsible position which the winking Somebody and Nobody now monopolise between them.

And this brings me back to Nobody; to the great irresponsible, guilty, wicked, blind giant of this time. O friends, countrymen, and lovers, look at that carcase smelling strong of prussic acid, (drunk out of a silver milkpot, which was a part of the plunder, or as the less pernicious thieves call it, the swag), cumbering Hampstead Heath by London town! Think of the history of which that abomination is at once the beginning and the end; of the dark social scenes daguerreotyped in it; and of the Lordship of your Treasury to which Nobody, driving a shameful bargain, raised this creature when he was alive. Follow the whole story, and finish by listening to the parliamentary lawyers as they tell you that Nobody knows anything about it; that Nobody is entitled (from the attorney point of view) to believe that there ever was such a business at all; that Nobody can be allowed to demand, for decency's sake, the swift expulsion from the lawmaking body of the surviving instrument in the heap of crime; that such expulsion is, in a word, just Nobody's business, and must at present be constitutionally left to Nobody to do.

There is a great fire raging in the land, and—by all the polite precedents and prescriptions!—you shall leave it to Nobody to put it out with a squirt, expected home in a year or so. There are inundations bursting on the valleys, and—by the same precedents and prescriptions!—you shall trust to Nobody to bale the water out with a bottomless tin kettle. Nobody being responsible to you for his perfect success in these little feats, and you confiding in him, you shall go to Heaven. Ask for Somebody in his stead, and you shall go in quite the contrary direction.

And yet, for the sake of Everybody, give me Somebody! I raise my voice in the wilderness for Somebody. My heart, as the ballad says, is sore for Somebody. Nobody has done more harm in this single generation than Everybody can mend in ten generations. Come, responsible Somebody; accountable Blockhead, come!

THE MURDERED PERSON

[October 11, 1856]

In an early number of this journal,[1] we made some reference to the fact that in the highly improving accounts which are given to the public of the last moments of murderers, the murdered person may be usually observed to be entirely dismissed from the moral discourses with which the murderer favours his admiring audience, except as an incidental and tributary portion of his own egotistical story.

To what lengths this dismissal of the very objectionable personage who persisted in tempting the Saint in the condemned cell to murder him, may be carried, we have had a recent opportunity of considering, in the case of the late lamented Mr. Dove. That amiable man, previous to taking the special express-train to Paradise which is vulgarly called the Gallows, indited a document wherein he made it manifest to all good people that the mighty and beneficent Creator of the vast Universe had specially wrought to bring it about that he should cruelly and stealthily torture, torment, and by inches slay, a weak sick woman, and that woman his wife, in order that he, Dove, as with the wings of a Dove (a little blood-stained or so, but that's not much) should be put in the way of ascending to Heaven.

Frightful as this statement is, and sickening as one would suppose it must be, to any mind capable of humbly and reverentially approaching at an inconceivable distance the idea of the Divine Majesty, there it stands in the printed records of the day : a part of the Gaol Court-Newsman's account of the visitors whom the chosen vessel received in his cell, of his proposing to sing hymns in chorus in the night season, and of the 'Prison Philanthropist' declaring him to be a pattern penitent.

Now, to the Prison Philanthropist we concede all good intentions. We take it for granted that the venerable gentleman did not confer his alliterative title on himself, and that he is no more

[1] *Pet Prisoners.*

THE MURDERED PERSON

responsible for it, than a public-house is for its sign, or a ship for
her figure-head. Yet, holding this horrible confusion of mind on
the part of the inhuman wretch to whom he devoted so much
humanity, to be shocking in itself and widely perilous in its influences, we plainly avow that we for our part cannot accept good
intentions as any set-off against the production of such a mental
state, and that we think the condemned cells everywhere (left to
their appointed ministers of religion who are very rarely deficient
in kindness and zeal) would be better without such philanthropy.
What would the Home Secretary say to Professor Holloway, if that
learned man applied for free admission to the condemned cells
throughout England, in order that he might with his ointment
anoint the throats of the convicts about to be hanged, so that under
the influences of the application their final sensations should be of a
mild tickling? What would the Home Secretary reply to the
august members of the Hygeian Council of the British College of
Health, if they made a similar request, with a view to the internal
exhibition for a similar purpose of that great discovery, Morrison's
pills? Even if some regular medical hand of eminence were to seek
the same privilege, with a view to a drugging within the limits of
the pharmacopœia—say for the philanthropic purpose of making the
patient maudlin drunk with opium and peppermint, and sending
him out of this world with a leer—how would the Home Secretary
receive that edifying proposal? And is there nothing of greater
moment involved in this revolting conceit, setting its heel on the
murdered body, and daring eternity on the edge of the murderer's
grave?

Pursue this advance made by the late Mr. Dove on the usual calm
dismissal of the murdered person, and see where it ends. There are
sent into this world two human creatures: one, a highly interesting
individual in whom Providence is much concerned—Mr. Dove: one,
a perfectly uninteresting individual of no account whatever, here or
hereafter—Mrs. Dove. Mr. Dove being expressly wanted in the
regions of the blessed, Mrs. Dove is delivered over to him, soul and
body, to ensure his presence there, and provide against disappointment. There is no escape from this appalling, this impious conclusion. The special Gaol-Call which was wanting to, and was found
by, Mr. Dove who is hanged, was wanting to, and was not found by,
Mrs. Dove who is poisoned. Thus, the New Drop usurps the place

of the Cross; and Saint John Ketch is preached to the multitude as the latest and holiest of the Prophets!

Our title is so associated with the remembrance of this exhibition, that we have been led into the present comments on it. But, the purpose with which we adopted the title was rather to illustrate the general prevalence of the practice of putting the murdered person out of the question, and the extensive following which the custom of criminals has found outside the gaols.

Two noble lords at loggerheads, each of whom significantly suggests that he thinks mighty little of the capabilities of the other, are blamed for certain disasters which did undoubtedly befall, under their distinguished administration of military affairs. They demand enquiry. A Board of their particular friends and admirers is appointed 'to enquire'—much as its members might leave their cards for the noble lords with that inscription. The enquiry is in the first instance directed by one of the noble lords to the question —not quite the main question at issue—whether the Board can muzzle the Editor of the *Times*? The Board have the best will in the world to do it, but, finding that the Editor declines to be muzzled, perforce confess their inability to muzzle him. The enquiry then proceeds into anything else that the noble lords like, and into nothing else that the noble lords don't like. It ends in eulogiums on the soldierly qualities and conduct of both lords, and clearly shows their fitness for command to have been so completely exemplified, in failing, that the inference is, if they had succeeded they would have failed. The compliments ended, the Board breaks up (the best thing it could possibly do, and the only function it is fit for), the noble lords are decorated, and there is an end of the matter.

How like the case of the late Mr. Dove! The murdered person —by name the wasted forces and resources of England—is not to be thought of; or, if thought of, is only to be regarded as having been expressly called into being for the noble lords to make away with, and mount up to the seventh Heaven of merit upon. The President of the Board (answering to the Prison Philanthropist) sings pæans in the dark to any amount, and the only thing wanting in the parallel, is, the finishing hand of Mr. Calcraft.

Let us pass to another instance. The Law of Divorce is in such condition that from the tie of marriage there is no escape to be had, no absolution to be got, except under certain proved circumstances not necessary to enter upon here, and then only on payment of an enormous sum of money. Ferocity, drunkenness, flight, felony, madness, none of these will break the chain, without the enormous sum of money. The husband who, after years of outrage, has abandoned his wife, may at any time claim her for his property and seize the earnings on which she subsists. The most profligate of women, an intolerable torment, torture, and shame to her husband, may nevertheless, unless he be a very rich man, insist on remaining handcuffed to him, and dragging him away from any happier alliance, from youth to old age and death. Out of this condition of things among the common people, out of the galling knowledge of the impossibility of relief — aggravated, in cottages and single rooms, to a degree not easily imaginable by ill-assorted couples who live in houses of many chambers, and who, both at home and abroad, can keep clear of each other and go their respective ways—vices and crimes arise which no one with open eyes and any fair experience of the people can fail often to trace, from the Calendars of Assizes, back to this source. It is proposed a little to relax the severity of a thraldom prolonged beyond the bounds of morality, justice, and sense, and to modify the law. Instantly the singing of pæans begins, and the murdered person disappears! Authorities, lay and clerical, rise in their parliamentary places to deliver panegyrics on Marriage as an Institution (which nobody disputes to be just); they have much to relate concerning what the Fathers thought of it, and what was written, said, and done about it hundreds of years before these evils were; they set up their fancy whipping-tops, and whip away; they utter homilies without end upon the good side of the question, which is in no want of them; but, from their exalted state of vision the murdered person utterly vanishes. The tortures and wrongs of the sufferer have no place in their speeches. They felicitate themselves, like the murderers, on their own glowing state of mind, and they mount upon the mangled creature to deliver their orations, much as the Duke's man in the sham siege took his post on the fallen governor of Barataria.

So in the case of overstrained Sunday observance, and denial of innocent popular reliefs from labour. The murdered person—the consumptive, scrofulous, rickety worker in unwholesome places, the wide prevalence of whose reduced physical condition has rendered it necessary to lower the standard of health and strength for recruiting into the army, and caused its ranks to be reinforced in the late war by numbers of poor creatures notoriously in an unserviceable bodily state—the murdered person, in this phase of his ubiquity, is put out of sight, as a matter of course. We have flaming and avenging speeches made, as if a bold peasantry, their country's pride, models of cheerful health and muscular development, were in every hamlet, town, and city, once a week ardently bent upon the practice of asceticism and the renunciation of the world ; but, the murdered person, Legion, who cannot at present by any means be got at once a week, and who does nothing all that day but gloom and grumble and deteriorate, is put out of sight as if none of us had ever heard of him ! What is it to the holders forth, that wherever we live, or wherever we go, we see him, and see him with so much pity and dismay that we want to make him better by other human means than those which have missed him ? To get rid of his memory, in the murdering way, and vaunt ourselves instead, is much easier.

Bankrupts are declared, greedy speculators smash, and bankers break. Who does not hear of the reverses of those unfortunate gentlemen ; of the disruption of their establishments ; of their wives being reduced to live upon their settlements ; of the sale of their horses, equipages, pictures, wines ; of the mighty being fallen, and of their magnanimity under their reverses ? But, the murdered person, the creditor, investor, depositor, the cheated and swindled under whatsoever name, whose mind does he trouble ? The mind of the fraudulent firm ? Enquire at the House of Detention, Clerkenwell, London, and you will find that the last great fraudulent firm was no more troubled about *him*, than Mr. Dove or Mr. Palmer was by the client whom he 'did for,' in the way of his different line of business.

And, lastly, get an order of admission to Sir Charles Barry's palace any night in the session, and you will observe the murdered person to be as comfortably stowed away as he ever is at Newgate. What In said to Out in eighteen hundred and thirty-five, what Out retorted upon In in eighteen hundred and forty-seven, why In would have been Out in eighteen hundred and fifty-four but for Out's unparalleled magnanimity in not coming in, this, with all the contemptible ins and outs of all the Innings and Outings, shall be discoursed upon, with abundance of hymns and pæans on all sides, for six months together. But, the murdered old gentleman Time, and the murdered matron, Britannia, shall no more come in question than the murdered people do in the cells of the penitents—unless indeed they are reproduced, as in the odious case with which we began, to show that they were expressly created for the exaltation of the speech-makers.

MURDEROUS EXTREMES

[JANUARY 3, 1857]

OUR title may suggest a reference in the reader's mind, to those much maligned persons, the ticket-of-leave men, who at present favour the metropolis with more of their exemplary business-trans-actions than is appreciated with becoming gratitude by an ungrateful public. It is not intended, however, to have that significance. We have over and over again in these pages dwelt upon the consequences to which a preposterous encouraging and rewarding of prison hypocrisy, were inevitably leading. Whether they have ensued in sufficient abundance (being met by a corresponding decrease of efficiency in the Police), and whether the issuing of an Order in Council, any time within the last six months, for the incarceration and severe punishment of convicted offenders enlarged upon commuted sentences, unable to show that they were honestly employed, would have been as good a symptom as the Income Tax of our really living under a Government ; all our readers can judge for themselves.

The Murderous Extremes to which we will, in very few words, entreat serious attention, appear to us to have a remarkable bearing on, and to be forcibly illustrated in, the Parliament Street Murder ; than which an outrage more barbarous in itself, or more disgraceful to the country, has not been committed in England within a hundred years.

The only circumstances in this act of brutality which our present object requires us to revive, are, that it was committed in a public shop (made the more public by being extraordinarily small, and nearly all window), at an early hour of the evening, in a great main thoroughfare of London ; that it was committed with bystanders looking on, and by-passers asking what was the matter; that the blows of the murderer, and the feeble groans of the murdered, were audible in the public street to several persons; and that not one of them interfered, saving a poor errand boy.

Is it worth any man's while to ask himself the question, how does it happen that a passiveness so shocking was displayed in such a case? Is it worth any man's while to ask himself the question, how does it happen that a similar passiveness, in similar cases, is actually becoming a part of the national character, brave and generous though it is? For, we assume that few can stop short at the Parliament Street example, and comfortably tick it off as a Phenomenon, who read with the least attention the reports of the Police Courts and of the Criminal Trials: in which records, the same ugly feature is constantly observable.

We have made bold to question our own mind on this painful subject, and we find the answer plainly, in two murderous extremes —in two wrestings of things good in themselves, to unnatural and ridiculous proportions.

Extreme the first:

It has been, for many years, a misfortune of the English People to be, by those in authority, both over-disparaged and over-praised. The disparagement has grown out of mere arrogance and ignorance; the praise, out of a groundless fear of the people, and a timid desire to keep them well in hand.

A due respect for the Law is the basis of social existence. Without it, we come to the Honourable Preston S. Brooks, Kansas, and those two shining constellations among the bright Stars of Freedom, known by the names of Bowie-knife and Revolver. But, have none of us Englishmen heard this tuneful fiddle with one string played upon, until our souls have sickened of it? From the Bench, from the Bar, from the Pulpit, from the Platform, from the Floor of the House of Commons, from all the thousand fountain-heads of boredom, have none of us been badgered and baited with an Englishman's respect for the Law, until, in the singular phraseology of Mr. Morier's Persian hero, our faces have turned upside down, and our livers have resolved themselves into water? We take leave to say, Yes; most emphatically, Yes! We avow for our own part, that whensoever, at public meeting, dinner, testimonial-presentation, charity-election, or other spoutation ceremony, we find (which we always do), an orator approaching an Englishman's respect for the Law, our heart dries up within us, and terror paralyses our frame. As the dreadful old clap-trap begins to jingle, we become the prey of a deep-seated melancholy and a miserable despair. We know the thing to have passed into a fulsome form, out of which the life has gone, and into which putrefaction has come. On common lips we perceive it to be a thing of no meaning, and on lips of authority we perceive it to have gradually passed into a thing of most pernicious meaning.

For, what does it mean? What is it? What has it come to? ' My good man, John Bull, hold up your hand and hear me! You are on no account to do anything for yourself. You are by no means to stir a finger to help yourself, or to help another man. Law has undertaken to take care of you, and to take care of the other man, whoever he may be. You are the foremost man of all this world, in regard of respecting the Law. Call in the Law, John, on all occasions. If you can find the Law round the corner, run after it and bring it on the scene when you see anything wrong; but, don't you touch the wrong on any consideration. Don't *you* interfere, whatever you see. It's not *your* business. Call in the Law, John. You shall not take the Law into your own hands. You are a good boy, John, and your business is to be a bystander, and a looker on, and to be thought for, and to be acted for. That's the station of life unto which *you* are called. Law is an edge-tool, John, and a strong arm, and you have nothing to do with it. Therefore, John, leave this all-sufficient Law alone, to achieve everything for you, and for everybody else. So shall you be ever, ever, the pride and glory of the earth ; so will we make patriotic speeches about you, and sing patriotic songs about you, out of number ! ' So, by degrees, it is our sincere conviction, John gets to be humbugged into believing that he is a first-rate citizen if he looks in at a shop-window while a man is being murdered, and if he quietly leaves the transaction entirely to Law, in the person of the policeman who is not there. So, when Law itself is down on the pavement in the person of the policeman, with Brute Force dancing jigs upon his body, John looks on with a faith in Law's coming uppermost somehow or other, and with a perfect conviction that it is Law's business, and not his.

Extreme the second :

MISCELLANEOUS PAPERS

Technicalities and forms of law, *in reason*, are essential to the preservation of the liberties and rights of all classes of men. No man has a greater or lesser interest in them than another, since any man may be, at any time, in the position of needing impartial justice. But, in its unreason, Westminster Hall is a nuisance; and, supposing Westminster Hall in its unreason conspicuously to back up this grievous error of John's, and conspicuously to supply him with a new distrust of the terrible consequences of his not leaving murderers with blood upon their hands to be taken solely by the Law, Westminster Hall would be a very great nuisance and a well-nigh insupportable nuisance. Supposing Westminster Hall to make this mischievous idiot of itself at a very critical time and under very famous circumstances, before the Parliament Street Murder was committed; why, then Westminster Hall might, in a pictorial representation of that terrible cruelty, be reasonably represented as holding John's hands while he looked in at the window, and as menacing John from interfering.

Will the reader who may not remember the facts, look back to what Westminster Hall said about the case of one Barthélémy, who, having had the misfortune to murder an old gentleman in Warren Street, Tottenham Court Road, was escaping over a garden fence, when, being collared by a meddlesome individual labouring under the absurd idea that he ought to stop a Murderer as Law was not there to stop him, he became virtuously indignant, and shot that meddlesome person dead? In that case, which attracted great attention, Westminster Hall solemnly argued and contended before Lord Campbell that the meddlesome man shot dead, had no right to stop the Murderer, and that the Murderer had a right to shoot the meddlesome man shot dead, for stopping him! Before as upright and as sagacious a Judge as ever graced the Bench, this almost incredible absurdity could not prevail, and Westminster Hall was reduced to the last feeble resource of moaning at the clubs until the ill-used Murderer was hanged.

Turn from these two extremes to the window in Parliament Street; see the people looking in, coming up, listening, exchanging a word or two, and passing on; and say whether, at the close of the year eighteen hundred and fifty-six, we find for the first time Smoke without Fire.

STORES FOR THE FIRST OF APRIL

[MARCH 7, 1857]

ALL FOOLS'-DAY drawing near, it is a seasonable occupation to calculate what we have in store for the occasion, and to take stock of the provision in reserve, to meet the great demand of the anniversary.

First (for the moment postponing the substantials of the annual feast, and beginning with the spirits), we are happy to report the existence in England, in its third volume, of a Spiritual Telegraph ' and British Harmonial Advocate.' Walled up in the flesh, as it is our personal and peculiar misfortune to be, we are not in a condition to report upon the derivation or meaning of the British adjective, Harmonial. Unknown to Dr. Johnson in the body, it has probably been revealed to him in the spirit, and by him been communicated to some favoured ' Medium.' The Harmonial Advocate is published in one of the northern counties erewhile renowned for horses, and which may yet be destined to establish a celebrity for its acquaintance with another class of quadrupeds.

In the January Harmonial, we find a Bank for the First of April, on which we will present our readers with a few small drafts, which may enable them to form a proximate idea of the value of its Rest. Its following extract from ' the British Court Journal,' of this last blessed eighteen hundred and fifty-sixth Christmas-time, will show how far we have travelled in all those years.

' One of our greatest English poets being in communication with the medium, asked for the summons of Dante. The presence of the latter was immediately made manifest by the written answers returned to the questions of the inquirer, and Mr. B—— then asked the medium to request the great Italian to make himself visible! Presently there arose, as if from the ground beneath the table, two long, thin, yellow hands, unmistakable as to their Italian origin, undeniable as to their having belonged to a student and a gentleman. While the assembly were yet gazing in breathless awe, and may be something of terror likewise, the hands floated away, or were rather borne, as it were, across the room, and rose to the marble console opposite, upon which stood a vase containing an orange tree

129

in blossom. The hands slowly and softly, without noise, but visibly to all, plucked from the stem a sprig of orange flower with its leaves and buds, and returning to the table, paused above the head of Mrs. B——, the poet's wife, herself an exquisite and beautiful poet likewise, and, placing the sprig upon her raven hair, disappeared gradually from sight, seeming once more to sink to the floor, while the audience remained speechless and awe-struck, and but little inclined to renew the experiment, that same night, at all events. The sprig of orange blossom is religiously preserved by Mrs. B——, whose honour and truth are unimpeachable; while the witnesses gathered round the table at the time of the occurrence all testify to the apparition, as well as to the utter unconsciousness of the medium, who neither spoke nor moved during the whole time the circumstance was taking place.'—

We happen to have had communicated to our humble bodily individuality by a letter of the alphabet, remarkably like B, some emphatic references to a similar story; and they were not merely associated with the production of two hands, but with the threatened production of one foot—the latter not a spiritual, but a corporeal foot, considered as a means of impelling the biped, Man, down a staircase.

We learn from the same pages that Mr. J. J. of Peckham, went into an appointed house at Sandgate-by-the-Sea, last autumn, at four of the clock in the afternoon, and unto him entered the Medium, evidently suffering from physical prostration'; spiritual knockings immediately afterwards hailed the advent of J. J., and in answer to the question, Were the spirits pleased with Mr. J. J. of Peckham being there? 'the rappings, as if on the under-side of the table, were rapid and joyous, and as loud as if made with a hand-hammer'; being probably made, we would deferentially suggest, by the ghost of the celebrated 'Harmonial' blacksmith. In the evening a loo-table politely expressed its happiness in making the acquaintance of the visitor from Peckham, by suspending itself in the air 'clear of the floor, about eight inches.' On another occasion, a lady of London, attending her uncle during his last illness, was gratified by a spectacle such as has been hitherto hidden from the ardent desires of the best of mankind, and saw her uncle 'floating out from under the bedclothes,' accompanied by two angels with whom he floated out of window, 'and continued to float and rise till out of sight.' This lady is described as Mrs. G., and may, perhaps, have been Mrs. Gamp, in professional attendance on the late Mr. Harris. On another occasion, Mr. J. G. had the following little experience: 'One evening, after having seen a great many extraordinary lifts, by the table frequently springing from the floor to a great height, and in that manner keeping time to tunes, etc., *with an understanding that the performer was the Spirit of Burns the poet*, the company had nearly all retired, leaving only the medium, her father, and myself at the table, when finally the father fell asleep, and the medium retired to a distance from the table, leaving me alone sitting at the table reading Burns's Poems, by the light of a candle placed on the middle of the table; I was just in the act of reading the song called Wandering Willie, and was making a remark to the medium that it was an old favourite of mine, when I heard a movement, and the medium said, "the table is moving of its own accord." I instantly stopped reading, and having heard of tables moving without touch, I thought I might perhaps be gratified with a movement of that kind. I therefore said, " *If this is really the Spirit of Burns, will he be kind enough to gratify me by a movement of the table without any human touch?* " Almost immediately afterwards, it commenced cracking as if a heavy weight had been pressing upon it, and it then gave a sudden rush on the floor, perhaps to the distance of a foot, when it stopped.' On another occasion the same gentleman saw 'a very heavy oak-table, weighing some few stones, fly up *like a rocket*,' and heard a lady make the singular request to her husband's spirit, that he would, as a particular favour, ' throw ' this heavy oak-table, weighing some few stones, ' over on her knee,' and ' upset it into her lap.' These extra-ordinary proofs of a love surviving beyond the grave, her husband affectionately accorded, but with what painful results to the lady's legs is not mentioned. On another occasion Mrs. Coan, Medium, was tested by ' the New York Philosophical Society of the Mechanics' Institution,' when a Spirit made the following startling disclosure: ' Did you leave a wife? Yes.—Did you leave children? No answer. —Did you leave a child? Yes.—Was it a girl? No.—*Was it a boy? Yes.*'

Mr. Robert Owen, who, as was formerly announced in this journal, received a special message from the spiritual world informing him that he would certainly succeed in his object of re-modelling society, if he inserted an advertisement in the *Morning Post*, has made large provision for the First of April. It is at present stored in a warehouse called the *Millennial Gazette*, established for the purpose of proclaiming to mankind that: 'A Congress of the advanced minds of the world, to consider the best immediate practicable mode of gradually superseding the false, ignorant, unjust, cruel, wicked, and most irrational system of society, opposed to the righteous laws of God and nature, and which hitherto has been the only system known to man,—by the true, enlightened, just, merciful, good, and rational system of society, in strict accordance with the all-wise laws of God and nature, will be opened at noon precisely, on the fourteenth of May next, in St. Martin's Hall, Long Acre, London, the present metropolis of the world—when will be explained the outline of the change which is highly to benefit all of the human race through futurity, and to injure none, even while passing through its first or transition generation, preliminary to the attainment of its full change, which will be the commencement of the long-promised millennium.'

It is foreseen that the debates of this assemblage (to which Mr. Owen invites 'the Sovereign Powers of the civilised world to send their most talented representatives, possessing firm integrity of character'—who will no doubt attend in great numbers) will take time. It is therefore announced that the Congress ' will be continued day by day, from ten A.M. to three P.M., until this great work of reformation for the lasting advantage of all of humankind shall be brought to a satisfactory termination.' We fear this may cause Mr. Hullah some little inconvenience; but, it is pleasant to consider, on the other hand, what an enormous amount of rent that respected gentleman will receive for the long occupation of his Hall. ' Superior spirits,' it appears, are taking great interest in the Congress, and among the mortals who will attend, we hope Mr. Samuel Clark, Medium, of ' Beaverton, Boone Co., Ill., U.S.' may be expected. This gentleman writes to the convener: ' DEAR SIR, I never heard your name nor the right foundation of the principles that you are advocating to the world until a few weeks ago I came into my house at noon and there lay your *Millennial Gazette*, but the cover not removed, and as I took it into my hand to open it a divine spiritual influence dropt over me, as if a mantle of light and harmony was cast over me by some invisible power. It vibrated through my entire system, and by that I knew I held something holy and true in my hand. I opened and great was my delight there to find the principles plainly laid before me, which I had been trying to advocate in public for some time past, with spiritualism combined, having been a medium some ten months, speaking in public, *languages that I do not understand, and sometimes no person present understood not even one word.* I have seen spirits and had them touch me, have seen the most beautiful visions, and healed the sick by laying on of hand by the same invisible power.' Mr. Clark sends likewise this apostrophe from Beaverton, Boone Co., Ill., U.S.: 'But I should love to see and hear thee, oh thou noble champion of truth. One favour I ask. If you are taken to the purer spiritual life before me, then throw thy holy influence on me, to convince the sceptical, and to help me speak the truth, impress me with your ideas. This you can do on a medium, by and through the laws of unity which exist between individual spirits of pure harmony.'

There appears to be no doubt that important communications from this gentleman may be confidently expected (in the language of which nobody understands one word), on the First of April.

Dismissing, here, this branch of the preparations for the feast of unreason, we pass to a joke happily conceived for the First of April, though we doubt its success in making as complete a fool of the British Public as is desired. An old captain of the Welsh Fusileers has translated into French and published at Brussels, for the edification and something-else-ification of the French people, a paper originally written by Mr. Hayward for an English Review, and therein published in the English tongue. Mr. Hayward is correctly described in the Preface as 'Queen's Counsel, and distinguished man of letters'; and he is further described as having, for the purposes of the translation, corrected his work, and enlarged it with a variety of information drawn from the most authentic sources. Its object is to show that the English people had, in the beginning, the most exaggerated expectations of the war with Russia; that they were fully persuaded that everything would go on of itself (que tout marcherait tout seul), though we suppose they may be allowed to have had some dim impression, at least, that a vast amount of their money would go off in helping it on; that nearly all the privations and sufferings of the English army 'may be accounted for without imputing any serious blame to any minister, civil or military officer, or chief of department, whether in London or whether in the Crimea'; and that 'nobody of good faith who is acquainted with the spirited reply of Lord Lucan (!), who has read the lucid address of Sir Richard Airey (!), or who has studied the extraordinary evidence of Colonel Tulloch before the Chelsea commission (!), will hesitate to pronounce a sentence of honourable acquittal.' The sufficient cause and reason of any little British failure (if any) that ill-conditioned journalists pretended to observe in the Crimea, and of any slight superfluous suffering and death (if any) that occurred among the British troops, is to be found in the alterations rendered necessary in the character of the army's operations, after those operations were arranged at Varna, and in the remissness of the French; the soldiers of which distracted nation (with the occasional exception of a Zouave or so) were never ready, were always behind time, were not to be relied upon, and were handled by their generals with timidity and incertitude. M. de Bazancourt having, with the not very generous concurrence of his master the Emperor, written a turbid, inflated, and partial account of the War in the Crimea (which, making every allowance for a Frenchman's not being specially predestined to write in the style of the Duke of Wellington, he has indisputably done), Mr. Hayward sets the matter right, and brings the French mind to a perfect understanding of the truth, by means of these lights and explanations (éclaircissements) on the subject.

It happens, however—perversely, with a view to the First of April—that Colonel Tulloch, who seems to have no relish for All Fools'-day, and no perception of the humour of the jokes appropriate to it, comes out arrayed in plain English attire, at about the same time as Mr. Hayward appears in his French suit, and offers *his* little lights and explanations on the same subject. Colonel Tulloch's ' éclaircissements ' are contained in a Review of the Proceedings and Report of the Chelsea Board ; and they incontestably prove, beyond the power of disproof by man of woman born, every conceivable detail of murderous muddle and mismanagement, by English administrators of one kind or another in the Crimea, on every imaginable head on which it was possible to do wrong, from the article of coatees up to hospital medicines and down again to coffee. They prove these imbecilities, too, out of the lips of his own opponents, making their own statements in their own defence before a one-sided tribunal constantly wresting the case out of the truth, by stopping short when they see that damnatory pea in danger of rolling out from among the thimbles. Whether Colonel Tulloch shows the spirited replyer, Lord Lucan, to have called cavalry officers to prove that nothing more could have been done than was done towards the sheltering of the horses, whom he had himself, in writing, under his own hand, severely censured for 'doing nothing' towards that sheltering for five long winter weeks; whether he shows that in the Crimea the same noble and spirited replyer would not hear of sail-cloth for the covering-in of horses, and that at Aldershot it is now extensively used for that very purpose; or whether he shows that the vast idea never presented itself to the collective wisdom of a whole brigade in want of barley, that it was possible, instead of sending horses all the way to Balaclava to fetch it, to send them half the way, and there let them meet the commissariat beasts, relieve them of their load, and turn back again; or whether he shows the English soldiers to have been perishing by thousands, abject scarecrows in rags that would not hold together, 'while their knapsacks were on the Black Sea, their squad-bags at Scutari, thousands of pairs of trousers missing, thousands of coatees unused, and tens of thousands of great-coats, blankets, and rugs, filling the Quarter-Master General's stores, or the harbour of Balaclava'; or whether he shows the Board to attribute the non-supply of those vital essentials, to the deficiency of transport to the front, whereas that very kind of transport was at that very time going on with shot and shell and the like to an enormous extent, and whereas Sir John Campbell and Sir Richard England both positively stated to the Board, that they had never received any intimation whatever from the Quarter-Master General, that such things were to be got for the sending for, or were there at all; or whether he shows it to be alleged as a reason for not issuing coatees to the men, that they were too small, 'by reason of the great quantity of under-clothing worn by them,' at a time when the identical men are to a dead certainty known to have had no under-clothing whatever; or whether he shows the Assistant Commissary General's accounts to pretend that within a certain time three hundred and fifty thousand pounds weight (in round numbers), of vegetables were issued to the starving troops, of which quantity two hundred and seventy-three thousand pounds weight (in round numbers), are afterwards admitted *to have been destroyed*, while the greater part of the rest was scrambled for in Balaclava harbour and never issued ; or whether he shows that when the Chelsea Board compassionate the Commissary General for having no transports to get fresh meat in, while the soldiers were dying of diseases caused by salt meat, there were Sixteen available transports lying idle at their moorings in Balaclava harbour ; or whether he shows the same Commissary when the men where dying for want of lime-juice, never to have reported to Lord Raglan that there was the small item of twenty thousand pounds weight of lime-juice stored there, in the Crimea, on the spot, ready for use ; or whether he shows the Chelsea Board in their Report, after all the mischief is done and all the misery is irreparable, to be still, to the last, so like their own championed Incapables, as, in their printed report, to be found quoting evidence that was never given, and assigning explanations to witnesses who never offered them ; in whatever he does from the first to the last page of his Review of a Board whose constitution and proceedings were an outrage on common sense, the lights of Colonel Tulloch make the lights of Mr. Hayward darkness, rout the whole host of spirited replyers with frightful loss and discomfiture, and show no toleration whatever of the First of April.

To us, who admire that institution, and love to contemplate the provision made and making for it, this is no service. We regard Colonel Tulloch as rather a dull man, wanting the due zest and relish for a joke, and conscious of no compunction in knocking a choice one on the head. Yet we descry a kind of humour in him, too, when he quotes this letter from the late Duke of Wellington to General Fane.

'I wish I had it in my power to give you well-clothed troops, or to hang those who ought to have given them their clothing.
'Believe me, etc.,
'WELLINGTON.'

—which is really an 'éclaircissement' extremely satisfactory to our odd way of thinking, and perhaps the next spirited reply on record after Lord Lucan's.

Consenting, in the good humour with which this pithy document inspires us, to consider Colonel Tulloch reconciled to the First of April, we will pass to a cursory examination of some more of its stores.

STORES FOR THE FIRST OF APRIL

A contribution to the general stock, of a rather remarkable nature, has been made by the reverend Ordinary of Newgate, in his report to the Lord Mayor and court of aldermen, as we find it quoted in the *Times* of Wednesday the eleventh of February. The reverend gentleman writes (in singular English):

'I have often thought, and still think, that the origin of garotte robberies took place from the exhibition of the way the Thugs in India strangle and plunder passengers, as exhibited in the British Museum. However valuable as illustrations of Indian manners such representations may be, I could heartily wish that these models were placed in some more obscure position, and cease to be that which I fear they have been, the means of giving to men addicted to crime and violence an idea how their evil purposes may be accomplished.'

Now, setting aside the fact notorious to all men—on the first of April—that the desperate characters of the metropolis are in the habit of fatiguing themselves with the study of the British Museum, and that the worst of the Ticket-of-leave men may be invariably found there, between the hours of ten and four, annotating their catalogues with great diligence, we take leave to protest against this reverend gentleman's doctrine, as utterly nonsensical in itself, and surpassingly insulting to the people. Here indeed is our old enemy Sloggins, with the broken nose, the black eye, and the bull-dog, at his old work in a rampant state! Because Sloggins abuses, nobody shall use. There is habitual drunkenness in the house of Sloggins, and therefore there shall not be temperate enjoyment in the house of Moderation; there is perversion of every gift of a gracious Creator on the part of this beast, and therefore the gifts shall be taken away from a million of well-conducted people. We declare that we believe the cruelty (however unintentional) of the reverend gentleman's proposition to be as gigantic as its injustice. It is a striking illustration of the purblind, one-sided, left-handed, monomaniacal vice of the time, which, deferring to the pests of society, would make England, for its toiling and much-enduring honest masses, one vast Penitentiary. Of what entertainment, of what knowledge, of what artificial relief that this earth can afford them, may the people out of Newgate not be deprived by a parity of reasoning? All traces of Mr. Layard's discoveries must be instantly put out of the way. They shew the Ordinary's precious charges how to bind people's hands behind their backs, and how to lop off people's heads. Peter's part in the New Testament must be sealed up, or we shall have a policeman's ear cut off. *Romeo and Juliet* must be interdicted, in remembrance of Mr. Palmer's having purchased poison, and lest Mr. Sloggins should think of administering a sleeping-draught. The publication of *King Lear* must be stopped by the Attorney-General, or a fiendish way of plotting against his brother will inevitably be put into young Mr. Sloggins's head. Tolerate *Hamlet* again, on any stage, and you shall hear from the Ordinary of there being somebody ' in trouble,' on suspicion of having poured poison into the ear of a near relation. The *Merchant of Venice* must be got with all dispatch into the State Gazette, or, so sure as you are born, Mr. Sloggins will have a pound of flesh from you as you go home one night. Prohibit *Paradise Lost* without a moment's loss of time, or Mr. Sloggins will get all the arguments of the Evil One into his head, and will misquote them against the Ordinary himself before he is a Sessions older. Burns must not be heard; Hogarth must not be seen. Sloggins never had a holiday that he did not misuse; therefore let no man have a holiday any more. Sloggins would raise a Devil out of any Art or Grace in life; therefore hamstring all the Arts and Graces, and lock the cripples up. Yet, even when you have done all this, and have cast the Thug figures into impenetrable obscurity, so ingenious is Mr. Sloggins, and such a knack of distorting the purest models has that exacting gentleman, that who shall ensure the Ordinary, after all, against Mr. Sloggins's declaring, one fine First of April, that ' he bin and got the idea o' garrotin',' from a certain lawful procession at eight o'clock in the morning, in which the Ordinary himself formed a conspicuous figure !

Among the commodities in store for All Fools'-day, we find a large quantity of expectations. It is expected to be known, then, by whose authority comfortable little arrangements are made for the absence of the Police when the worst characters in London come together to describe the Police as their natural and implacable enemies—which, it is to be hoped, they will long remain. It is expected to be known, then (and that through the agency of some Member of Parliament), whether the managing Police Commissioner takes the responsibility of this very dangerous proceeding, or whether the Home Secretary takes it ; and whether the responsibility of either functionary is a sufficient justification of it. On the same occasion it is expected that Somebody (official) will rise in both houses of Parliament, with a plain speech to this effect: 'We hear, my lords and gentlemen, a great deal said about youthful profligacy and corruption, in search of which we are perpetually poking our heads into Singing Rooms and Acting Rooms, and where not, and worrying mankind grey with the shying and backing and jibbing of a variety of hobbies; but, at any rate, we may all know, through the evidence of our own ears, that one of the most prolific sources of that profligacy and corruption is always rife and unchecked in our streets: where more abominable language is currently and openly used chiefly by young boys and young men than in all the rest of Europe. Now, my lords and gentlemen, we have the remedy for this, ready made, in the last Police Bill, where the use of bad language, in any public place, is made an offence punishable by fine or imprisonment. And, to begin plainly, at the beginning, without any prancing of hobbies in circles, we have just come to the conclusion that this law shall not be suffered to remain a Dead Letter, but shall, on special instruction, be enforced by the Police; and so, with GOD's help and yours, we will, at least, shut one of the stable-doors, standing wide open in our full view, before the steed is stolen.'[1] On the same occasion, the same Somebody (still speaking officially) is expected to announce, within the compass of half an hour by the clock, that he holds in his hand a Bill for the taking into custody by the strong arm, of every neglected or abandoned child of either sex, found in the streets of any town in this kingdom; for the training and education of that child, in honest knowledge and honest labour; for the heavy punishment of the parents if they can by any means be found; for making it compulsory on them to contribute to the costs and charges of the rearing of those children out of their earnings, no matter what; but, for their summary and final deprivation of all rights, as parents, over the young creatures they would have driven to perdition; and for the transfer of those rights to the State. It is expected that the Preamble of such Bill will set forth that the human heart can no longer bear the affecting spectacle of

---

[1] The writer has himself obtained a conviction by a police magistrate, under this Act, for this shameful and demoralising offence—which is as common and as public as the mud in the streets. He obtained it with difficulty, the charge not being within the experience of any one concerned; but, he insisted on the law, and it was clear (wonderful to relate !), and was enforced.

beautiful childhood made repulsive and shocking, which every great town presents; and that human faith cannot believe in the Divine endurance of such iniquity as the standing by and looking at it, without a terrible retribution.

It is further expected that the subject will occasion half as much interest at Westminster, and draw half as full a Lower House, as a pitched battle of 'I say you did' and 'I say you didn't' between M. and N., or as the appearance arm-in-arm, instead of fist to fist, of A. and Z. This extravagant notion, as by far the greatest of all the extravagances we have recorded, may aptly close the list of Stores for the Day of All Fools.

THE BEST AUTHORITY

[June 20, 1857]

I wish he was not so ubiquitous.

I wish he was not always having people to dine with him, into whom he crams all manner of confidences, and who come from his too hospitable board to harass my soul with special intelligence (which is never true), upon all the subjects that arise in Europe, Asia, Africa, and America. I wish to Heaven he would dine out!

Yet, that is a weak wish, because he does dine out. He makes a habit of dining out. He is always dining out. How could I be the confused, perplexed, benighted wretch I am, but for everybody I know, meeting him at dinner everywhere, and receiving information from him which they impart to me? I wish he would hold his tongue!

Yet, that is another weak wish, because when he does hold his tongue, I am none the better for it. His silence is used against me. If I mention to my friend, Pottington, any little scrap of fact or which in my very humble way I may have become possessed, Pottington says, that's very odd, he hardly thinks it can be, he will tell me why; dining yesterday at Croxford's he happened to sit next to the Best Authority, and had a good deal of talk with him, and yet he never said a word to lead him to suppose—

This brings me to inquire how does it happen that everybody

140

always sits next him? At a dinner of eighteen persons, I have known seventeen sit next him. Nay, at a public dinner of one hundred and thirty, I have known one hundred and twenty-nine sit next him. How is it done? In his ardent desire to impart special intelligence to his fellow-men, does he shift his position constantly, and sit upon all the chairs in the social circle successively? If he does so, it is obvious that he has no moral right to represent to each individual member of the company that his communication is of an exclusive character, and that he is impelled to it by strong personal consideration and respect. Yet I find that he invariably makes some such representation. I augur from this, that he is a deceiver.

What is his calling in life, that it leaves him so much time upon his hands? He is always at all the clubs—must spend a respectable income in annual club subscriptions alone. He is always in all the streets, and is met in the market-places by all sorts and conditions of men. Who is his bootmaker? Who cuts his corns? He is always going up and down the pavements, and must have corns of a prodigious size.

I object to his being addicted to compliments and flattery. I boldly publish this accusation against him, because I have several respected friends who would scorn to compliment themselves, whom he is always complimenting. For example. He meets my dear Flounceby (whom I regard as a brother), at a mutual friend's— there again! He is mutual friends with everybody!—and I find that he prefaces his communications to Flounceby, with such expressions as these: 'Mr. Flounceby, I do not wish what I am about to mention, to go any further; it is a matter of some little delicacy which I should not consider myself justified in speaking of to general society; but, knowing your remarkable powers, your delicate discrimination, and great discretion,' etc. All of which, my dear Flounceby, in the modest truthfulness of his nature, feels constrained to repeat to me! This is the Best Authority's didactic style; but, I observe him also, by incidental strokes, artfully to convey complimentary touches of character into casual dialogue. As when he remarks, in reference to some handsome reticence on my friend's part, 'Ah Flounceby! Your usual reserve in committing others!' Or, 'Your expressive eye, my dear Mr. Flounceby, discloses what your honourable tongue would desire to conceal!' And the like. All of which, Flounceby, in his severe determination to convey to me the truth, the whole truth, and nothing but the truth, repeats, with evident pain to his modesty.

Is he a burglar, or of the swell mob? I do not accuse him of occupying either position (which would be libellous), but I ask for information. Because my mind is tormented by his perpetually getting into houses into which he would seem to have no lawful open way, and by his continually diving into people's pocket-books in an otherwise inexplicable manner. In respect of getting into the Queen's Palace, the Boy Jones was a fool to him. He knows everything that takes place there. On a late auspicious occasion when the nation was hourly expecting to be transported with joy for the ninth time, it is surprising what he knew on the question of Chloroform. Now, Doctor Locock is known to be the most trustworthy even of doctors; and Her Majesty's self-reliance and quiet force of character have passed into an axiom. I want to know, therefore, How, When, Where, and From Whom, did the Best Authority acquire all that chloroform information which he was, for months, prowling about all the clubs, going up and down all the streets, having all London to dine with him, and going out to dine with all London, for the express purpose of diffusing? I hope society does not demand that I should be slowly bothered to death by any man, without demanding this much satisfaction. How did he come by his intelligence, I ask? The Best Authority must have had an authority. Let it be produced.

I have mentioned the pocket-books in which he deciphers secret entries; many of them written, probably, in invisible ink, for they are non-existent even to the owner's eyes. How does he come by all the ambassadors' letter-bags, and by all the note-books of all the judges? Who gave him all the little scraps of paper that the late Mr. Palmer wrote and handed about in the course of his protracted trial? He tells all sorts of people what was in them all; he must have seen them, surely. Who made out for him the accounts of this journal? Who calculated for him the sum total of profit? And when will it be quite convenient to him to name an early day for handing over to the Conductor the very large balance, with several ciphers at the end of it, which clearly must be owing the said Conductor, as he has never laid hands on it yet?

How did he get into the Russian lines? He was always there; just as he was always in the English camp, and always coming home to put Mr. Russell right, and going back again. It was he who found out that the Commissariat wouldn't give the *Times* rations of pork, and that the porkless *Times* would never afterwards leave the Commissariat alone. Had he known much of the Russian leaders before the war, that he began to talk of them so familiarly by their surnames as soon as the first gun was fired? Will any of us ever forget while memory holds her seat in these distracted globes, our aching heads, what we suffered from this man in connection with the Redan? Can the most Christian of us ever forgive the lies he told us about the Malakhoff? I might myself overlook even those injuries, but for his having put so many people up to making plans of that detested fortress, on tablecloths, with salt-spoons, forks, dessert-dishes, nut-crackers, and wine-glasses. Which frightful persecution, a thousand times inflicted on me, upon his authority—the best—I hereby swear never to condone! Never shall the Sapping and Mining knowledge, stamped in characters of lead upon this burning brow, remain with me but as a dreadful injury stimulating me to devote the residue of my life to vengeance on the Best Authority. If I could have his blood, I would! I avow it, in fell remembrance of the baying hounds of Boredom with which he hunted me in the days of the Russian war.

Will he, on this public challenge, stand forward foot to foot against me, his mortal enemy, and declare how he can justify his behaviour? Why am I, a free-born Briton, who never, never will—or rather who never, never would, if I could help it—why am I to truckle to this tyrant all the days of my life? Why is the Best Authority, Gesler-like, to set his hat upon a pole in the épergne of every dinner table, in the hall of every club-house, in the stones of every street, and, violating the Charter proclaimed by the Guardian Angels who sang that strain, to demand me for his slave? What does he mean by his unreasonable requirement that I shall make over my five senses to him? Who is he that he is to absorb my entity into his non-entity? And are not these his appetites? I put it to Flounceby.

Flounceby is rather an obstinate character (Mrs. Flounceby says the most obstinate of men; but, that may be her impulsive way of expressing herself), and will argue with you on any point, for any length of time you like—or don't like. He is certain to beat you, too, by a neat method he has of representing you to have said something which you never did say, or so much as think of, and then indignantly contradicting it. No further back than within this month, Flounceby was holding forth at a great rate on the most argumentative question of all questions—which every question is with him, and therefore I simply mean any question—and had made out his case entirely to his own satisfaction, and was pounding his dinner-company of six with it, as if they were plastic metal, and he and the question were the steam-hammer; when an unknown man of faint and fashionable aspect (one of the six) slided out from under the hammer without any apparent effort, and flatly denied Flounceby's positions, one and all, 'on the best authority.' If he had contested them on any ground of faith, reason, probability, or analogy, Flounceby would have pinned him like a bull-dog; but, the mere mention of the Best Authority (it was a genteel question in its bearings) instantly laid Flounceby on his back. He turned pale, trembled, and gave in. It happened, however, as it always does at Flounceby's, that the next most argumentative question of questions came on immediately afterwards. Upon that point I, deriving courage from the faint and fashionable man, who by the way from the moment of his victory, retired, like Iago, and word spake never more—opposed myself to Flounceby. I had not been rolled and flattened under the steam-hammer two minutes, when Flounceby, throwing the machinery out of gear, gave me one final crush from the Best Authority, and left me for dead. Goaded to distraction by the anonymous oppressor, I wildly cried that I cared nothing for the Best Authority. A shudder went round the table, and all present shrank from me, as if I had distinctly made the one greatest and most audacious denial of which humanity is capable.

Still goaded by this oppressor—always goaded by this oppressor—I ask, Who is he? Whence does he come when he goes out to dinner; where does he give those dinners at which so many people dine? Was he enrolled in the last census? Does he bear his part in the light burdens of the country? Is he assessed to the equitable income-tax? I call upon the Best Authority to stand forth.

On more than one occasion I have thought I had him. In that portion of Pall Mall, London, which is bounded on the east by the Senior United Service Club House, and on the west by the Carlton Club House—a miasmatic spot, in which I suppose more boredom to be babbled daily, than in any two thousand square miles on the surface of the earth—into that dismal region I had sometimes tracked the despot, and there lost him. One day, upon the steps of the Athenæum, of which eminent institution I have the honour to be a member, I found a fellow-member, Mr. Prowler, of the Royal Society of Arts, lying in wait, under the portico, to pour a drop of special information into the ear of every man and brother who approached the temple. Mr. Prowler is a grave and secret personage, always specially informed, who whispers his way through life ; incessantly acting Midas to everybody else's Reed. He goes about, like a lukewarm draught of air, breathing intelligence into the ears of his fellow-men, and passing on. He had often previously brought me into trouble, and caused me to be covered with confusion and shame. On this occasion the subject-matter of his confidence was—if I may be allowed the expression—so much more than usually impossible that I took the liberty to intimate my sense of its irreconcilability with all laws human and divine, and to ask him from whom he had his information ? He replied, from the Best Authority ; at the same time implying, with a profound and portentous movement of his head, that that mysterious Being had just gone in. I thought the hour was come—rushed into the hall— and found nobody there, but a weak old gentleman, to all appearance harmlessly idiotic, who was drying his pocket-handkerchief before the fire, and gazing over his shoulder at two graceful leathern institutions, in the form of broken French bedsteads without the pole, which embellish that chaste spot and invite to voluptuous repose.

On another occasion, I was so near having my hand at my enemy's throat and he so unaccountably eluded me, that a brief recital of the circumstances may aptly close this paper. The pursuit and escape occurred at the Reform Club, of which eminent Institution likewise, I have the honour to be a member. As I know the Best Authority to pervade that building constantly, my eye had frequently sought him, with a vague sense of the supernatural and an irresistible feeling of dread, in the galleries overhanging the hall where I had but too often heard him quoted. No trace of his form, however, had revealed itself to me. I had frequently been close upon him ; I had heard of him as having 'just gone down to the House,' or 'just come up'; but, between us there had been a

MISCELLANEOUS PAPERS

void. I should explain that in the palatial establishment of which I write, there is a dreadful little vault on the left of the Hall, where we hang up our hats and coats ; the gloom and closeness of which vault, shade the imagination. I was crossing the Hall to dinner, in the height of the then Session of Parliament, when my distinguished friend, O'Boodleom (Irish Member), being disappointed of a man of title, whom he was waiting to stun with a piece of information which he had just telegraphed to Erin, did me the honour to discharge that weapon upon me. As I had every conceivable reason to know that it could not possibly be correct, I deferentially asked O'Boodleom from whom he had received it ? 'Bedad, sir,' says he—and, knowing his sensitive bravery, I really felt grateful to him, for not saying, 'Blood, sir !'—' Bedad, sir,' says he, 'I had it, a while ago, from the Best Authority, and he's at this moment hanging up the entire of his coat and umberreller in the vault.' I dashed into the vault, and seized (as I fondly thought) the Best Authority, to cope with him at last in the death-struggle. It was only my cousin Cackles, admitted on all hands to be the most amiable ass alive, who inoffensively asked me if I had heard the news ?

The Best Authority was gone ! How gone, whither gone, I am in no condition to say. I again, therefore, raise my voice, and call upon him to stand forward and declare himself.

CURIOUS MISPRINT IN THE 'EDINBURGH REVIEW'.

[August 1, 1857]

The *Edinburgh Review*, in an article in its last number, on 'The License of Modern Novelists,' is angry with Mr. Dickens and other modern novelists, for not confining themselves to the mere amusement of their readers, and for testifying in their works that they seriously feel the interest of true Englishmen in the welfare and honour of their country. To them should be left the making of easy occasional books for idle young gentlemen and ladies to take up and lay down on sofas, drawing-room tables, and window-seats ; to the *Edinburgh Review* should be reserved the settlement of all social and political questions, and the strangulation of all complainers. Mr. Thackeray may write upon Snobs, but there must be none in the superior government departments. There is no positive objection to Mr. Reade having to do, in a Platonic way, with a Scottish fishwoman or so ; but he must by no means connect himself with Prison Discipline. That is the inalienable property of official personages ; and, until Mr. Reade can show that he has so much a-year, paid quarterly, for understanding (or not understanding) the subject, it is none of his, and it is impossible that he can be allowed to deal with it.

The name of Mr. Dickens is at the head of this page, and the hand of Mr. Dickens writes this paper. He will shelter himself under no affectation of being any one else, in having a few words of earnest but temperate remonstrance with the *Edinburgh Review*, before pointing out its curious misprint. Temperate, for the honour of Literature ; temperate, because of the great services which the *Edinburgh Review* has rendered in its time to good literature, and good government ; temperate, in remembrance of the loving affection of Jeffrey, the friendship of Sydney Smith, and the faithful sympathy of both.

The License of Modern Novelists is a taking title. But it suggests another,—the License of Modern Reviewers. Mr. Dickens's libel on the wonderfully exact and vigorous English government, which is always ready for any emergency, and which, as everybody knows, has never shown itself to be at all feeble at a pinch within the memory of men, is License in a novelist. Will the *Edinburgh Review* forgive Mr. Dickens for taking the liberty to point out what is License in a Reviewer ?

'Even the catastrophe in *Little Dorrit* is evidently borrowed from the recent fall of houses in Tottenham Court Road, which happens to have appeared in the newspapers at a convenient period.'

Thus, the Reviewer. The Novelist begs to ask him whether there is no License in his writing those words and stating that assumption as a truth, when any man accustomed to the critical examination of a book cannot fail, attentively turning over the pages of *Little Dorrit*, to observe that that catastrophe is carefully prepared for from the very first presentation of the old house in the story ; that when Rigaud, the man who is crushed by the fall of the house, first enters it (hundreds of pages before the end), he is beset by a mysterious fear and shuddering; that the rotten and crazy state of the house is laboriously kept before the reader, whenever the house is shown; that the way to the demolition of the man and the house together, is paved all through the book with a painful minuteness and reiterated care of preparation, the necessity of which (in order that the thread may be kept in the reader's mind through nearly two years), is one of the adverse incidents of that serial form of publication? It may be nothing to the question that Mr. Dickens now publicly declares, on his word and honour, that that catastrophe was written, was engraven on steel, was printed, had passed through the hands of compositors, readers for the press, and pressmen, and was in type and in proof in the Printing House of Messrs. Bradbury and Evans, before the accident in Tottenham Court Road occurred. But, it is much to the question that an honourable reviewer might have easily traced this out in the internal evidence of the book itself, before he stated, for a fact, what is utterly and entirely, in every particular and respect, untrue. More; if the Editor of the *Edinburgh Review* (unbending from the severe official duties of a blameless branch of the Circumlocution Office) had happened to condescend to cast his eye on the passage, and had referred even its mechanical probabilities and improbabilities to his publishers, those experienced gentlemen must have warned him that he was getting into danger; must have told him that on a comparison of dates, and with a reference to the number printed of *Little Dorrit*, with that very incident illustrated, and to the date of the publication of the completed book in a volume, they hardly perceived how Mr. Dickens *could* have waited, with such a desperate Micawberism, for a fall of houses in Tottenham Court Road, to get him out of his difficulties, and yet could have come up to time with the needful punctuality. Does the *Edinburgh Review* make no charges at random? Does it live in a blue and yellow glass house, and yet throw such big stones over the roof? Will the licensed Reviewer apologise to the licensed Novelist, for *his* little Circumlocution Office? Will he ' examine the justice ' of his own ' general charges,' as well as Mr. Dickens's? Will he apply his own words to himself, and come to the conclusion that it really is, 'a little curious to consider what qualifications a man ought to possess, before he could with any kind of propriety hold this language'?

MISPRINT IN THE 'EDINBURGH REVIEW'

The Novelist now proceeds to the Reviewer's curious misprint. The Reviewer, in his laudation of the great official departments, and in his indignant denial of there being any trace of a Circumlocution Office to be detected among them all, begs to know, 'what does Mr. Dickens think of the whole organisation of the Post-Office, and of the system of cheap Postage?' Taking St. Martins-le-grand in tow, the wrathful Circumlocution steamer, puffing at Mr. Dickens to crush him with all the weight of that first-rate vessel, demands, 'to take a single and well-known example, how does he account for the career of Mr. Rowland Hill? A gentleman in a private and not very conspicuous position, writes a pamphlet recommending what amounted to a revolution in a most important department of the Government. Did the Circumlocution Office neglect him, traduce him, break his heart, and ruin his fortune? They adopted his scheme, and gave him the leading share in carrying it out, and yet this is the government which Mr. Dickens declares to be a sworn foe to talent, and a systematic enemy to ingenuity.'

The curious misprint, here, is the name of Mr. Rowland Hill. Some other and perfectly different name must have been sent to the printer. Mr. Rowland Hill!! Why, if Mr. Rowland Hill were not, in toughness, a man of a hundred thousand; if he had not had in the struggles of his career a steadfastness of purpose overriding all sensitiveness, and steadily staring grim despair out of countenance, the Circumlocution Office would have made a dead man of him long and long ago. Mr. Dickens, among his other darings, dares to state, that the Circumlocution Office most heartily hated Mr. Rowland Hill; that the Circumlocution Office most characteristically opposed him as long as opposition was in any way possible; that the Circumlocution Office would have been most devoutly glad if it could have harried Mr. Rowland Hill's soul out of his body, and consigned him and his troublesome penny project to the grave together.

Mr. Rowland Hill!! Now, see the impossibility of Mr. Rowland Hill being the name which the *Edinburgh Review* sent to the printer. It may have relied on the forbearance of Mr. Dickens towards living gentlemen, for his being mute on a mighty job that was jobbed in that very Post-Office when Mr. Rowland Hill was *taboo* there, and it shall not rely upon his courtesy in vain: though there be breezes on the southern side of mid-Strand, London, in which the scent of it is yet strong on quarter-days. But, the *Edinburgh Review* never can have put up Mr. Rowland Hill for the putting down of Mr. Dickens's idle fiction of a Circumlocution Office. The ' license ' would have been too great, the absurdity would have been too transparent, the Circumlocution Office dictation and partisanship would have been much too manifest.

'The Circumlocution Office adopted his scheme, and gave him the leading share in carrying it out.' The words are clearly not applicable to Mr. Rowland Hill. Does the Reviewer remember the history of Mr. Rowland Hill's scheme? The Novelist does, and will state it here, exactly ; in spite of its being one of the eternal decrees that the Reviewer, in virtue of his license, shall know everything, and that the Novelist, in virtue of *his* license, shall know nothing.

Mr. Rowland Hill published his pamphlet on the establishment of one uniform penny postage, in the beginning of the year eighteen hundred and thirty-seven. Mr. Wallace, member for Greenock, who had long been opposed to the then existing Post-Office system, moved for a Committee on the subject. Its appointment was opposed by the Government—or, let us say, the Circumlocution Office—but was afterwards conceded. Before that Committee, the Circumlocution Office and Mr. Rowland Hill were perpetually in conflict on questions of fact ; and it invariably turned out that Mr. Rowland Hill was always right in his facts, and that the Circumlocution Office was always wrong. Even on so plain a point as the average number of letters at that very time passing through the Post-Office, Mr. Rowland Hill was right, and the Circumlocution Office was wrong.

Says the *Edinburgh Review*, in what it calls a ' general ' way, ' The Circumlocution Office adopted his scheme.' Did it ? Not just then, certainly ; for, nothing whatever was done, arising out of the enquiries of that Committee. But, it happened that the Whig Government afterwards came to be beaten on the Jamaica question, by reason of the Radicals voting against them. Sir Robert Peel was commanded to form a Government, but failed, in consequence of the difficulties that arose (our readers will remember them) about the Ladies of the Bedchamber. The Ladies of the Bedchamber brought the Whigs in again, and then the Radicals (being always for the destruction of everything) made it one of the conditions of their rendering their support to the new Whig Government that the penny-postage system should be adopted. This was two years after the appointment of the Committee: that is to say, in eighteen hundred and thirty-nine. The Circumlocution Office had, to that time, done nothing towards the penny postage, but oppose, delay, contradict, and show itself uniformly wrong.

'They adopted his scheme, and gave him the leading share in carrying it out.' Of course they gave him the leading share in carrying it out, then, at the time when they adopted it, and took the credit and popularity of it? Not so. In eighteen hundred and thirty-nine, Mr. Rowland Hill was appointed—not to the Post-Office, but to the Treasury. Was he appointed to the Treasury to carry out his own scheme? No. He was appointed ' to advise.' In other words, to instruct the ignorant Circumlocution Office how to do without him, if it by any means could. On the tenth of January, eighteen hundred and forty, the penny-postage system was adopted. Then, of course, the Circumlocution Office gave Mr. Rowland Hill 'the leading share in carrying it out'? Not exactly, but it gave him the leading share in carrying himself out: for, in eighteen hundred and forty-two, it summarily dismissed Mr. Rowland Hill altogether!

When the Circumlocution Office had come to that pass in its patriotic course, so much admired by the *Edinburgh Review*, of protecting and patronising Mr. Rowland Hill, whom any child who is not a Novelist can perceive to have been its peculiar *protégé*, the public mind (always perverse) became much excited on the subject. Sir Thomas Wilde moved for another Committee. Circumlocution Office interposed. Nothing was done. The public subscribed and presented to Mr. Rowland Hill, Sixteen Thousand Pounds. Circumlocution Office remained true to itself and its functions. Did nothing; would do nothing. It was not until eighteen hundred and forty-six, four years afterwards, that Mr. Rowland Hill was appointed to a place in the Post-Office. Was he appointed, even then, to the 'leading share in carrying out' his scheme? He was permitted to creep into the Post-Office up the back stairs, through having a place created for him. This post of dignity and honour, this Circumlocution Office crown, was called 'Secretary to the Post-Master General'; there being already a Secretary to the Post-Office, of whom the Circumlocution Office had declared, as its reason for dismissing Mr. Rowland Hill, that his functions and Mr. Rowland Hill's could not be made to harmonise.

MISCELLANEOUS PAPERS

They did not harmonise. They were in perpetual discord. Penny postage is but one reform of a number of Post-Office reforms effected by Mr. Rowland Hill; and these, for eight years longer, were thwarted and opposed by the Circumlocution Office, tooth and nail. It was not until eighteen hundred and fifty-four, fourteen years after the appointment of Mr. Wallace's Committee, that Mr. Rowland Hill (having, as was openly stated at the time, threatened to resign and to give his reasons for doing so), was at last made sole Secretary at the Post-Office, and the inharmonious secretary (of whom no more shall be said) was otherwise disposed of. It is only since that date of eighteen hundred and fifty-four, that such reforms as the amalgamation of the general and district posts, the division of London into ten towns, the earlier delivery of letters all over the country, the book and parcels post, the increase of letter-receiving houses everywhere, and the management of the Post-Office with a greatly increased efficiency, have been brought about by Mr. Rowland Hill for the public benefit and the public convenience.

If the *Edinburgh Review* could seriously want to know ' How Mr. Dickens accounts for the career of Mr. Rowland Hill,' Mr. Dickens would account for it by his being a Birmingham man of such imperturbable steadiness and strength of purpose, that the Circumlocution Office, by its utmost endeavours, very freely tried, could not weaken his determination, sharpen his razor, or break his heart. By his being a man in whose behalf the public gallantry was roused, and the public spirit awakened. By his having a project, in its nature so plainly and directly tending to the immediate benefit of every man, woman, and child in the State, that the Circumlocution Office could not blind them, though it could for a time cripple it. By his having thus, from the first to the last, made his way in spite of the Circumlocution Office, and dead against it as his natural enemy.

But, the name is evidently a curious misprint and an unfortunate mistake. The Novelist will await the Reviewer's correction of the press, and substitution of the right name.

Will the *Edinburgh Review* also take its next opportunity of manfully expressing its regret that in too distempered a zeal for the Circumlocution Office, it has been betrayed, as to that Tottenham Court Road assertion, into a hasty substitution of untruth for truth; the discredit of which, it might have saved itself, if it had been sufficiently cool and considerate to be simply just? It will, too possibly, have much to do by that time in championing its Circumlocution Office in new triumphs on the voyage out to India (God knows that the Novelist has his private as well as his public reasons for writing the foreboding with no triumphant heart!); but even party occupation, the reviewer's license, or the editorial plural, does not absolve a gentleman from a gentleman's duty, a gentleman's restraint, and a gentleman's generosity.

Mr. Dickens will willingly do his best to 'account for' any new case of Circumlocution Office protection that the *Review* may make a gauntlet of. He may be trusted to do so, he hopes, with a just respect for the *Review*, for himself, and for his calling; beyond the sound, healthy, legitimate uses and influences of which, he has no purpose to serve, and no ambition in life to gratify.

WELL-AUTHENTICATED RAPPINGS

[FEBRUARY 20, 1858]

THE writer, who is about to record three spiritual experiences of his own in the present truthful article, deems it essential to state that, down to the time of his being favoured therewith, he had not been a believer in rappings, or tippings. His vulgar notions of the spiritual world, represented its inhabitants as probably advanced, even beyond the intellectual supremacy of Peckham or New York; and it seemed to him, considering the large amount of ignorance, presumption, and folly with which this earth is blessed, so very unnecessary to call in immaterial Beings to gratify mankind with bad spelling and worse nonsense, that the presumption was strongly against those respected films taking the trouble to come here, for no better purpose than to make supercrogatory idiots of themselves.

This was the writer's gross and fleshy state of mind at so late a period as the twenty-sixth of December last. On that memorable morning, at about two hours after daylight,—that is to say, at twenty minutes before ten by the writer's watch, which stood on a table at his bedside, and which can be seen at the publishing-office, and identified as a demi-chronometer made by Bautte of Geneva, and numbered 67,709—on that memorable morning, at about two hours after daylight, the writer, starting up in bed with his hand to his

153

forehead, distinctly felt seventeen heavy throbs or beats in that region. They were accompanied by a feeling of pain in the locality, and by a general sensation not unlike that which is usually attendant on biliousness. Yielding to a sudden impulse, the writer asked:

'What is this?'

The answer immediately returned (in throbs or beats upon the forehead) was, 'Yesterday.'

The writer then demanded, being as yet but imperfectly awake:

'What was yesterday?'

Answer: 'Christmas Day.'

The writer, being now quite come to himself, inquired, 'Who is the Medium in this case?'

Answer: 'Clarkins.'

Question: 'Mrs. Clarkins, or Mr. Clarkins?'

Answer: 'Both.'

Question: 'By Mr., do you mean Old Clarkins, or Young Clarkins?'

Answer: 'Both.'

Now, the writer had dined with his friend Clarkins (who can be appealed to, at the State-Paper Office) on the previous day, and spirits had actually been discussed at that dinner, under various aspects. It was in the writer's remembrance, also, that both Clarkins Senior and Clarkins Junior had been very active in such discussion, and had rather pressed it on the company. Mrs. Clarkins too had joined in it with animation, and had observed, in a joyous if not an exuberant tone, that it was 'only once a year.'

Convinced by these tokens that the rapping was of spiritual origin, the writer proceeded as follows:

'Who are you?'

The rapping on the forehead was resumed, but in a most incoherent manner. It was for some time impossible to make sense of it. After a pause, the writer (holding his head) repeated the inquiry in a solemn voice, accompanied with a groan:

'Who ARE you?'

Incoherent rappings were still the response.

The writer then asked, solemnly as before, and with another groan:

'What is your name?'

The reply was conveyed in a sound exactly resembling a loud

hiccough. It afterwards appeared that this spiritual voice was distinctly heard by Alexander Pumpion, the writer's footboy (seventh son of Widow Pumpion, mangler), in an adjoining chamber.

Question : 'Your name cannot be Hiccough? Hiccough is not a proper name?'

No answer being returned, the writer said : ' I solemnly charge you, by our joint knowledge of Clarkins the Medium—of Clarkins Senior, Clarkins Junior, and Clarkins Mrs.—to reveal your name !'

The reply rapped out with extreme unwillingness, was, 'Sloe-Juice, Logwood, Blackberry.'

This appeared to the writer sufficiently like a parody on Cobweb, Moth, and Mustard-Seed, in the *Midsummer Night's Dream,* to justify the retort :

' *That* is not your name?'

The rapping spirit admitted, ' No.'

'Then what do they generally call you?'

A pause.

'I ask you, what do they generally call you?'

The spirit, evidently under coercion, responded, in a most solemn manner, 'Port !'

This awful communication caused the writer to lie prostrate, on the verge of insensibility, for a quarter of an hour : during which the rappings were continued with violence, and a host of spiritual appearances passed before his eyes, of a black hue, and greatly resembling tadpoles endowed with the power of occasionally spinning themselves out into musical notes as they swam down into space. After contemplating a vast Legion of these appearances, the writer demanded of the rapping spirit :

' How am I to present you to myself? What, upon the whole, is most like you?'

The terrific reply was, ' Blacking.'

As soon as the writer could command his emotion, which was now very great, he inquired :

' Had I better take something?'

Answer : 'Yes.'

Question : ' Can I write for something?'

Answer : 'Yes.'

A pencil and a slip of paper which were on the table at the bed-side immediately bounded into the writer's hand, and he found himself forced to write (in a curiously unsteady character and all downhill, whereas his own writing is remarkably plain and straight) the following spiritual note.

'Mr. C. D. S. Pooney presents his compliments to Messrs. Bell and Company, Pharmaceutical Chemists, Oxford Street, opposite to Portland Street, and begs them to have the goodness to send him by Bearer a five-grain genuine blue pill and a genuine black draught of corresponding power.'

But, before entrusting this document to Alexander Pumpion (who unfortunately lost it on his return, if he did not even lay himself open to the suspicion of having wilfully inserted it into one of the holes of a perambulating chestnut-roaster, to see how it would flare), the writer resolved to test the rapping spirit with one conclusive question. He therefore asked, in a slow and impressive voice :

' Will these remedies make my stomach ache ? '

It is impossible to describe the prophetic confidence of the reply. ' Yes.' The assurance was fully borne out by the result, as the writer will long remember ; and after this experience it were needless to observe that he could no longer doubt.

The next communication of a deeply interesting character with which the writer was favoured, occurred on one of the leading lines of railway. The circumstances under which the revelation was made to him—on the second day of January in the present year—were these : He had recovered from the effects of the previous remarkable visitation, and had again been partaking of the compliments of the season. The preceding day had been passed in hilarity. He was on his way to a celebrated town, a well-known commercial emporium where he had business to transact, and had lunched in a somewhat greater hurry than is usual on railways, in consequence of the train being behind time. His lunch had been very reluctantly administered to him by a young lady behind a counter. She had been much occupied at the time with the arrangement of her hair and dress, and her expressive countenance had denoted disdain. It will be seen that this young lady proved to be a powerful Medium.

The writer had returned to the first-class carriage in which he chanced to be travelling alone, the train had resumed its motion, he had fallen into a doze, and the unimpeachable watch already mentioned recorded forty-five minutes to have elapsed since his interview with the Medium, when he was aroused by a very singular musical instrument. This instrument, he found to his admiration not unmixed with alarm, was performing in his inside. Its tones were of a low and rippling character, difficult to describe; but, if such a comparison may be admitted, resembling a melodious heart-burn. Be this as it may, they suggested that humble sensation to the writer.

Concurrently with his becoming aware of the phenomenon in question, the writer perceived that his attention was being solicited by a hurried succession of angry raps in the stomach, and a pressure on the chest. A sceptic no more, he immediately communed with the spirit. The dialogue was as follows:

Question: 'Do I know your name?'

Answer: '*I* should think so!'

Question: 'Does it begin with a P?'

Answer (second time): '*I* should think so!'

Question: 'Have you two names, and does each begin with a P?'

Answer (third time): '*I* should think so!'

Question: 'I charge you to lay aside this levity, and inform me what you are called.'

The spirit, after reflecting for a few seconds, spelt out P. O. R. K. The musical instrument then performed a short and fragmentary strain. The spirit then recommenced, and spelt out the word 'P. I. E.'

Now, this precise article of pastry, this particular viand or comestible, actually had formed—let the scoffer know—the staple of the writer's lunch, and actually had been handed to him by the young lady whom he now knew to be a powerful Medium! Highly gratified by the conviction thus forced upon his mind that the know-ledge with which he conversed was not of this world, the writer pursued the dialogue.

Question: 'They call you Pork Pie?'

Answer: 'Yes.'

Question (which the writer timidly put, after struggling with some natural reluctance): 'Are you, in fact, Pork Pie?'

Answer: 'Yes.'

It were vain to attempt a description of the mental comfort and relief which the writer derived from this important answer. He proceeded:

Question: 'Let us understand each other. A part of you is Pork, and a part of you is Pie?'

157

Answer : ' Exactly so.'

Question : ' What is your Pie-part made of ? '

Answer : ' Lard.' Then came a sorrowful strain from the musical instrument. Then the word ' Dripping.'

Question : ' How am I to present you to my mind ? What are you most like ? '

Answer (very quickly) : ' Lead.'

A sense of despondency overcame the writer at this point. When he had in some measure conquered it, he resumed :

Question : ' Your other nature is a Porky nature. What has that nature been chiefly sustained upon ? '

Answer (in a sprightly manner) : ' Pork, to be sure ! '

Question : ' Not so. Pork is not fed upon Pork ? '

Answer : ' Isn't it, though ! '

A strange internal feeling, resembling a flight of pigeons, seized upon the writer. He then became illuminated in a surprising manner, and said :

' Do I understand you to hint that the human race, incautiously attacking the indigestible fortresses called by your name, and not having time to storm them, owing to the great solidity of their almost impregnable walls, are in the habit of leaving much of their contents in the hands of the Mediums, who with such pig nourish the pigs of the future pies ? '

Answer : ' That 's it ! '

Question : ' Then to paraphrase the words of our immortal bard :——'

Answer (interrupting) :

> ' The same pork in its time, makes many pies,
> Its least being seven pasties.'

The writer's emotion was profound. But, again desirous still further to try the Spirit, and to ascertain whether, in the poetic phraseology of the advanced seers of the United States, it hailed from one of the inner and more elevated circles, he tested its knowledge with the following

Question : ' In the wild harmony of the musical instrument within me, of which I am again conscious, what other substances are there airs of, besides those you have mentioned ? '

Answer: 'Cape. Gamboge. Camomile. Treacle. Spirits of wine. Distilled Potatoes.'

Question: 'Nothing else?'

Answer: 'Nothing worth mentioning.'

Let the scorner tremble and do homage; let the feeble sceptic blush! The writer at his lunch had demanded of the powerful Medium, a glass of Sherry, and likewise a small glass of Brandy. Who can doubt that the articles of commerce indicated by the Spirit were supplied to him from that source under those two names?

One other instance may suffice to prove that experiences of the foregoing nature are no longer to be questioned, and that it ought to be made capital to attempt to explain them away. It is an exquisite case of Tipping.

The writer's Destiny had appointed him to entertain a hopeless affection for Miss L. B., of Bungay, in the county of Suffolk. Miss L. B. had not, at the period of the occurrence of the Tipping, openly rejected the writer's offer of his hand and heart; but it has since seemed probable that she had been withheld from doing so, by filial fear of her father, Mr. B., who was favourable to the writer's pretensions. Now, mark the Tipping. A young man, obnoxious to all well-constituted minds (since married to Miss L. B.), was visiting at the house. Young B. was also home from school. The writer was present. The family party were assembled about a round table. It was the spiritual time of twilight in the month of July. Objects could not be discerned with any degree of distinctness. Suddenly, Mr. B., whose senses had been lulled to repose, infused terror into all our breasts, by uttering a passionate roar or ejaculation. His words (his education was neglected in his youth) were exactly these: 'Damme, here's somebody a shoving of a letter into my hand, under my own mahogany!' Consternation seized the assembled group. Mrs. B. augmented the prevalent dismay by declaring that somebody had been softly treading on her toes, at intervals, for half an hour. Greater consternation seized the assembled group. Mr. B. called for lights. Now, mark the Tipping. Young B. cried (I quote his expressions accurately), 'It's the spirits, father! They've been at it with me this last fortnight.' Mr. B. demanded with irascibility, 'What do you mean, sir? What have they been at?' Young B. replied, 'Wanting to make a regular Post-office of me, father. They're always handing impalpable letters to me, father.

A letter must have come creeping round to you by mistake. I must be a Medium, father. O here 's a go !' cried young B. 'If I ain't a jolly Medium !' The boy now became violently convulsed, sputtering exceedingly, and jerking out his legs and arms in a manner calculated to cause me (and which did cause me) serious inconvenience ; for, I was supporting his respected mother within range of his boots, and he conducted himself like a telegraph before the invention of the electric one. All this time Mr. B. was looking about under the table for the letter, while the obnoxious young man, since married to Miss L. B., protected that young lady in an obnoxious manner. ' O here 's a go !' Young B. continued to cry without intermission, ' If I an't a jolly Medium, father ! Here 's a go ! There 'll be a Tipping presently, father. Look out for the table !' Now mark the Tipping. The table tipped so violently as to strike Mr. B. a good half-dozen times on his bald head while he was looking under it ; which caused Mr. B. to come out with great agility, and rub it with much tenderness (I refer to his head), and to imprecate it with much violence (I refer to the table). I observed that the tipping of the table was uniformly in the direction of the magnetic current ; that is to say, from south to north, or from young B. to Mr. B. I should have made some further observations on this deeply interesting point, but that the table suddenly revolved, and tipped over on myself, bearing me to the ground with a force increased by the momentum imparted to it by young B., who came over with it in a state of mental exaltation, and could not be displaced for some time. In the interval, I was aware of being crushed by his weight and the table's, and also of his constantly calling out to his sister and the obnoxious young man, that he foresaw there would be another Tipping presently.

None such, however, took place. He recovered after taking a short walk with them in the dark, and no worse effects of the very beautiful experience with which we had been favoured, were perceptible in him during the rest of the evening, than a slight tendency to hysterical laughter, and a noticeable attraction (I might almost term it fascination) of his left hand, in the direction of his heart or waistcoat-pocket.

Was this, or was it not a case of Tipping ? Will the sceptic and the scoffer reply ?

AN IDEA OF MINE

[MARCH 13, 1858]

EMERGING, the other day, into the open street from an exhibition of pictures at the West End of London, I was much impressed by the contrast between the polite bearing of the Fine Arts, and the rudeness of real life. Inside the gallery, all the people in the pictures had pointedly referred to me in every cock of their highly feathered hats, in every wrinkle of their highly slashed doublets, in every stride and straddle of their highly muscular legs. Outside, I did not observe that I exercised any influence on the crowd who were pursuing their business or their pleasure ; or that those insensible persons at all altered the expression of their countenances for my sake. Inside, nothing could be done without me. Were a pair of eyes in question, they must smirk at me ; were a pair of spurs in question, they must glint at me ; were a pair of boots in question, they must stretch themselves out on forms and benches to captivate me. Whereas, it appeared to me, that the eyes and the spurs and the boots that were outside, all had more or less of their own to do, and did it ; thereby reducing me to the station of quite an unimportant personage. I had occasion to make the same remark in reference to the Passions. Nothing could exceed the good-breeding with which, inside the gallery, they had entreated me not to disturb myself on their account, and had begged me to observe that they were what the children call, ' only in fun.' Outside, on the other hand, they were quite obstreperous, and no more cared to preserve a good understanding with me than if I had been one of the sparrows in the gutter. A similar barbarous tendency to reality, to change and movement, and to the knowledge of the Present as a something of interest sprung out of the Past and melting into the Future, was to be noted on every external object : insomuch that the passing from the inside of the gallery to the outside was like the transition from Madame Tussaud's waxwork, or a tawdry fancy ball in the Sleeping Beauty's palace during the hundred years of enchantment, to a windy mountain or the rolling sea. I understood now, what I had never understood before, why there were

161

two sentries at the exhibition-door. These are not to be regarded as mere privates in the Foot Guards, but as allegorical personages, stationed there with gun and bayonet to keep out Purpose, and to mount guard over the lassitude of the Fine Arts, laid up in the lavender of other ages.

I was so charmed by these discoveries, and particularly the last, that I stepped into my club (the Associated Bores), with the idea of writing an essay, to be entitled The Praise of Painting. But, as I am of a discriminatory turn, even in my admiration, I meditated in its stead a little project of reform, which I proceed to submit to the Royal Academy of Arts—of whose co-operation I have no doubt—and to the public.

Devoted as I am to the pictures which it is the pride and privilege of the present age to produce in this land of the free and refuge of the slave, I cannot disguise from myself the fact that I know all the Models. I cannot shut my eyes to the gloomy truth, that my fellow-countrymen and countrywomen are but too well acquainted by sight with every member of that limited profession which sits to painters at so much an hour. I cannot be deaf to the whisper of my conscience that we have had enough of them. I am unable to silence the still small voice which tells me that I am tired to death of that young man with the large chest, and that I would thankfully accept a less symmetrical young man with a smaller chest, or even with a chest in which the stethoscope might detect a weakness. Immaculate as that other young man's legs are, I am sick of his legs. A novelty, even though it were bandy, would be a sweet and soothing relief to me.

My feelings are, I say, the feelings of thousands who suffer with me under the oppression of this nightmare of Models, and I therefore reckon with certainty on the general support in my project for curing the evil. My project is as follows :

1. That the young man with the large chest be promptly taken into custody, and confined in the Tower.

2. That the young man with the immaculate legs be promptly taken into custody, and confined in Greenwich Hospital ; and that his legs be there immediately amputated (under chloroform), and decently buried within the precincts of the building.

3. That the young woman with the long eyelashes be sent to the Magdalen until further orders.

162

4. That every other Model be immediately seized, veiled, and placed in solitary confinement.

5. That the fancy-dress establishment of the Messrs. Nathan in Titchbourne Street, Haymarket, be razed to the ground, and the stock-in-trade seized; and further, that all slashed dresses of the period of Charles the Second, all buff jerkins of the Commonwealth, and all large boots of whatsoever description, found in such stock, be publicly burnt, as old and incorrigible offenders.

6. That the premises of the Messrs. Pratt in Bond Street, as being in the occupation of the leaders of the Still-life Model Department, be rigidly searched, and that all the old curiosity shops in Wardour Street and elsewhere be likewise rigidly searched, and that all offensively notorious property found therein be brought away. That is to say: all steel-caps and armour of whatsoever description, all large spurs and spur-leathers, all bossy tankards, all knobby drinking glasses, all ancient bottles and jugs, all high-backed chairs, all twisted-legged tables, all carpets, covers, and hangings, all remarkable swords and daggers, all strangely bound old books, and all spinning wheels. (The last-named to be broken on the spot.)

It may be objected by the scrupulous, that the loss of property thus caused would fall heavily on individuals, and would be a greater punishment than could be justified, even by the immense provocation the public has received. My answer is, that my project is based on principles of justice, and that I therefore propose to compensate these persons by paying the fair purchase-price of all the articles seized.

For this purpose (and for another to be presently mentioned), I propose that the government be empowered to raise by the issue of exchequer bills, a sum not exceeding three millions sterling. Inasmuch as it would be necessary to purchase of Messrs. Hunt and Roskell, goldsmiths and jewellers of New Bond Street, and likewise of Mr. Hancock, goldsmith and jeweller of the same place, various highly-exasperating tall cups and covers wrought in precious metals, which daily find their way into pictures, to the persecution, terror, and exhaustion of the public, my calculation is, that two millions of the three would be sunk in the payments indispensable to the public relief.

The remaining million to be devoted to the two remaining objects now to be described.

MISCELLANEOUS PAPERS

Firstly, to the construction of a large building (if no edifice suffi-ciently inconvenient and hideous to serve a national purpose be already in existence), in which the seized property shall be deposited in strict seclusion for ever. As the public, after its long and terrible experience of the contents of this dismal storehouse, will naturally shun it, and as all good parents may confidently be expected to teach their children in awestricken whispers to avoid it, it would be super-fluous to take precautions against the intrusion of any casual visitors. But, it will be necessary (so touching is the constancy and so enthralling the affection with which painters cling to Models), to make it capital for any professor of the art of painting to be found in the Institution on any pretence whatever; and to render it incumbent on the judges of the land, receiving proof of such offence according to the usual laws of evidence, to sentence the offender to death, without hope of mercy.

The east and west sides of this building to be fitted up, each with its own sleeping rooms, domestic offices, dining-hall, and chapel. The east side to be called The Side of the Male Models; the west side to be called The Side of the Female Models. Every preparation being completed for the reception of these unhappy persons, hither would be brought: from the Tower, the young man with the large chest; from Greenwich Hospital, the young man without the immaculate legs; from the Magdalen, the young woman with the long eyelashes. Hither too, would be brought, all in close custody and heavily veiled, the whole offending family of live Models. Hither, a procession of hearses would convey them in the dead of night; the first hearse containing the aggravating patriarch with the white beard, and the pious grandmother with the veinous hands; the last, containing the innocent but misguided child who has long been accustomed to sit on a cruelly knotty bench, and blow bubbles from a pipe. From this place of seclusion and expiation, they should never more be permitted to come forth. And adapting an idea from the eloquent pamphlet of Mr. Com-missioner Phillips on capital punishment, I would have a gorgeous flag perpetually waving from the apex of the roof, on which should be inscribed, in mediæval characters, THE GRAVE OF THE MODELS.

But, still respecting the eternal principles of justice, I would not confiscate the money-earning opportunities of the socially deceased.

164

AN IDEA OF MINE

This brings me to the last object to which the residue of the capital of three millions should be appropriated. Assuming, say the young man with the large chest, to have been able to earn by that chest two shillings an hour (I take that to be high, but his chest is very large), for six hours a day during six months of the year, that young man's gains, in round numbers, would amount to ninety pounds per annum. I would pay that young man that income, and, though civilly dead, he should retain the power of disposing of his property by will. Neither would I amputate the legs of that other young man, without allowing him, besides, a pension for their loss in the public service. The rights of the young woman with the eyelashes would be similarly respected. No Model would suffer, except in liberty, by the incalculable addition to the stock of general comfort and happiness. Over and above these great advantages, I would concede to the Models the right of encasing themselves in all the armour, wearing all the fancy dresses, lolling in all the high-backed chairs, putting on the boots of all periods and striding them under, over, or upon, all the twisted-legged tables, and pretending to drink out of all the knobby glasses and bossy tankards, in the collection. As they have seldom done anything else, and, happily for themselves, have seldom been used to do this to any purpose but the display of themselves and the property, I conceive that they would hardly discern a difference between their being under the proposed restraint and being still at large.

This is my project. Whether the withdrawal of the Models would reduce our men of genius, who paint pictures, to the shameful necessity of wresting their great art to the telling of stories and conveying of ideas, is a question upon which I do not feel called to enter. To close with quite another head of remark, I will observe that I may be told that the Act of Parliament necessary for carrying out my purpose, is a sweeping one, and might be opposed. I have considered that, too, and have discovered the remedy. It is (which can be easily done), but to get some continental sovereign to demand it, on a threat of invasion, fire, sword, and extermination ; and a spirited Minister will do his utmost to pass it with the greatest alacrity.

165

PLEASE TO LEAVE YOUR UMBRELLA

[MAY 1, 1858]

I MADE a visit the other day to the Palace at Hampton Court. I may have had my little reason for being in the best of humours with the Palace at Hampton Court; but that little reason is neither here (ah! I wish it were here!) nor there.

In the readiest of moods for complying with any civil request, I was met, in the entrance-hall of the public apartments at Hampton Court, by the most obliging of policemen, who requested me to leave my umbrella in his custody at the foot of the stairs. 'Most willingly,' said I, 'for my umbrella is very wet.' So the policeman hung it on a rack, to drip on the stone floor with the sound of an irregular clock, and gave me a card of authority to reclaim it when I should come out again. Then, I went prosperously through the long suites of deserted rooms, now looking at the pictures, and now leaning over the broad old window-seats and looking down into the rainy old gardens, with their formal gravel walks, clipped trees, and trim turf banks—gardens with court-suits on. There was only one other visitor (in very melancholy boots) at Hampton Court that blessed day: who soon went his long grave way, alternately dark in the piers and light in the windows, and was seen no more.

'I wonder,' said I, in the manner of the Sentimental Journeyer, 'I wonder, Yorick, whether, with this little reason in my bosom, I should ever want to get out of these same interminable suites of rooms, and return to noise and bustle! It seems to me that I could stay here very well until the grisly phantom on the pale horse came at a gallop up the staircase, seeking me. My little reason should make of these queer dingy closet-rooms, these little corner chimney-pieces tier above tier, this old blue china of squat shapes, these dreary old state bedsteads with attenuated posts, nay, dear Yorick,' said I, stretching forth my hand towards a stagnant pool of blacking in a frame, 'should make, even of these very works of art, an encompassing universe of beauty and happiness. The fountain in the staid red and white courtyard without (for we had turned that angle of the building), would never fall too monotonously on my ear, the

166

four chilled sparrows now fluttering on the brink of its basin would never chirp a wish for change of weather, no bargeman on the rain-speckled river; no wayfarer rain-belated under the leafless trees in the park, would ever come into my fancy as examining in despair those swollen clouds, and vainly peering for a ray of sunshine. I and my little reason, Yorick, would keep house here, all our lives, in perfect contentment; and when we died, our ghosts should make of this dull Palace the first building ever haunted happily!

I had got thus far in my adaptation of the *Sentimental Journey* when I was recalled to my senses by the visible presence of the Blacking which I just now mentioned. 'Good Heaven!' I cried, with a start; 'now I think of it, what a number of articles that policeman below-stairs required me to leave with him!'

'Only an umbrella. He said no more than, Please to leave your umbrella.'

'Faith, Yorick,' I returned, 'he insisted on my putting so much valuable property into my umbrella, and leaving it all at the foot of the stairs before I entered on the contemplation of many of these pictures, that I tremble to think of the extent to which I have been despoiled. That policeman demanded of me, for the time being, all the best bumps in my head. Form, colour, size, proportion, distance, individuality, the true perception of every object on the face of the earth or the face of the Heavens, he insisted on my leaving at the foot of the stairs, before I could confide in the catalogue. And now I find the moon to be really made of green cheese; the sun to be a yellow wafer or a little round blister; the deep wild sea to be a shallow series of slate-coloured festoons turned upside down; the human face Divine to be a smear; the whole material and immaterial universe to be sticky with treacle and polished up with blacking. Conceive what I must be, through all the rest of my life, if the police-man should make off with my umbrella and never restore it!'

Filled with the terrors of this idea, I retraced my steps to the top of the stairs, and looked over the hand-rail for my precious property. It was still keeping time on the stone pavement like an irregular clock, and the policeman (evidently possessed by no dishonest spirit) was reading a newspaper. Calmed and composed, I resumed my musing way through the many rooms.

Please to leave your umbrella. Of all the Powers that get your umbrella from you, Taste is the most encroaching and insatiate.

MISCELLANEOUS PAPERS

Please to put into your umbrella, to be deposited in the hall until you come out again, all your powers of comparison, all your experience, all your individual opinions. Please to accept with this ticket for your umbrella the individual opinions of some other personage whose name is Somebody, or Nobody, or Anybody, and to swallow the same without a word of demur. Be so good as to leave your eyes with your umbrellas, gentlemen, and to deliver up your private judgment with your walking-sticks. Apply this ointment, compounded by the learned Dervish, and you shall see no end of camels going with the greatest ease through needles' eyes. Leave your umbrella-full of property which is not by any means to be poked at this collection, with the police, and you shall acknowledge, whether you will or no, this hideous porcelain-ware to be beautiful, these wearisomely stiff and unimaginative forms to be graceful, these coarse daubs to be masterpieces. Leave your umbrella and take up your gentility. Taste proclaims to you what is the genteel thing; receive it and be genteel! Think no more of your umbrellas—be they the care of the Police of Scotland Yard! Think no more for yourselves —be you the care of the Police of Taste!

I protest that the very Tax-gatherer does not demand so much of me as the Powers who demand my umbrella. The Tax-gatherer will not allow me to wear hair-powder unmolested; but the Umbrella-gatherer will not allow me to wear my head. The Tax-gatherer takes toll of my spade; but the Umbrella-gatherer will not permit me to call my spade, a spade. Longinus, Aristotle, Doctor Waagen, and the Musical Glasses, Parliamentary Commissions, the Lord-Knows-Who, Marlborough House, and the Brompton Boilers, have declared my spade to be a mop-stick. And I must please to give up my umbrella, and believe in the mop-stick.

Again. The moral distinctions, and the many remembrances, and balances of This and That, which I am required by other authorities to put into my so-often demanded umbrella and to leave in the lobby, are as numerous as the Barnacle family. It was but a sessions or two ago, that I went to the gallery at the Old Bailey, to hear a trial. Was my umbrella all that I was called upon to leave behind me, previous to taking my seat? Certainly not. I was requested to put so many things into it that it became, though of itself a neat umbrella, more bulgy than Mrs. Gamp's. I found it insisted upon, that I should cram into this unfortunate article all the weighty comparisons I had ever made in my life between the guilt of laying hands upon a pound of scrag of mutton, and upon hundreds of thousands of pounds of sterling money. I found it insisted upon, that I should leave with my umbrella before I went into Court, any suspicions I had about me (and I happened to have a good many), that distortion and perversion of the truth, plainly for the purpose of so much gain, and for the enhancement of a professional reputation, were to be observed there, outside the dock and beyond the prisoner. I found myself required to take a ticket, conventionally used in that place, in exchange for my natural perception of many painfully ludicrous things that should have become obsolete long ago. Not that I complain of this particular demand at the door; for otherwise how could I have borne the fearful absurdity of the Judge being unable to discharge the last awful duty of his office without putting on a strange little comical hat, only used for the dismissal of a blood-stained soul into eternity? Or how could I have withheld myself from bursting out into a fit of laughter, which would have been contempt of court, when the same exalted functionary and two virtuous Counsel (I never in my life had the pleasure of hearing two gentlemen talk so much virtue) were grimly pleasant on the dressing-up in woollen wigs of certain Negro Singers whose place of entertainment had been innocently the scene of a manslaughter. While the exalted functionary himself, and the two virtuous counsel themselves, were at that very moment dressed up in woolly wigs, to the full as false and ridiculous as any theatrical wigs in the world, only they were not of the negro colour!

But, when I went to the Strangers' Gallery of the House of Commons, I had a greater load to leave with my umbrella than Christian had to lay down in the *Pilgrim's Progress*. The difference between Black and White, which is really a very large one and enough to burst any Umbrella, was the first thing I had to force into mine. And it was well for me that this was insisted on by the Police, or how could I have escaped the Serjeant-at-Arms, when the very same Member who on the last occasion of my going to the very same place I had with my own ears heard announce with the profoundest emotion that he came down to that house expressly to lay his hand upon his heart and declare that Black was White and there was no such thing as Black, now announced with the profoundest emotion that he came down to that house expressly to lay his hand upon his heart and declare that White was Black and there was no such thing as White? If you have such an article about you (said the Umbrella-taker to me in effect) as the distinction between very ill-constructed common places, and sound patriotic facts, you are requested to leave it at the door here.—By all means, said I.—You have there a Noun of Multitude or signifying many, called The Country; please to put that too, in your Umbrella.—Willingly, said I.—Your belief that public opinion is not the lobby of this place and the bores of the clubs, will be much in your way, and everybody else's hereabouts; please to leave that likewise.—You are welcome to it, said I.—But I am bound to admit that, thus denuded, I passed quite a pleasant evening; which I am certain I could not have done, if I had been allowed to take my Umbrella and its cumbrous contents in with me.

Please to leave your Umbrella. I have gone into churches where I have been required to leave my Umbrella in a sham mediæval porch, with hundreds of eventful years of History squeezed in among its ribs. I have gone into public assemblages of great pretensions—even into assemblages gathered together under the most sacred of names—and my Umbrella, filled to the handle with my sense of Christian fairness and moderation, has been taken from me at the door. All through life, according to my personal experience, I must please to leave my Umbrella, or I can't go in.

I had reached this point and was about to apostrophise Yorick once more, when a civil voice requested me, in obliging tones, to ' claim my Umbrella.' I might have done that, without a ticket, as there was no other on the rack in the hall at Hampton Court Palace, whither I had now worked my way round by another course, without knowing it. However, I gave back my ticket, and got back my Umbrella, and then I and my little reason went dreaming away under its shelter through the fast-falling spring rain, which had a sound in it that day like the rustle of the coming summer.

NEW YEAR'S DAY

[JANUARY 1, 1859]

WHEN I was a little animal revolting to the sense of sight (for I date from the period when small boys had a dreadful high-shouldered sleeved strait-waistcoat put upon them by their keepers, over which their dreadful little trousers were buttoned tight, so that they roamed about disconsolate, with their hands in their pockets, like dreadful little pairs of tongs that were vainly looking for the rest of the fire-irons); when I was this object of just contempt and horror to all well-constituted minds, and when, according to the best of my remembrance and self-examination in the past, even my small shirt was an airy superstition which had no sleeves to it and stopped short at my chest; when I was this exceedingly uncomfortable and dis-reputable father of my present self, I remember to have been taken, upon a New Year's Day, to the Bazaar in Soho Square, London, to have a present bought for me. A distinct impression yet lingers in my soul that a grim and unsympathetic old personage of the female gender, flavoured with musty dry lavender, dressed in black crape, and wearing a pocket in which something clinked at my ear as we went along, conducted me on this occasion to the World of Toys. I remember to have been incidentally escorted a little way down some conveniently retired street diverging from Oxford Street, for the purpose of being shaken; and nothing has ever slaked the burning thirst for vengeance awakened in me by this female's manner of insisting upon wiping my nose herself (I had a cold and a pocket-handkerchief), on the screw principle. For many years I was unable to excogitate the reason why she should have undertaken to make me a present. In the exercise of a matured judgment, I have now no doubt that she had done something bad in her youth, and that she took me out as an act of expiation.

Nearly lifted off my legs by this adamantine woman's grasp of my glove (another fearful invention of those dark ages—a muffler, and fastened at the wrist like a handcuff), I was haled through the Bazaar. My tender imagination (or conscience) represented certain small apartments in corners, resembling wooden cages, wherein I

171

have since seen reason to suppose that ladies' collars and the like are tried on, as being, either dark places of confinement for refractory youth, or dens in which the lions were kept who fattened on boys who said they didn't care. Suffering tremendous terrors from the vicinity of these avenging mysteries, I was put before an expanse of toys, apparently about a hundred and twenty acres in extent, and was asked what I would have to the value of half-a-crown? Having first selected every object at half-a-guinea, and then staked all the aspirations of my nature on every object at five shillings, I hit, as a last resource, upon a Harlequin's Wand—painted particoloured, like Harlequin himself.

Although of a highly hopeful and imaginative temperament, I had no fond belief that the possession of this talisman would enable me to change Mrs. Pipchin at my side into anything agreeable. When I tried the effect of the wand upon her, behind her bonnet, it was rather as a desperate experiment founded on the conviction that she could change into nothing worse, than with any latent hope that she would change into something better. Howbeit, I clung to the delusion that when I got home I should do something magical with this wand; and I did not resign all hope of it until I had, by many trials, proved the wand's total incapacity. It had no effect on the staring obstinacy of a rocking-horse; it produced no live Clown out of the hot beefsteak-pie at dinner; it could not even influence the minds of my honoured parents to the extent of suggesting the decency and propriety of their giving me an invitation to sit up to supper.

The failure of this wand is my first very memorable association with a New Year's Day. Other wands have failed me since, but the Day itself has become their substitute, and is always potent. It is the best Harlequin's Wand I have ever had. It has wrought strange transformations—no more of them—its power in reproducing the Past is admirable. Nothing ever goes wrong with that trick. I throw up and catch my little wand of New Year's Day, beat the dust of years from the ground at my feet with it, twinkle it a little, and Time reverses his hour-glass, and flies back, much faster than he ever flew forward.

New Year's Day. What Party can that have been, and what New Year's Day can that have been, which first rooted the phrase, 'A New Year's Day Party,' in my mind? So far back do my recollections of childhood extend, that I have a vivid remembrance of the sensation of being carried downstairs in a woman's arms, and holding tight to her, in the terror of seeing the steep perspective below. Hence, I may have been carried into this Party, for anything I know; but, somehow or other, I most certainly got there, and was in a doorway looking on; and in that look a New Year's Party revealed itself to me, as a very long row of ladies and gentlemen sitting against a wall, all drinking at once out of little glass cups with handles, like custard-cups. What can this Party have been! I am afraid it must have been a dull one, but I *know* it came off. Where can this Party have been! I have not the faintest notion where, but I am absolutely certain it was somewhere. Why the company should all have been drinking at once, and especially why they should all have been drinking out of custard-cups, are points of fact over which the Waters of Oblivion have long rolled. I doubt if they can have been drinking the Old Year out and the New One in, because they were not at supper and had no table before them. There was no speech-making, no quick movement and change of action, no demonstration of any kind. They were all sitting in a long row against the wall—very like my first idea of the good people in Heaven, as I derived it from a wretched picture in a Prayer-book —and they had all got their heads a little thrown back, and were all drinking at once. It is possible enough that I, the baby, may have been caught up out of bed to have a peep at the company, and that the company may happen to have been thus occupied for the flash and space of a moment only. But, it has always seemed to me as if I looked at them for a long time—hours—during which they did nothing else; and to this present time, a casual mention in my hearing, of a Party on a New Year's Day, always revives that picture.

On what other early New Year's Day can I possibly have been an innocent accomplice in the secreting—in a coal cellar too—of a man with a wooden leg! There was no man with a wooden leg, in the circle of my acknowledged and lawful relations and friends. Yet, I clearly remember that we stealthily conducted the man with the wooden leg—whom we knew intimately—into the coal cellar, and that, in getting him over the coals to hide him behind some partition there was beyond, his wooden leg bored itself in among the small coals, and his hat flew off, and he fell backward and lay prone:

a spectacle of helplessness. I clearly remember that his struggles to get up among the small coals, and to obtain any purchase on himself in those slippery and shifting circumstances, were a work of exceeding difficulty, involving delay and noise that occasioned us excessive terror. I have not the least idea who 'we' were, except that I had a little sister for another innocent accomplice, and that there must have been a servant girl for principal: neither do I know whether the man with the wooden leg robbed the house, before or afterwards, or otherwise nefariously distinguished himself. Nor, how a cat came to be connected with the occasion, and had a fit, and ran over the top of a door. But, I know that some awful reason compelled us to hush it all up, and that we 'never told.' For many years, I had this association with a New Year's Day entirely to myself, until at last, the anniversary being come round again, I said to the little sister, as she and I sat by chance among our children, 'Do you remember the New Year's Day of the man with the wooden leg?' Whereupon, a thick black curtain which had overhung him from her infancy, went up, and she saw just this much of the man, and not a jot more. (A day or so before her death, that little sister told me that, in the night, the smell of the fallen leaves in the woods where we had habitually walked as very young children, had come upon her with such strength of reality that she had moved her weak head to look for strewn leaves on the floor at her bedside.)

New Year's Day. It was on a New Year's Day that I fought a duel. Furious with love and jealousy, I 'went out' with another gentleman of honour, to assert my passion for the loveliest and falsest of her sex. I estimate the age of that young lady to have been about nine—my own age, about ten. I knew the Queen of my soul, as 'the youngest Miss Clickitt but one.' I had offered marriage, and my proposals had been very favourably received, though not definitively closed with. At which juncture, my enemy—Paynter, by name—arose out of some abyss or cavern, and came between us. The appearance of the Fiend Paynter, in the Clickitt Paradise, was altogether so mysterious and sudden, that I don't know where he came from; I only know that I found him, on the surface of this earth, one afternoon late in the month of December, playing at hot boiled beans and butter with the youngest Miss Clickitt but one. His conduct on that occasion was such, that I sent a friend to Paynter. After endeavouring with levity to evade the question, by pulling the friend's cap off and throwing it into a cabbage-garden, Paynter referred my messenger to his cousin—a goggle-eyed Being worthy of himself. Preliminaries were arranged, and by my own express stipulation the meeting was appointed for New Year's Day, in order that one of us might quit this state of existence on a day of mark. I passed a considerable portion of the last evening of the old year in arranging my affairs. I addressed a pathetic letter, and a goldfinch, to the youngest Miss Clickitt but one (to be delivered into her own hands by my friend, in case I should fall), and I wrote another letter for my mother, and made a disposition of my property : which consisted of books, some coloured engravings of Bamfylde Moore Carew, Mrs. Shipton, and others, in a florid style of art, and a rather choice collection of marbles. While engaged in these last duties, I suffered the keenest anguish, and wept abundantly. The combat was to begin with fists, but was to end anyhow. Dark presentiments overshadowed my mind, because I had heard, on reliable authority, that Paynter (whose father was paymaster of some regiment stationed in the seaport where the conflict impended), had a dirk and meant the worst. I had no other arms, myself, than a blank cartridge, of which ammunition we used to get driblets from the soldiers when they practised, by following them up with tobacco, and bribing them with pipes-full screwed in old copies, to pretend to load and not to do it. This cartridge my friend and second had specially recommended me, on the combat's assuming a mortal appearance, to explode on the fell Paynter: which I, with some indefinite view of blowing that gentleman up, had undertaken to do, though the engineering details of the operation were not at all adjusted. We met in a sequestered trench, among the fortifications. Paynter had access to some old military stores, and appeared on the ground in the regulation-cap of a full-grown Private of the Second Royal Veteran Battalion.—I see the boy now, coming from among the stinging-nettles in an angle of the trench, and making my blood run cold by his terrible appearance. Preliminaries were arranged, and we were to begin the struggle— this again was my express stipulation—on the word being given, 'The youngest Miss Clickitt but one!' At this crisis, a difference of opinion arose between the seconds, touching the exact construction of that article in the code of honour which prohibits 'hitting below the waistcoat'; and I rather think it arose from *my* second's having manœuvred the whole of *my* waistcoat into the neighbour-hood of my chin. However it arose, expressions were used which Paynter, who I found had a very delicate sense of honour, could not permit to pass. He immediately dropped his guard, and appealed to me whether it was not our duty most reluctantly to forego our own gratification until the two gentlemen in attendance on us had established their honour? I warmly assented; I did more; I immediately took my friend aside, and lent him the cartridge. But, so unworthy of our confidence were those seconds that they declined, in spite alike of our encouragements and our indignant re-monstrances, to engage. This made it plain both to Paynter and myself, that we had but one painful course to take; which was, to leave them ('with loathing,' Paynter said, and I highly approved), and go away arm in arm. He gave me to understand as we went along that he too was a victim of the perfidy of the youngest Miss Clickitt but one, and I became exceedingly fond of him before we parted.

And here is another New Year's Day coming back under the influence of the Wand which is better than Harlequin's! What New Year's Day is this? This is the New Year's Day of the annual gathering of later times at Boles's. Mr. Boles lives in a high, bleak, Down-country, where the wind never leaves off whistling all the year round, unless it takes to roaring. Mr. Boles has chimney-corners in his house, as big as other people's rooms; Mr. Boles's larder is as the larder of an amiable giant, and Mr. Boles's kitchen corresponds thereto. In Mr. Boles's Boudoirs sits Miss Boles: a blessed creature: a Divinity. In Mr. Boles's bed-chambers, is a ghost. In Mr. Boles's house, in short, is everything desirable—and under Mr. Boles's house is Mr. Boles's cellar. So many are the New Year's Days I have passed at Mr. Boles's, that I have won my way, like an enlisted Son of the vanished French Republic one and indivisible, through a regular series of promotions: beginning with the non-commissioned bedrooms, passing through the subaltern bedrooms, ascending in the scale until, on the New Year's Day now obedient to the Wand, I inhabit the Field-Marshal bedroom. But, where is Mr. Boles, now I have risen so high in the service? Alack! I go out, now-a-days, into the windy snow-drift, or the windy frost, or windy rain, or windy sunshine—of a certainty into the windy weather, let it be what else it may—to look at Mr. Boles's tomb in the little churchyard:

176

NEW YEAR'S DAY

where, while the avenue of elms is gustily tossed and troubled, like Life, the one dark yew-tree in the shadow of the bell-tower is solemnly at rest, like Death. And Miss Boles? She, too, is departed, though only into the world of matrons, not of shadows; and she is my hostess now; and she is a blessed creature (in the byegone sense of making the ground she walks on, worshipful), no more; and I have outlived my passion for her, and I perceive her appetite to be healthy, and her nose to be red. What of that? Are the seasons to stop for me? There are Boleses coming on, though under the different name into which the blessed creature gone for ever, (if she ever really came) sunk her own. In the old Boles boudoirs, there are still blessed creatures and divinities—to somebody, though not to me. If I suspect that the present non-commissioned officers and subalterns don't love as I did when I held those ranks, are not half as unselfishly faithful as I was, not half as tenderly devoted as I was, not half as passionately miserable as I was, what then? It may be so; it may not be so; but the world is, on the whole, round, and it is ever turning. If my old type has disappeared for the moment, it will come up again in its right place, when its right time brings it upward. Moreover, what am I, even as I know myself, that I should bemoan the disappearance, real or fancied, of the like of Me? Because I am *not* virtuous, shall there be no cakes but of my kneading, no ale but of my brewing? Far from me be the thought! When it comes near me, and stays by me, I may know of a surety that New Year's Days are finally closing in around me, and that, in a scheme where nothing created stops, I cannot too soon cease to be an insignificant anomaly. Therefore, O New Year's Days of the old Boles time, and of all my old time, may you be ever welcome! Therefore, non-commissioned officers, subalterns, lieutenants, all, of the Boles spare bedrooms, I, from the Field-Marshal chamber stretch out my poor hand, entreating cordiality of union among all degrees, and cheerfully declaring my readiness to join as well as I can, in the last new figures of the Dance of Life, rather than growl and grumble, with no partner, down the Dance of Death.

And here is another New Year's Day responsive to the Wand of the season before I have dismissed the last. An Italian New Year's Day, this, and the bright Mediterranean, with a stretch of violet and purple shore, formed the first leaf in the book of the New Year

177

that I turned at daybreak this morning. On the steep hill-sides between me and the sea, diversified by many a patch of cypress-trees and tangled vines, is a wild medley of roof upon roof, church upon church, terrace upon terrace, wall upon wall, tower upon tower. Questioning myself whether I am not descended, without having thought of it before, in a direct line from the good Haroun Alraschid, I tread the tesselated pavement of the garden-terrace, watch the gold-fish in the marble fountains, loiter in the pleasant grove of orange-trees, and become a moving pillar of fragrance by unromantically pocketing a green lemon, now and then, with an eye to Punch to-night in the English manner. It is not the New Year's Day of a dream, but of broad awake fact, that finds me housed in a palace, with a highly popular ghost and twenty-five spare bed-rooms: over the stone and marble floors of which deserted halls, the highly popular ghost (unquiet spirit of a Porter, one would think), drags all the heavy furniture at dead of night. Down in the town, in the street of Happy Charles, at the shop of the Swiss confectioner, there is at this moment, and is all day, an eager group examining the great Twelve-cake—or, as my good friend and servant who speaks all languages and knows none, renders it to the natives, *pane dolce numero dodici*—sweet bread number twelve—which has come as a present all the way from Signor Gunter's della Piazza Berkeley, Londra, Inghilterra, and which got cracked in coming, and is in the street of Happy Charles to be mended, and the like of which has never been seen. It comes back at sunset (in order that the man who brings it on his head may get clear off before the ghost is due), and is set out as a show in the great hall. In the great hall, made as light as all our lights can make it—which is rather dark, it must be confessed—we assemble at night, to 'keep it up,' in the English manner; meaning by 'we,' the handful of English dwelling in that city, and the half handful of English who have married there into other nations, and the rare old Italian Cavaliere, who improvises, writes poetry, plays harps, composes music, paints pictures, and is always inaugurating somebody's bust in his little garden. Brown is the rare old Cavaliere's face, but green his young enthusiastic heart; and whatever we do upon this mad New Year's Night, the Cavaliere gaily bears his part in, and believes to be essentially an English custom, which all the English observe. When we enact grotesque charades, or disperse in the

wildest exaggeration of an obsolete country-dance through the
five-and-twenty empty rooms, the Cavaliere, ever foremost, believes
in his soul that all provincial respectability and metropolitan variety,
all Canterbury Precinct, Whitfield Tabernacle, Saint James's Parish,
Clapham, and Whitechapel, are religiously doing the same thing;
and he cries, 'Dear England, merry England, the young and
joyous, home of the Fancy, free as the air, playful as the child!'
So enchanted is the dear Cavaliere (at about three in the morning,
and after the lemons), that he folds my hand flat, inside his white
waistcoat, folds his own two over it, and walks me up and down the
Hall, meekly prisoner, while he improvises an enormous poem on
the sports of England; which poem, I think, throughout, I am
going to begin to understand presently, but of which I do not
comprehend one lonely word. Nor, does even this severe intellectual
exercise use up the Cavaliere, for, after going home and playing the
harp I don't know how many hours, he flies out of bed, seizes pen
ink and paper—the mechanical appliances of the whole circle of
the Arts are always at his bedside, ready against inspiration in the
night—and writes quite a Work on the same subject: as the blotted,
piebald manuscript he sends to me before I am up next day,
affectingly testifies. Said manuscript is inscribed to myself, most
illustrious Signor, kissing my hands, and is munificently placed
at the disposal of any English publisher whom it may please to
undertake a translation.

And here is another New Year's Day invoked by the Wand of the
time, and this New Year's Day is a French one, and a bitter, bitter
cold one. All Paris is out of doors. Along the line of the Boule-
vards runs a double row of stalls, like the stalls at an English fair;
and surely those are hard to please, in all small wares and all small
gambling, who cannot be pleased here. Paris is out of doors in
its newest and brightest clothes. Paris is making presents to the
Universe—which is well known to be Paris. Paris will eat more
bon-bons this day, than in the whole bon-bon eating year. Paris
will dine out this day, more than ever. In homage to the day, the
peculiar glory of the always-glorious plate-glass windows of the
Restorers in the Palais Royal, where rare summer-vegetables from
Algiers contend with wonderful great pears from the richest soils of
France, and with little plump birds of exquisite plumage, direct from
the skies. In homage to the day, the glittering brilliancy of the

sweet-shops, teeming with beautiful arrangement of colours, and with beautiful tact and taste in trifles. In homage to the day, the new Review—Dramas at the Theatre of Varieties, and the Theatre of Vaudevilles, and the Theatre of the Palais Royal. In homage to the day, the new Drama in seven acts, and incalculable pictures, at the Ambiguously Comic Theatre, the Theatre of the Gate of Saint Martin, and the Theatre of Gaiety: at which last establishment particularly, a brooding Englishman can, by intensity of interest, get himself made wretched for a fortnight. In homage to the day, the extra-announcing of these Theatres, and fifty more, and the queues of blouses already, at three o'clock in the afternoon, penned up in the cold wind on the cold stone pavement outside them. Spite of wind and frost, the Elysian Fields and the Wood of Boulogne are filled with equipages, equestrians, and pedestrians: while the strange, rackety, rickety, up-all-night looking world of eating-house, tomb-stone maker, ball-room, cemetery, and wine-shop, outside the Barriers, is as thickly - peopled as the Paris streets themselves; with one universal tendency observable in both hemispheres, to sit down upon any public seat at a risk of being frozen to death, and to go round and round on a hobby-horse in any roundabout, to the music of a barrel organ, as a severe act of duty. And now, this New Year's Day tones down into night, and the brilliantly lighted city shines out like the gardens of the Wonderful Lamp, and the penned blouses flutter into the Theatres in orderly line, and the confidential men, not unaccustomed to lean on umbrellas as they survey mankind of an afternoon, who have tickets to sell cheap, are very busy among them, and the women money-takers shut up in strong iron-cages are busy too, and the three men all of a row behind a breast-work who take the checks are busy too, and the women box-openers with their foot-stools begin to be busy too, but as yet not very, and the curtain goes up for the curtain-rising piece, and the gloomy young gentle-man with the tight black head and the new black moustache is as much in love as ever with the young lady whose eyebrows are very arched and whose voice is very thin, and the gloomy young gentle-man's experienced friend (generally chewing something, by the bye, and I wonder what), who leans his back against the chimney-piece and reads him lessons of life, is just as cool as he always was, and an amazing circumstance to me is, that they are always doing this thing and no other thing, and that I don't find them to have any place in the great event of the evening, and that I want to know whether they go home when they have done it, or what becomes of them. Meanwhile, gushes of cookery rise with the night air from the Restorer's kitchens; and the guests at the Café of Paris, and the Café of the Three Provincial Brothers, and the Café Vefour, and the Café Verey, and the Gilded House, and others of first class, are reflected in wildernesses of looking-glass, and sit on red velvet and order dinner out of red velvet books; while the citizens at the Café Champeaux near the Bourse, and others of second class, sit on rush-bottomed chairs, and have their dinner-library bound in plain leather, though they dine well too; while both kinds of company have plenty of children with them (which is pleasant to me, though I think they begin life biliously), and both unite in eating everything that is set before them. But, now it is eight o'clock upon this New Year's evening. The new Dramas being about to begin, bells ring violently in the Theatre lobbies and rooms, and cigars, coffee cups, and small glasses are hastily abandoned, and I find myself assisting at one of the Review-pieces: where I notice that the English gentleman's stomach isn't very like, because it doesn't fit him, and wherein I doubt the accurate nationality of the English lady's walking on her toes with an upward jerk behind. The Review is derived from various times and sources, and when I have seen David the Psalmist in his droll scene with Mahomet and Abd-el-Kader, and have heard the best joke and best song that Eve (a charming young lady, but liable, I should fear, to take cold) has in her part (which occurs in her scene with the Sieur Framboisie), I think I will step out to the Theatre of Gaiety, and see what they are about there. I am so fortunate as to arrive in the nick of time to find the very estimable man just eloped with the wife of the much less estimable man whom Destiny has made a bore, and to find her honest father just arriving from the country by one door, encountering the father of the very estimable man just arriving from the country by another door, and to hear them launch cross-curses—her father at him: his father at her—which so deeply affects a martial gentleman of tall stature and dark complexion, in the next stall to mine, that, taking his handkerchief from his hat to dry his eyes, he pulls out with it several very large lumps of sugar which he abstracted when he took his coffee, and showers them over my legs—exceedingly to my confusion, but not at all to his. The drop-curtain being, to appearance, down for a long time, I think I will step on a little further—say to the Theatre of the Scavengers—and see what they are doing there. At the Theatre of the Scavengers, I find Pierrot on a voyage. I know he is aboard ship, because I can see nothing but sky; and I infer that the crew are aloft from the circumstance of two rope-ladders crossing the stage and meeting at top; about midway on each of which hangs, contemplating the public, an immovable young lady in male attire, with highly unseamanlike pink legs. This spectacle reminds me of another New Year's Day at home in England, where I saw the brave William, lover of Black-Eyed Susan, tried by a Court Martial composed entirely of ladies, wearing perceptible combs in their heads : with the exception of the presiding Admiral, who was so far gone in liquor that I trembled to think what could possibly be done respecting the catastrophe, if he should take it in his head to record the verdict ' Not guilty.' On this present New Year's Day, I find Pierrot suffering, in various ways, so very much from sea-sickness, that I soon leave the congregated Scavengers in possession of him ; but not before I have gathered from the bill that in the case even of his drama, as of every other French piece, it takes at least two men to write it. So, I pass this New Year's evening, which is a French one, looking about me until midnight : when, going into a Boulevard café on my way home, I find the elderly men who are always playing dominoes there, or always looking on at one another playing dominoes there, hard at it still, not in the least moved by the stir and novelty of the day, not in the least minding the New Year.

CHIPS

[July 6, 1850]

THERE is a saying that a good workman is known by his chips. Such a prodigious accumulation of chips takes place in our Manufactory, that we infer we must have some first-rate workmen about us.

There is also a figure of speech, concerning a chip of the old block. The chips with which *our* old block (aged fifteen weeks) is

CHIPS

overwhelmed every week, would make some five-and-twenty blocks of similar dimensions.

There is a popular simile—an awkward one in this connexion—founded on the dryness of a chip. This has almost deterred us from our intention of bundling a few chips together now and then. But, reflection on the natural lightness of the article has reassured us; and we here present a few to our readers,—and shall continue to do so from time to time.

THE INDIVIDUALITY OF LOCOMOTIVES

[September 21, 1850]

It is a remarkable truth, and, well applied, it might be profitable to us, in helping us to make fair allowance for the differences between the temperaments of different men—that every Locomotive Engine running on a Railway, has a distinct individuality and character of its own.

It is perfectly well known to experienced practical engineers, that if a dozen different Locomotive Engines were made, at the same time, of the same power, for the same purpose, of like materials, in the same Factory—each of those Locomotive Engines would come out with its own peculiar whims and ways, only ascertainable by experience. One engine will take a great meal of coke and water at once ; another will not hear of such a thing, but will insist on being coaxed by spades-full and buckets-full. One is disposed to start off, when required, at the top of his speed ; another must have a little time to warm at his work, and to get well into it. These peculiarities are so accurately mastered by skilful drivers, that only particular men can persuade particular engines to do their best. It would seem as if some of these 'excellent monsters' declared, on being brought out of the stable, 'If it's Smith who is to drive me, I won't go. If it's my friend Stokes, I am agreeable to anything!'

All Locomotive Engines are low-spirited in damp and foggy weather. They have a great satisfaction in their work when the air is crisp and frosty. At such a time they are very cheerful and brisk ; but they strongly object to haze and Scotch mists. These are points of character on which they are all united. It is in

183

their peculiarities and varieties of character that they are most remarkable.

The Railway Company who should consign all their Locomotives to one uniform standard of treatment, without any allowance for varying shades of character and opinion, would soon fall as much behind-hand in the world as those greater Governments are, and ever will be, who pursue the same course with the finer piece of work called Man.

HOMŒOPATHY

[November 15, 1851]

We have never been subjects of the Homœopathic mode of treatment, nor have we ever been concerned in making others so. But as we desire to state the Homœopathic Doctrine fairly, like all other doctrines to which we make any reference, and as it has been suggested to us that we may have scarcely done so in a passing allusion to it at page 592 of the last volume of this journal, we will here reprint the following extract from a work in explanation of Homœopathic principles, by Dr. Epps.

'It is not maintained that a millionth part of a grain or a drop (to take a given, though a large quantity, in homœopathic administration,) will produce any visible action on the man in health ; nor is it maintained that a millionth part of a grain or of a drop will act on the man in disease : but it is maintained that the millionth part of a grain or of a drop will act on the man in disease, if between the diseased state of the man and the medicine, infinitesimally administered, there is a homœopathic relationship.   In other words, the homœopathists do not vaguely say that medicines in infinitesimal dozes cure diseases ; but they do say that medicines given for the cure of diseases to which they are homœopathic, do cure these diseases when administered in infinitesimal quantities; to repeat, the homœopathist, in maintaining the efficacy of medicines in infinitesimal quantities, regards three requirements as necessary : — First, the development of virtues in medicines by the process of preparation ; second, the increased receptivity to impression produced by disease ; and third, the selection of the right remedy.'

CHIPS

[MARCH 13, 1852]

THERE is a picture now lodged at the Amateur Gallery, 121 Pall Mall, which, apart from its own merits, is rendered interesting by being the first large picture ever painted, or (by many people) ever seen, in Australia.

It is an illustration of the Scripture, 'Suffer little children to come unto me.' The painter is Mr. Marshall Claxton. It was produced under the following circumstances.

In the summer of the year 1850, a munificent lady residing in London, and distinguished everywhere for her gentle generosity and goodness, commissioned Mr. Claxton to paint this picture for the interior decoration of an Infant School. Mr. Claxton was then on the eve of emigrating to Sydney. If he might only consider the subject on the voyage, he said, and paint it in the land of his adoption, what a pride he would have in showing it to his new countrymen, and what a testimony it would be to them that he was not slighted in Old England! The commission was freely entrusted to him to be so dealt with; and away he sailed, light of heart and strong of purpose.

How he studied it, and sketched it, month after month, during the long voyage; and how he found it a companion in whom there was always something new to be discovered, and of whom he never tired; needs not to be told. But when he came to Sydney, he could find no house suited to his requirements, with a room large enough to paint the picture in. So, he asked the Committee of the Sydney College for the loan of that building; and, it being handsomely conceded, went to work there.

It may be questioned whether any Australian models had ever sat before, to painting man. At all events, models or not models, the general population of Sydney became so excited about this picture, and were so eager to see it in every stage of its progress, that seven thousand persons, first and last, dropped in to look at it. And such an object was as new to many of them, as the travelling elephant was to the young men on the banks of the Mississippi, when he made a pilgrimage 'a while ago,' with his caravan, to those far-off regions.

185

MISCELLANEOUS PAPERS

Thus, the Picture was imagined, painted, and sent home. Thus, it is, at the present writing, lodged in Pall Mall—the dawn perhaps of the longest day for the fine arts, as for all the arts of life, that ever rose upon the world. As the bright eyes of the children in the Infant School will often, in these times, rest upon it with the awe and wonder of its having come so far over the deep sea; so, perhaps, Mr. Macaulay's traveller, standing, in a distant age, upon the ruins of an old cathedral once called St. Paul's, in the midst of a desert once called London, will look about him with similar emotions for any broken stones that may possibly be traces of the School, said in the Australian nursery-legend to have contained the first important picture painted in that ancient country.

THE GHOST OF THE COCK LANE GHOST WRONG AGAIN

[JANUARY 15, 1853]

THE exhibitor of the spirit-rapping at the small charge of one guinea per head, or five guineas for a party of ten; the Mr. Stone who 'begs leave to inform the nobility and gentry, that he has just returned from the United States, accompanied by Mrs. M. B. Hayden, for the purpose of Demonstrating the wonderful Phenomena known in that country as Spiritual Manifestations, and which have created the most intense excitement among all classes of society,'—as described at page 217 of our present volume [1]—has been exhibiting Electro-Biology in London to certain dismal little audiences; and has attempted to enliven the very dreary performances by pressing the name of Mr. Charles Dickens into his service, and delivering himself of accounts of a personal interview held by himself and his Medium with that gentleman at the house in Upper Seymour Street, Portman Square, where all classes of society are intensely excited every day at from eleven to two, and from four to six.

As a further warning to the gullible who may be disposed to put their trust in this exhibitor's 'facts,' we may inform them that he, and his Medium, with their troops of spirits and their electro-biological penetration to boot, are as wide of the truth in this as in everything else. Mr. Dickens was never at the intensely exciting

[1] Refers to *Household Words*. See a previous article entitled *The Spirit Business*.

house and never beheld any of its intensely exciting inhabitants. Two trustworthy gentlemen attached to this Journal tested the spirit rappers at his request, and found them to be the egregious absurdity described.

READY WIT

[FEBRUARY 4, 1854]

As an instance of a correspondent who thoroughly understands a joke, and possesses a quick wit and a happy comprehension, we cannot resist the temptation that is upon us to print the following genuine letter :—

'SIR,—I happened this afternoon to take up the last number of your *Household Words*, whilst waiting to see my doctor, at whose house I had called. It has often struck me, when reading your writings, that the tendency of your mind is to hold up to derision those of the higher classes. I refer you for the present to the Ignoble Nobleman as written by you and published this month. Now we find recorded in Scripture the world described as hateful and hating one another, and I would call your attention to the third chapter of Paul's Epistle to Titus; read the first six verses, and see what believers in——the son of the living——are called upon to do, and then judge yourself, that ye be not judged. I would invoke you into a kinder spirit, and be ye a doer of the word and not a hearer only.

'I am, Sir,
'Your very obedt.,
'A COMMONER.'

SUPPOSING

[APRIL 20, 1850]

SUPPOSING, we were to change the Property and Income Tax a little, and make it somewhat heavier on realised property, and somewhat lighter on mere income, fixed and uncertain, I wonder whether we should be committing any violent injustice !

Supposing, we were to be more Christian and less mystical, agreeing more about the spirit and fighting less about the letter, I

187

wonder whether we should present a very irreligious and indecent spectacle to the mass of mankind!

Supposing, the Honourable Member for White troubled his head a little less about the Honourable Member for Black, and *vice versâ*, and that both applied themselves a little more in earnest to the real business of the honourable people and the honourable country, I wonder whether it would be unparliamentary!

Supposing, that, when there was a surplus in the Public Treasury, we laid aside our own particular whims, and all agreed that there were four elements necessary to the existence of our fellow-creatures, to wit, earth, air, fire, and water, and that these were the first grand necessaries to be uncooped and untaxed, I wonder whether it would be unreasonable!

Supposing, we had at this day a Baron Jenner, or a Viscount Watt, or an Earl Stephenson, or a Marquess of Brunel, or a dormant Shakespeare peerage, or a Hogarth baronetcy, I wonder whether it would be cruelly disgraceful to our old nobility!

Supposing, we were all of us to come off our pedestals and mix a little more with those below us, with no fear but that genius, rank, and wealth, would always sufficiently assert their own superiority, I wonder whether we should lower ourselves beyond retrieval!

Supposing, we were to have less botheration and more real education, I wonder whether we should have less or more compulsory colonisation, and Cape of Good Hope very natural indignation!

Supposing, we were materially to simplify the laws, and to abrogate the absurd fiction that everybody is supposed to be acquainted with them, when we know very well that such acquaintance is the study of a life in which some fifty men may have been proficient perhaps in five times fifty years, I wonder whether laws would be respected less?

Supposing, we maintained too many of such fictions altogether, and found their stabling come exceedingly expensive!

Supposing, we looked about us, and seeing a cattle-market originally established in an open place, standing in the midst of a great city because of the unforeseen growth of that great city all about it, and, hearing it asserted that the market was still adapted to the requirements and conveniences of the great city, made up our

SUPPOSING!

minds to say that this was stark-mad nonsense and we wouldn't bear it, I wonder whether we should be revolutionary!

Supposing, we were to harbour a small suspicion that there was too much doing in the diplomatic line of business, and that the world would get on better with that shop shut up three days a-week, I wonder whether it would be a huge impiety!

Supposing, Governments were to consider public questions less with reference to their own time, and more with reference to all time, I wonder how we should get on then!

Supposing, the wisdom of our ancestors should turn out to be a mere phrase, and that if there were any sense in it, it should follow that we ought to be believers in the worship of the Druids at this hour, I wonder whether any people would have talked mere moonshine all their lives!

Supposing, we were clearly to perceive that we cannot keep some men out of their share in the administration of affairs, and were to say to them, 'Come, brothers, let us take counsel together, and see how we can best manage this; and don't expect too much from what you get; and let us all in our degree put our shoulders to the wheel, and strive; and let us all improve ourselves and all abandon something of our extreme opinions for the general harmony,' I wonder whether we should want so many special constables on any future tenth of April, or should talk so much about it any more!

I wonder whether people who are quite easy about anything, usually *do* talk quite so much about it!

Mr. Lane, the traveller, tells us of a superstition the Egyptians have, that the mischievous Genii are driven away by iron, of which they have an instinctive dread. Supposing, this should foreshadow the disappearance of the evil spirits and ignorances besetting this earth, before the iron steam-engines and roads, I wonder whether we could expedite their flight at all by iron energy!

Supposing, we were just to try two or three of these experiments!

[August 10, 1850]

Supposing a Royal Duke were to die. Which is not a great stretch of supposition,

> For golden lads and lasses must,
> Like chimney-sweepers, come to dust:

189

Supposing he had been a good old Duke with a thoroughly kind heart, and generous nature, always influenced by a sincere desire to do right, and always doing it, like a man and a gentleman, to the best of his ability :

And supposing, this Royal Duke left a son, against whom there was no imputation or reproach, but of whom all men were disposed to think well, and had no right or reason to think otherwise :

And supposing, this Royal Duke, though possessed of a very handsome income in his life-time, had not made provision for this son ; and a rather accommodating Government (in such matters) were to make provision for him, at the expense of the public, on a scale wholly unsuited to the nature of the public burdens, past, present, and prospective, and bearing no proportion to any kind of public reward, for any sort of public service :

I wonder whether the country could then, with any justice, complain, that the Royal Duke had not himself provided for his son, instead of leaving his son a charge upon the people !

I should think the question would depend upon this :—Whether the country had ever given the good Duke to understand, that it, in the least degree, expected him to provide for his son. If it never did anything of the sort, but always conveyed to him, in every possible way, the rapturous assurance that there was a certain amount of troublesome Hotel business to be done, which nobody but a Royal Duke could by any possibility do, or the business would lose its grace and flavour, then, I should say, the good Duke aforesaid might reasonably suppose that he made sufficient provision for his son, in leaving him the Hotel business ; and that the country would be a very unreasonable country, if it made any complaint.

Supposing the country *did* complain, though, after all. I wonder what it would still say, in Committee, Sub Committee, Charitable Association, and List of Stewards, if any ungenteel person were to propose ignoble chairmen !

Because I should like the country to be consistent.

[JUNE 7, 1851]

SUPPOSING a stipendiary magistrate, honourably distinguished for his careful, sensible, and upright decisions, were to have brought before him, a Socialist or Chartist, proved to have wilfully, and without any

SUPPOSING!

palliative circumstance whatsoever, assaulted the police in the execution of their duty :

And supposing that stipendiary magistrate committed that Socialist or Chartist to prison for the offence, steadfastly refusing to adopt the alternative unjustly and partially allowed him by the law, of permitting the offender to purchase immunity by the payment of a fine :

And supposing one of the great unpaid county magistrates were to take upon himself virtually to abrogate the rules observed, in all other cases, in that prison, by introducing, say fourteen visitors, to that Socialist or Chartist during his one week's imprisonment :

I wonder whether Sir George Grey, or any other Home Secretary for the time being, would then consider it his duty to take a very decided course of objection to the proceedings of that county magistrate.

And supposing that the prisoner, instead of being a Socialist or Chartist, were a gentleman of good family, and that County Magistrate did exactly this same thing, I wonder what Sir George Grey, or any other Home Secretary for the time being, would do then.

Because, supposing he did nothing, I should strongly doubt his doing right.

[SEPTEMBER 6, 1851]

SUPPOSING that among the news in a Weekly Newspaper—say, the *Examiner* for Saturday the twenty-third of August in the present year — there were stated in succession two cases, presenting a monstrous contrast.

Supposing that the first of these cases were the case of an indigent woman, the wife of a labouring man, who died in a most deplorable and abject condition, neglected and unassisted by the parish authorities :

Supposing that the second of these cases were the case of an infamous woman, drunken and profligate, a convicted felon, a returned transport, an habitual inmate of Houses of Correction, destitute of the lowest attributes of decency, a Pet Prisoner in the Model Prison, where the interesting creature was presented with a large gratuity for her excellent conduct :

191

MISCELLANEOUS PAPERS

I wonder whether it would occur to any governing power in the country, that there might be something wrong here!

Because I make bold to say, that such a shocking instance of Pet Prisoning and Pet Poor Law administering has profounder depths of mischief in it than Red Tape can fathom.

[FEBRUARY 10, 1855]

SUPPOSING that a gentleman named Mr. Sidney Herbert were to get up in the House of Commons, to make the best case he could of a system of mismanagement that had filled all England with grief and shame:

And supposing that this gentleman were to expatiate to the House of Commons on the natural helplessness of our English soldiers, consequent on their boots being made by one man, their clothes by another, their houses by another, and so forth—blending a sentimental political economy with Red Tape, in a very singular manner:

I wonder, in such case, whether it would be out of order to suggest the homely fact that indeed it is not the custom to enlist the English Soldier in his cradle; that there really are instances of his having been something else before becoming a soldier; and that perhaps there is not a Regiment in the service but includes within its ranks, a number of men more or less expert in every handicraft-trade under the Sun.

MISCELLANIES

FROM

'ALL THE YEAR ROUND'

1859-1869

ADDRESS WHICH APPEARED SHORTLY PREVIOUS TO THE COMPLETION OF THE TWENTIETH VOLUME (1868) OF INTIMATING A NEW SERIES OF 'ALL THE YEAR ROUND'

I BEG to announce to the readers of this Journal, that on the completion of the Twentieth Volume on the Twenty-eighth of November, in the present year, I shall commence an entirely New Series of *All the Year Round*. The change is not only due to the convenience of the public (with which a set of such books, extending beyond twenty large volumes, would be quite incompatible), but is also resolved upon for the purpose of effecting some desirable improvements in respect of type, paper, and size of page, which could not otherwise be made. To the Literature of the New Series it would not become me to refer, beyond glancing at the pages of this Journal, and of its predecessor, through a score of years; inasmuch as my regular fellow-labourers and I will be at our old posts, in company with those younger comrades, whom I have had the pleasure of enrolling from time to time, and whose number it is always one of my pleasantest editorial duties to enlarge.

As it is better that every kind of work honestly undertaken and discharged, should speak for itself than be spoken for, I will only remark further on one intended omission in the New Series. The Extra Christmas Number has now been so extensively, and regularly, and often imitated, that it is in very great danger of becoming tiresome. I have therefore resolved (though I cannot add, willingly) to abolish it, at the highest tide of its success.

CHARLES DICKENS.

THE POOR MAN AND HIS BEER [1]

[April 30, 1859]

My friend Philosewers and I, contemplating a farm-labourer the other day, who was drinking his mug of beer on a settle at a road-side ale-house door, we fell to humming the fag-end of an old ditty, of which the poor man and his beer, and the sin of parting them, form the doleful burden. Philosewers then mentioned to me that a friend of his in an agricultural county—say a Hertfordshire friend—had, for two years last past, endeavoured to reconcile the poor man and his beer to public morality, by making it a point of honour between himself and the poor man that the latter should use his beer and not abuse it. Interested in an effort of so unobtrusive and un-speechifying a nature, 'O Philosewers,' said I, after the manner of the dreary sages in Eastern apologues, 'Show me, I pray, the man who deems that temperance can be attained without a medal, an oration, a banner, and a denunciation of half the world, and who has at once the head and heart to set about it!'

Philosewers expressing, in reply, his willingness to gratify the dreary sage, an appointment was made for the purpose. And on the day fixed, I, the Dreary one, accompanied by Philosewers, went down Nor'-West per railway, in search of temperate temperance. It was a thunderous day; and the clouds were so immoderately watery, and so very much disposed to sour all the beer in Hertfordshire, that they seemed to have taken the pledge.

But, the sun burst forth gaily in the afternoon, and gilded the old gables, and old mullioned windows, and old weathercock and old clock-face, of the quaint old house which is the dwelling of the man we sought. How shall I describe him? As one of the most famous practical chemists of the age? That designation will do as well as another—better, perhaps, than most others. And his name? Friar Bacon.

'Though, take notice, Philosewers,' said I, behind my hand, 'that the first Friar Bacon had not that handsome lady-wife beside him. Wherein, O Philosewers, he was a chemist, wretched and forlorn, compared with his successor. Young Romeo bade the holy father

THE POOR MAN AND HIS BEER

Lawrence hang up philosophy, unless philosophy could make a Juliet. Chemistry would infallibly be hanged if its life were staked on making anything half so pleasant as this Juliet.' The gentle Philosewers smiled assent.

The foregoing whisper from myself, the Dreary one, tickled the ear of Philosewers, as we walked on the trim garden terrace before dinner, among the early leaves and blossoms; two peacocks, apparently in very tight new boots, occasionally crossing the gravel at a distance. The sun, shining through the old house-windows, now and then flashed out some brilliant piece of colour from bright hangings within, or upon the old oak panelling; similarly, Friar Bacon, as we paced to and fro, revealed little glimpses of his good work.

'It is not much,' said he. 'It is no wonderful thing. There used to be a great deal of drunkenness here, and I wanted to make it better if I could. The people are very ignorant, and have been much neglected, and I wanted to make *that* better, if I could. My utmost object was, to help them to a little self-government and a little homely pleasure. I only show the way to better things, and advise them. I never act for them; I never interfere; above all, I never patronise.'

I had said to Philosewers as we came along Nor'-West that patronage was one of the curses of England; I appeared to rise in the estimation of Philosewers when thus confirmed.

'And so,' said Friar Bacon, 'I established my Allotment-club, and my pig-clubs, and those little Concerts by the ladies of my own family, of which we have the last of the season this evening. They are a great success, for the people here are amazingly fond of music. But there is the early dinner-bell, and I have no need to talk of my endeavours when you will soon see them in their working dress.'

Dinner done, behold the Friar, Philosewers, and myself the Dreary one, walking, at six o'clock, across the fields, to the 'Club-house.'

As we swung open the last field-gate and entered the Allotment-grounds, many members were already on their way to the Club, which stands in the midst of the allotments. Who could help thinking of the wonderful contrast between these club-men and the club-men of St. James's Street, or Pall Mall, in London! Look at yonder prematurely old man, doubled up with work, and leaning on a rude stick more crooked than himself, slowly trudging to the club-house, in a shapeless hat like an Italian harlequin's, or an old brown-paper bag, leathern leggings, and dull green smock-frock, looking as though duck-weed had accumulated on it—the result of its stagnant life—or as if it were a vegetable production, originally meant to blow into something better, but stopped somehow. Compare him with Old Cousin Feenix, ambling along St. James's Street, got up in the style of a couple of generations ago, and with a head of hair, a complexion, and a set of teeth, profoundly impossible to be believed in by the widest stretch of human credulity. Can they both be men and brothers? Verily they are. And although Cousin Feenix has lived so fast that he will die at Baden-Baden, and although this club-man in the frock has lived, ever since he came to man's estate, on nine shillings a week, and is sure to die in the Union if he die in bed, yet he brought as much into the world as Cousin Feenix, and will take as much out—more, for more of him is real.

A pretty, simple building, the club-house, with a rustic colonnade outside, under which the members can sit on wet evenings, looking at the patches of ground they cultivate for themselves; within, a well-ventilated room, large and lofty, cheerful pavement of coloured tiles, a bar for serving out the beer, good supply of forms and chairs, and a brave big chimney-corner, where the fire burns cheerfully. Adjoining this room, another:

'Built for a reading-room,' said Friar Bacon; 'but not much used—yet.'

The dreary sage, looking in through the window, perceiving a fixed reading-desk within, and inquiring its use:

'I have Service there,' said Friar Bacon. 'They never went anywhere to hear prayers, and of course it would be hopeless to help them to be happier and better, if they had no religious feeling at all.'

'The whole place is very pretty.' Thus the sage.

'I am glad you think so. I built it for the holders of the Allotment-grounds, and gave it them: only requiring them to manage it by a committee of their own appointing, and never to get drunk there. They never have got drunk there.'

'Yet they have their beer freely?'

'O yes. As much as they choose to buy. The club gets its beer direct from the brewer, by the barrel. So they get it good; at

THE POOR MAN AND HIS BEER

once much cheaper, and much better, than at the public-house. The members take it in turns to be steward, and serve out the beer : if a man should decline to serve when his turn came, he would pay a fine of twopence. The steward lasts, as long as the barrel lasts. When there is a new barrel, there is a new steward.'

' What a noble fire is roaring up that chimney ! '

' Yes, a capital fire. Every member pays a halfpenny a week.'

' Every member must be the holder of an Allotment-garden ? '

' Yes ; for which he pays five shillings a year. The Allotments you see about us, occupy some sixteen or eighteen acres, and each garden is as large as experience shows one man to be able to manage. You see how admirably they are tilled, and how much they get off them. They are always working in them in their spare hours ; and when a man wants a mug of beer, instead of going off to the village and the public-house, he puts down his spade or his hoe, comes to the club-house and gets it, and goes back to his work. When he has done work, he likes to have his beer at the club, still, and to sit and look at his little crops as they thrive.'

' They seem to manage the club very well.'

' Perfectly well. Here are their own rules. They made them. I never interfere with them, except to advise them when they ask me.'

RULES AND REGULATIONS

MADE BY THE COMMITTEE,

From the 21st September, 1857.

One half-penny per week to be paid to the club by each member.

1.—Each member to draw the beer in order, according to the number of his allotment ; on failing, a forfeit of twopence to be paid to the club.

2.—The member that draws the beer to pay for the same, and bring his ticket up receipted when the subscriptions are paid ; on failing to do so, a penalty of sixpence to be forfeited and paid to the club.

3.—The subscriptions and forfeits to be paid at the club-room on the last Saturday night of each month.

4.—The subscriptions and forfeits to be cleared up every quarter ; if not, a penalty of sixpence to be paid to the club.

5.—The member that draws the beer to be at the club-room by six o'clock every evening, and stay till ten; but in the event of no member being there, he may leave at nine; on failing so to attend, a penalty of sixpence to be paid to the club.

6.—Any member giving beer to a stranger in this club-room, excepting to his wife or family, shall be liable to the penalty of one shilling.

7.—Any member lifting his hand to strike another in this club-room shall be liable to the penalty of sixpence.

8.—Any member swearing in this club-room shall be liable to a penalty of twopence each time.

9.—Any member selling beer shall be expelled from the club.

10.—Any member wishing to give up his allotment, may apply to the committee, and they shall value the crop and the condition of the ground. The amount of the valuation shall be paid by the succeeding tenant, who shall be allowed to enter on any part of the allotment which is uncropped at the time of notice of the leaving tenant.

11.—Any member not keeping his allotment-garden clear from seed-weeds, or otherwise injuring his neighbours, may be turned out of his garden by the votes of two-thirds of the committee, one month's notice being given to him.

12.—Any member carelessly breaking a mug, is to pay the cost of replacing the same.

I was soliciting the attention of Philosewers to some old old bonnets hanging in the Allotment-gardens to frighten the birds, and the fashion of which I should think would terrify a French bird to death at any distance, when Philosewers solicited my attention to the scrapers at the club-house door. The amount of the soil of England which every member brought there on his feet, was indeed surprising; and even I, who am professedly a salad-eater, could have grown a salad for my dinner, in the earth on any member's frock or hat.

'Now,' said Friar Bacon, looking at his watch, 'for the Pig-clubs!'

The dreary Sage entreated explanation.

'Why, a pig is so very valuable to a poor labouring man, and it is so very difficult for him at this time of the year to get money enough to buy one, that I lend him a pound for the purpose. But,

THE POOR MAN AND HIS BEER

I do it in this way. I leave such of the club members as choose it and desire it, to form themselves into parties of five. To every man in each company of five, I lend a pound, to buy a pig. But, each man of the five becomes bound for every other man, as to the repayment of his money. Consequently, they look after one another, and pick out their partners with care; selecting men in whom they have confidence.'

'They repay the money, I suppose, when the pig is fattened, killed, and sold?'

'Yes. Then they repay the money. And they do repay it. I had one man, last year, who was a little tardy (he was in the habit of going to the public-house); but even he did pay. It is an immense advantage to one of these poor fellows to have a pig. The pig consumes the refuse from the man's cottage and Allotment-garden, and the pig's refuse enriches the man's garden besides. The pig is the poor man's friend. Come into the club-house again.'

The poor man's friend. Yes. I have often wondered who really was the poor man's friend among a great number of competitors, and I now clearly perceive him to be the pig. *He* never makes any flourishes about the poor man. *He* never gammons the poor man—except to his manifest advantage in the article of bacon. *He* never comes down to this house, or goes down to his constituents. He openly declares to the poor man, 'I want my sty because I am a Pig. I desire to have as much to eat as you can by any means stuff me with, because I am a Pig.' *He* never gives the poor man a sovereign for bringing up a family. *He* never grunts the poor man's name in vain. And when he dies in the odour of Porkity, he cuts up, a highly useful creature and a blessing to the poor man, from the ring in his snout to the curl in his tail. Which of the poor man's other friends can say as much? Where is the M.P. who means Mere Pork?

The dreary Sage had glided into these reflections, when he found himself sitting by the club-house fire, surrounded by green smock-frocks and shapeless hats: with Friar Bacon lively, busy, and expert, at a little table near him.

'Now, then, come. The first five!' said Friar Bacon. 'Where are you?'

'Order!' cried a merry-faced little man, who had brought his young daughter with him to see life, and who always modestly hid his face in his beer-mug after he had thus assisted the business.

'John Nightingale, William Thrush, Joseph Blackbird, Cecil Robin, and Thomas Linnet!' cried Friar Bacon.

'Here, sir!' and 'Here, sir!' And Linnet, Robin, Blackbird, Thrush, and Nightingale, stood confessed.

We, the undersigned, declare, in effect, by this written paper, that each of us is responsible for the repayment of this pig-money by each of the other. 'Sure you understand, Nightingale?'

'Ees, sur.'

'Can you write your name, Nightingale?'

'Na, sur.'

Nightingale's eye upon his name, as Friar Bacon wrote it, was a sight to consider in after years. Rather incredulous was Nightingale, with a hand at the corner of his mouth, and his head on one side, as to those drawings really meaning him. Doubtful was Nightingale whether any virtue had gone out of him in that committal to paper. Meditative was Nightingale as to what would come of young Nightingale's growing up to the acquisition of that art. Suspended was the interest of Nightingale, when his name was done—as if he thought the letters were only sown, to come up presently in some other form. Prodigious, and wrong-handed was the cross made by Nightingale on much encouragement—the strokes directed from him instead of towards him; and most patient and sweet-humoured was the smile of Nightingale as he stepped back into a general laugh.

'Or—der!' cried the little man. Immediately disappearing into his mug.

'Ralph Mangel, Roger Wurzel, Edward Vetches, Matthew Carrot, and Charles Taters!' said Friar Bacon.

'All here, sir.'

'You understand it, Mangel?'

'Iss, sir, I unnerstaans it.'

'Can you write your name, Mangel?'

'Iss, sir.'

Breathless interest. A dense background of smock-frocks accumulated behind Mangel, and many eyes in it looked doubtfully at Friar Bacon, as who should say, 'Can he really though?' Mangel put down his hat, retired a little to get a good look at the paper, wetted his right hand thoroughly by drawing it slowly across his mouth, approached the paper with great determination, flattened it,

THE POOR MAN AND HIS BEER

sat down at it, and got well to his work. Circuitous and sea-serpent-like, were the movements of the tongue of Mangel while he formed the letters ; elevated were the eyebrows of Mangel and sidelong the eyes, as, with his left whisker reposing on his left arm, they followed his performance ; many were the misgivings of Mangel, and slow was his retrospective meditation touching the junction of the letter p with h ; something too active was the big forefinger of Mangel in its propensity to rub out without proved cause. At last, long and deep was the breath drawn by Mangel when he laid down the pen ; long and deep the wondering breath drawn by the back-ground—as if they had watched his walking across the rapids of Niagara, on stilts, and now cried, ' He has done it !'

But, Mangel was an honest man, if ever honest man lived. ' T"owt to be a hell, sir,' said he, contemplating his work, ' and I ha' made a t on 't.'

The over-fraught bosoms of the background found relief in a roar of laughter.

' Or—DER !' cried the little man. ' CHEER !' And after that second word, came forth from his mug no more.

Several other clubs signed, and received their money. Very few could write their names ; all who could not, pleaded that they could not, more or less sorrowfully, and always with a shake of the head, and in a lower voice than their natural speaking voice. Crosses could be made standing ; signatures must be sat down to. There was no exception to this rule. Meantime, the various club-members smoked, drank their beer, and talked together quite unrestrained. They all wore their hats, except when they went up to Friar Bacon's table. The merry-faced little man offered his beer, with a natural good-fellowship, both to the Dreary one and Philosewers. Both partook of it with thanks.

' Seven o'clock !' said Friar Bacon. ' And now we had better get across to the concert, men, for the music will be beginning.'

The concert was in Friar Bacon's laboratory ; a large building near at hand, in an open field. The bettermost people of the village and neighbourhood were in a gallery on one side, and, in a gallery opposite the orchestra. The whole space below was filled with the labouring people and their families, to the number of five or six hundred. We had been obliged to turn away two hundred to-night, Friar Bacon said, for want of room—and that,

203

not counting the boys, of whom we had taken in only a few picked ones, by reason of the boys, as a class, being given to too fervent a custom of applauding with their boot-heels.

The performers were the ladies of Friar Bacon's family, and two gentlemen; one of them, who presided, a Doctor of Music. A piano was the only instrument. Among the vocal pieces, we had a negro melody (rapturously encored), the Indian Drum, and the Village Blacksmith; neither did we want for fashionable Italian, having *Ah! non giunge*, and *Mi manca la voce*. Our success was splendid; our good-humoured, unaffected, and modest bearing, a pattern. As to the audience, they were far more polite and far more pleased than at the Opera; they were faultless. Thus for barely an hour the concert lasted, with thousands of great bottles looking on from the walls, containing the results of Friar Bacon's Million and one experiments in agricultural chemistry; and containing too, no doubt, a variety of materials with which the Friar could have blown us all through the roof at five minutes' notice.

God save the Queen being done, the good Friar stepped forward and said a few words, more particularly concerning two points; firstly, that Saturday half-holiday, which it would be kind in farmers to grant; secondly, the additional Allotment-grounds we were going to establish, in consequence of the happy success of the system, but which we could not guarantee should entitle the holders to be members of the club, because the present members must consider and settle that question for themselves : a bargain between man and man being always a bargain, and we having made over the club to them as the original Allotment-men. This was loudly applauded, and so, with contented and affectionate cheering, it was all over.

As Philosewers, and I the Dreary, posted back to London, looking up at the moon and discussing it as a world preparing for the habitation of responsible creatures, we expatiated on the honour due to men in this world of ours who try to prepare it for a higher course, and to leave the race who live and die upon it better than they found them.

FIVE NEW POINTS OF CRIMINAL LAW

[SEPTEMBER 24, 1859]

THE existing Criminal Law has been found in trials for Murder, to be so exceedingly hasty, unfair, and oppressive—in a word, to be so very objectionable to the amiable persons accused of that thoughtless act—that it is, we understand, the intention of the Government to bring in a Bill for its amendment. We have been favoured with an outline of its probable provisions.

It will be grounded on the profound principle that the real offender is the Murdered Person ; but for whose obstinate persistency in being murdered, the interesting fellow-creature to be tried could not have got into trouble.

Its leading enactments may be expected to resolve themselves under the following heads :

1. There shall be no Judge. Strong representations have been made by highly popular culprits that the presence of this obtrusive character is prejudicial to their best interests. The Court will be composed of a political gentleman, sitting in a secluded room commanding a view of St. James's Park, who has already more to do than any human creature can, by any stretch of the human imagination, be supposed capable of doing.

2. The Jury to consist of Five Thousand Five Hundred and Fifty-five Volunteers.

3. The Jury to be strictly prohibited from seeing either the accused or the witnesses. They are not to be sworn. They are on no account to hear the evidence. They are to receive it, or such representations of it, as may happen to fall in their way ; and they will constantly write letters about it to all the Papers.

4. Supposing the trial to be a trial for Murder by poisoning, and supposing the hypothetical case, or the evidence, for the prosecution to charge the administration of two poisons, say Arsenic and Antimony ; and supposing the taint of Arsenic in the body to be possible but not probable, and the presence of Antimony in the body, to be an absolute certainty ; it will then become the duty of

205

the Jury to confine their attention solely to the Arsenic, and entirely
to dismiss the Antimony from their minds.

5. The symptoms preceding the death of the real offender (or
Murdered Person) being described in evidence by medical practitioners
who saw them, other medical practitioners who never saw them shall
be required to state whether they are inconsistent with certain
known diseases—*but, they shall never be asked whether they are not
exactly consistent with the administration of Poison.* To illustrate this
enactment in the proposed Bill by a case :—A raging mad dog is seen
to run into the house where Z lives alone, foaming at the mouth.
Z and the mad dog are for some time left together in that house
under proved circumstances, irresistibly leading to the conclusion
that Z has been bitten by the dog. Z is afterwards found lying on
his bed in a state of hydrophobia, and with the marks of the dog's
teeth. Now, the symptoms of that disease being identical with
those of another disease called Tetanus, which might supervene on
Z's running a rusty nail into a certain part of his foot, medical
practitioners who never saw Z, shall bear testimony to that abstract
fact, and it shall then be incumbent on the Registrar-General to
certify that Z died of a rusty nail.

It is hoped that these alterations in the present mode of pro-
cedure will not only be quite satisfactory to the accused person
(which is the first great consideration), but will also tend, in a
tolerable degree, to the welfare and safety of Society. For it is not
sought in this moderate and prudent measure to be wholly denied
that it is an inconvenience to Society to be poisoned overmuch.

LEIGH HUNT. A REMONSTRANCE

[December 24, 1859]

' The sense of beauty and gentleness, of moral beauty and faithful
gentleness, grew upon him as the clear evening closed in. When he
went to visit his relative at Putney, he still carried with him his
work, and the books he more immediately wanted. Although his
bodily powers had been giving way, his most conspicuous qualities,
his memory for books, and his affection remained ; and when his hair
was white, when his ample chest had grown slender, when the very

proportion of his height had visibly lessened, his step was still ready, and his dark eyes brightened at every happy expression, and at every thought of kindness. His death was simply exhaustion : he broke off his work to lie down and repose. So gentle was the final approach, that he scarcely recognised it till the very last, and then it came without terrors. His physical suffering had not been severe ; at the latest hour he said that his only uneasiness was failing breath. And that failing breath was used to express his sense of the inexhaustible kindness he had received from the family who had been so unexpectedly made his nurses,—to draw from one of his sons, by minute, eager, and searching questions, all that he could learn about the latest vicissitudes and growing hopes of Italy, — to ask the friends and children around him for news of those whom he loved,— and to send love and messages to the absent who loved him.'

Thus, with a manly simplicity and filial affection, writes the eldest son of Leigh Hunt in recording his father's death. These are the closing words of a new edition of *The Autobiography of Leigh Hunt*, published by Messrs. Smith and Elder, of Cornhill, revised by that son, and enriched with an introductory chapter of remarkable beauty and tenderness. The son's first presentation of his father to the reader, ' rather tall, straight as an arrow, looking slenderer than he really was ; his hair black and shining, and slightly inclined to wave ; his head high, his forehead straight and white, his eyes black and sparkling, his general complexion dark ; in his whole carriage and manner an extraordinary degree of life,' completes the picture. It is the picture of the flourishing and fading away of man that is born of a woman and hath but a short time to live.

In his presentation of his father's moral nature and intellectual qualities, Mr. Hunt is no less faithful and no less touching. Those who knew Leigh Hunt, will see the bright face and hear the musical voice again, when he is recalled to them in this passage : ' Even at seasons of the greatest depression in his fortunes, he always attracted many visitors, but still not so much for any repute that attended him as for his personal qualities. Few men were more attractive, in society,' whether in a large company or over the fireside. His manners were peculiarly animated ; his conversation, varied, ranging over a great field of subjects, was moved and called forth by the response of his companion, be that companion philosopher or student, sage or boy, man or woman ; and he was equally ready for the most lively topics or for the gravest reflections—his expression easily adapting itself to the tone of his companion's mind. With much freedom of manners, he combined a spontaneous courtesy that never failed, and a considerateness derived from a ceaseless kindness of heart that invariably fascinated even strangers.' Or in this: 'His animation, his sympathy with what was gay and pleasurable; his avowed doctrine of cultivating cheerfulness, were manifest on the surface, and could be appreciated by those who knew him in society, most probably even exaggerated as salient traits, on which he himself insisted *with a sort of gay and ostentatious wilfulness.*'

The last words describe one of the most captivating peculiarities of a most original and engaging man, better than any other words could. The reader is besought to observe them, for a reason that shall presently be given. Lastly: 'The anxiety to recognise the right of others, the tendency to "refine," which was noted by an early school companion, and the propensity to elaborate every thought, made him, along with the direct argument by which he sustained his own conviction, recognise and almost admit all that might be said on the opposite side.' For these reasons, and for others suggested with equal felicity, and with equal fidelity, the son writes of the father, 'It is most desirable that his qualities should be known as they were; for such deficiencies as he had are the honest explanation of his mistakes; while, as the reader may see from his writings and his conduct, they are not, as the faults of which he was accused would be, incompatible with the noblest faculties both of head and heart. To know Leigh Hunt as he was, was to hold him in reverence and love.'

These quotations are made here, with a special object. It is not, that the personal testimony of one who knew Leigh Hunt well, may be borne to their truthfulness. It is not, that it may be recorded in these pages, as in his son's introductory chapter, that his life was of the most amiable and domestic kind, that his wants were few, that his way of life was frugal, that he was a man of small expenses, no ostentations, a diligent labourer, and a secluded man of letters. It is not, that the inconsiderate and forgetful may be reminded of his wrongs and sufferings in the days of the Regency, and of the national disgrace of his imprisonment. It is not, that their forbearance may be entreated for his grave, in right of his graceful fancy or his political labours and endurances, though—

LEIGH HUNT. A REMONSTRANCE

> Not only we, the latest seed of Time,
> New men, that in the flying of a wheel
> Cry down the past, not only we, that prate
> Of rights and wrongs, have loved the people well.

It is, that a duty may be done in the most direct way possible. An act of plain, clear duty.

Four or five years ago, the writer of these lines was much pained by accidentally encountering a printed statement, 'that Mr. Leigh Hunt was the original of Harold Skimpole in *Bleak House*.' The writer of these lines, is the author of that book. The statement came from America. It is no disrespect to that country, in which the writer has, perhaps, as many friends and as true an interest as any man that lives, good-humouredly to state the fact, that he has, now and then, been the subject of paragraphs in Transatlantic newspapers, more surprisingly destitute of all foundation in truth than the wildest delusions of the wildest lunatics. For reasons born of this experience, he let the thing go by.

But, since Mr. Leigh Hunt's death, the statement has been revived in England. The delicacy and generosity evinced in its revival, are for the rather late consideration of its revivers. The fact is this :

Exactly those graces and charms of manner which are remembered in the words we have quoted, were remembered by the author of the work of fiction in question, when he drew the character in question. Above all other things, that 'sort of gay and ostentatious wilfulness' in the humouring of a subject, which had many a time delighted him, and impressed him as being unspeakably whimsical and attractive, was the airy quality he wanted for the man he invented. Partly for this reason, and partly (he has since often grieved to think) for the pleasure it afforded him to find that delightful manner reproducing itself under his hand, he yielded to the temptation of too often making the character *speak* like his old friend. He no more thought, God forgive him ! that the admired original would ever be charged with the imaginary vices of the fictitious creature, than he has himself ever thought of charging the blood of Desdemona and Othello, on the innocent Academy model who sat for Iago's leg in the picture. Even as to the mere occasional manner, he meant to be so cautious and conscientious, that he privately referred the proof sheets of the first number of that book to two intimate literary friends of Leigh Hunt (both still living), and altered the whole of that part of the text on their discovering too strong a resemblance to his ' way.'

He cannot see the son lay this wreath on the father's tomb, and leave him to the possibility of ever thinking that the present words might have righted the father's memory and were left unwritten. He cannot know that his own son may have to explain his father when folly or malice can wound his heart no more, and leave this task undone.

THE TATTLESNIVEL BLEATER
[DECEMBER 31, 1859]

THE pen is taken in hand on the present occasion, by a private individual (not wholly unaccustomed to literary composition), for the exposure of a conspiracy of a most frightful nature ; a conspiracy which, like the deadly Upas-tree of Java, on which the individual produced a poem in his earlier youth (not wholly devoid of length), which was so flatteringly received (in circles not wholly unaccustomed to form critical opinions), that he was recommended to publish it, and would certainly have carried out the suggestion, but for private considerations (not wholly unconnected with expense).

The individual who undertakes the exposure of the gigantic conspiracy now to be laid bare in all its hideous deformity, is an inhabitant of the town of Tattlesnivel—a lowly inhabitant, it may be, but one who, as an Englishman and a man, will ne'er abase his eye before the gaudy and the mocking throng.

Tattlesnivel stoops to demand no championship from her sons. On an occasion in History, our bluff British monarch, our Eighth Royal Harry, almost went there. And long ere the periodical in which this exposure will appear, had sprung into being, Tattlesnivel had unfurled that standard which yet waves upon her battlements. The standard alluded to, is THE TATTLESNIVEL BLEATER, containing the latest intelligence, and state of markets, down to the hour of going to press, and presenting a favourable local medium for advertisers, on a graduated scale of charges, considerably diminishing in proportion to the guaranteed number of insertions.

THE TATTLESNIVEL BLEATER

It were bootless to expatiate on the host of talent engaged in formidable phalanx to do fealty to the Bleater. Suffice it to select, for present purposes, one of the most gifted and (but for the wide and deep ramifications of an un-English conspiracy), most rising, of the men who are bold Albion's pride. It were needless, after this preamble, to point the finger more directly at the LONDON CORRESPONDENT OF THE TATTLESNIVEL BLEATER.

On the weekly letters of that Correspondent, on the flexibility of their English, on the boldness of their grammar, on the originality of their quotations (never to be found as they are printed, in any book existing), on the priority of their information, on their intimate acquaintance with the secret thoughts and unexecuted intentions of men, it would ill become the humble Tattlesnivellian who traces these words, to dwell. They are graven in the memory ; they are on the Bleater's file. Let them be referred to.

But, from the infamous, the dark, the subtle conspiracy which spreads its baleful roots throughout the land, and of which the Bleater's London Correspondent is the one sole subject, it is the purpose of the lowly Tattlesnivellian who undertakes this revelation, to tear the veil. Nor will he shrink from his self-imposed labour, Herculean though it be.

The conspiracy begins in the very Palace of the Sovereign Lady of our Ocean Isle. Leal and loyal as it is the proud vaunt of the Bleater's readers, one and all, to be, the inhabitant who pens this exposure does not personally impeach, either her Majesty the queen, or the illustrious Prince Consort. But, some silken-clad smoothers, some purple parasites, some fawners in frippery, some greedy and begartered ones in gorgeous garments, he does impeach—ay, and wrathfully ! Is it asked on what grounds ? They shall be stated.

The Bleater's London Correspondent, in the prosecution of his important inquiries, goes down to Windsor, sends in his card, has a confidential interview with her Majesty and the illustrious Prince Consort. For a time, the restraints of Royalty are thrown aside in the cheerful conversation of the Bleater's London Correspondent, in his fund of information, in his flow of anecdote, in the atmosphere of his genius; her Majesty brightens, the illustrious Prince Consort thaws, the cares of State and the conflicts of Party are forgotten, lunch is proposed. Over that unassuming and domestic table, her Majesty communicates to the Bleater's London Correspondent that it is her intention to send his Royal Highness the Prince of Wales to inspect the top of the Great Pyramid—thinking it likely to improve his acquaintance with the views of the people. Her Majesty further communicates that she has made up her royal mind (and that the Prince Consort has made up his illustrious mind) to the bestowal of the vacant Garter, let us say on Mr. Roebuck. The younger Royal children having been introduced at the request of the Bleater's London Correspondent, and having been by him closely observed to present the usual external indications of good health, the happy knot is severed, with a sigh the Royal bow is once more strung to its full tension, the Bleater's London Correspondent returns to London, writes his letter, and tells the Tattlesnivel Bleater what he knows. All Tattlesnivel reads it, and knows that he knows it. But, *does* his Royal Highness the Prince of Wales ultimately go to the top of the Great Pyramid? *Does* Mr. Roebuck ultimately get the Garter? No. Are the younger Royal children even ultimately found to be well? On the contrary, they have—and on that very day had — the measles. Why is this? *Because the conspirators against the Bleater's London Correspondent have stepped in with their dark machinations.* Because her Majesty and the Prince Consort are artfully induced to change their minds, from north to south, from east to west, immediately after it is known to the conspirators that they have put themselves in communication with the Bleater's London Correspondent. It is now indignantly demanded, by whom are they so tampered with? It is now indignantly demanded, who took the responsibility of concealing the indisposition of those Royal children from their Royal and Illustrious parents, and of bringing them down from their beds, disguised, expressly to confound the London Correspondent of the Tattlesnivel Bleater? Who are those persons, it is again asked? Let not rank and favour protect them. Let the traitors be exhibited in the face of day!

Lord John Russell is in this conspiracy. Tell us not that his Lordship is a man of too much spirit and honour. Denunciation is hurled against him. The proof? The proof is here.

The Time is panting for an answer to the question, Will Lord John Russell consent to take office under Lord Palmerston? Good. The London Correspondent of the Tattlesnivel Bleater is in the act of writing his weekly letter, finds himself rather at a loss to settle this question finally, leaves off, puts his hat on, goes down to the lobby of the House of Commons, sends in for Lord John Russell, and has him out. He draws his arm through his Lordship's, takes him aside, and says, ' John, will you ever accept office under Palmerston ? ' His Lordship replies, ' I will not.' The Bleater's London Correspondent retorts, with the caution such a man is bound to use, ' John, think again ; say nothing to me rashly ; is there any temper here ? ' His Lordship replies, calmly, ' None whatever.' After giving him time for reflection, the Bleater's London Correspondent says, ' Once more, John, let me put a question to you. Will you ever accept office under Palmerston ? ' His Lordship answers (note the exact expressions), ' Nothing shall induce me, ever to accept a seat in a Cabinet of which Palmerston is the Chief.' They part, the London Correspondent of the Tattlesnivel Bleater finishes his letter, and—always being withheld by motives of delicacy, from plainly divulging his means of getting accurate information on every subject, at first hand—puts in it, this passage : ' Lord John Russell is spoken of, by blunderers, for Foreign Affairs ; but I have the best reasons for assuring your readers, that' (giving prominence to the exact expressions, it will be observed) ' " NOTHING WILL EVER INDUCE HIM, TO ACCEPT A SEAT IN A CABINET OF WHICH PALMERSTON IS THE CHIEF." On this you may implicitly rely.' What happens ? On the very day of the publication of that number of the Bleater—the malignity of the conspirators being even manifested in the selection of the day—Lord John Russell takes the Foreign Office ! Comment were superfluous.

The people of Tattlesnivel will be told, have been told, that Lord John Russell is a man of his word. He may be, on some occasions ; but, when overshadowed by this dark and enormous growth of conspiracy, Tattlesnivel knows him to be otherwise. ' I happen to be certain, deriving my information from a source which cannot be doubted to be authentic,' wrote the London Correspondent of the Bleater, within the last year, ' that Lord John Russell bitterly regrets having made that explicit speech of last Monday.' These are not roundabout phrases ; these are plain words. What does Lord John Russell (apparently by accident), within eight-and-forty hours after their diffusion over the civilised globe ? Rises in his place in Parliament, and unblushingly declares that if the occasion could arise five hundred times, for his making that very speech, he would make it five hundred times ! Is there no conspiracy here ? And is this

MISCELLANEOUS PAPERS

combination against one who would be always right if he were
not proved always wrong, to be endured in a country that boasts
of its freedom and its fairness?

But, the Tattlesnivellian who now raises his voice against intolerable oppression, may be told that, after all, this is a political conspiracy. He may be told, forsooth, that Mr. Disraeli's being in it,
that Lord Derby's being in it, that Mr. Bright's being in it, that
every Home, Foreign, and Colonial Secretary's being in it, that every
ministry's and every opposition's being in it, are but proofs that men
will do in politics what they would do in nothing else. Is this the
plea? If so, the rejoinder is, that the mighty conspiracy includes
the whole circle of Artists of all kinds, and comprehends all degrees
of men, down to the worst criminal and the hangman who ends
his career. For, all these are intimately known to the London
Correspondent of the Tattlesnivel Bleater, and all these deceive
him.

Sir, put it to the proof. There is the Bleater on the file—docu-
mentary evidence. Weeks, months, before the Exhibition of the
Royal Academy, the Bleater's London Correspondent knows the
subjects of all the leading pictures, knows what the painters first
meant to do, knows what they afterwards substituted for what they
first meant to do, knows what they ought to do and won't do, knows
what they ought not to do and will do, knows to a letter from whom
they have commissions, knows to a shilling how much they are to be
paid. Now, no sooner is each studio clear of the remarkable man to
whom each studio-occupant has revealed himself as he does not
reveal himself to his nearest and dearest bosom friend, than conspiracy and fraud begin. Alfred the Great becomes the Fairy
Queen; Moses viewing the Promised Land, turns out to be Moses
going to the Fair; Portrait of His Grace the Archbishop of Canterbury, is transformed, as if by irreverent enchantment of the dissent-
ing interest, into A Favourite Terrier, or Cattle Grazing; and the
most extraordinary work of art in the list described by the Bleater,
is coolly sponged out altogether, and asserted never to have had
existence at all, even in the most shadowy thoughts of its executant!
This is vile enough, but this is not all. Picture-buyers then come
forth from their secret positions, and creep into their places in the
assassin-multitude of conspirators. Mr. Baring, after expressly telling
the Bleater's London Correspondent that he had bought No. 39

214

for one thousand guineas, gives it up to somebody unknown for a couple of hundred pounds; The Marquis of Lansdowne pretends to have no knowledge whatever of the commissions to which the London Correspondent of the Bleater swore him, but allows a Railway Contractor to cut him out for half the money. Similar examples might be multiplied. Shame, shame, on these men! Is this England?

Sir, look again at Literature. The Bleater's London Correspondent is not merely acquainted with all the eminent writers, but is in possession of the secrets of their souls. He is versed in their hidden meanings and references, sees their manuscripts before publication, and knows the subjects and titles of their books when they are not begun. How dare those writers turn upon the eminent man and depart from every intention they have confided to him? How do they justify themselves in entirely altering their manuscripts, changing their titles, and abandoning their subjects? Will they deny, in the face of Tattlesnivel, that they do so? If they have such hardihood, let the file of the Bleater strike them dumb. By their fruits they shall be known. Let their works be compared with the anticipatory letters of the Bleater's London Correspondent, and their falsehood and deceit will become manifest as the sun; it will be seen that they do nothing which they stand pledged to the Bleater's London Correspondent to do; it will be seen that they are among the blackest parties in this black and base conspiracy. This will become apparent, sir, not only as to their public proceedings but as to their private affairs. The outraged Tattlesnivellian who now drags this infamous combination into the face of day, charges those literary persons with making away with their property, imposing on the Income Tax Commissioners, keeping false books, and entering into sham contracts. He accuses them on the unimpeachable faith of the London Correspondent of the Tattlesnivel Bleater. With whose evidence they will find it impossible to reconcile their own account of any transaction of their lives.

The national character is degenerating under the influence of the ramifications of this tremendous conspiracy. Forgery is committed, constantly. A person of note—any sort of person of note—dies. The Bleater's London Correspondent knows what his circumstances are, what his savings are (if any), who his creditors are, all about his children and relations, and (in general, before his body is cold) describes his will. Is that will ever proved? Never! Some other will is substituted; the real instrument, destroyed. And this (as has been before observed), is England!

Who are the workmen and artificers, enrolled upon the books of this treacherous league? From what funds are they paid, and with what ceremonies are they sworn to secrecy? Are there none such? Observe what follows. A little time ago the Bleater's London Correspondent had this passage: 'Boddleboy is pianoforte playing at St. Januarius's Gallery, with pretty tolerable success! He clears three hundred pounds per night. Not bad this!!' The builder of St. Januarius's Gallery (plunged to the throat in the conspiracy) met with this piece of news, and observed, with characteristic coarseness, 'that the Bleater's London Correspondent was a Blind Ass.' Being pressed by a man of spirit to give his reasons for this extraordinary statement, he declared that the Gallery, crammed to suffocation, would not hold two hundred pounds, and that its expenses were, probably, at least half what it did hold. The man of spirit (himself a Tattlesnivellian) had the Gallery measured within a week from that hour, and it would *not* hold two hundred pounds! Now, can the poorest capacity doubt that it had been altered in the meantime?

And so the conspiracy extends, through every grade of society, down to the condemned criminal in prison, the hangman, and the Ordinary. Every famous murderer within the last ten years has desecrated his last moments by falsifying his confidences imparted specially to the London Correspondent of the Tattlesnivel Bleater; on every such occasion, Mr. Calcraft has followed the degrading example; and the reverend Ordinary, forgetful of his cloth, and mindful only (it would seem, alas!) of the conspiracy, has committed himself to some account or other of the criminal's demeanour and conversation, which has been diametrically opposed to the exclusive information of the London Correspondent of the Bleater. And this (as has been before observed) is Merry England!

A man of true genius, however, is not easily defeated. The Bleater's London Correspondent, probably beginning to suspect the existence of a plot against him, has recently fallen on a new style, which, as being very difficult to countermine, may necessitate the organisation of a new conspiracy. One of his masterly letters, lately, disclosed the adoption of this style—which was remarked with profound sensation throughout Tattlesnivel—in the following passage:

THE TATTLESNIVEL BLEATER

' Mentioning literary small talk, I may tell you that some new and extraordinary rumours are afloat concerning the conversations I have previously mentioned, alleged to have taken place in the first floor front (situated over the street door), of Mr. X. Ameter (the poet so well known to your readers), in which, X. Ameter's great uncle, his second son, his butcher, and a corpulent gentleman with one eye universally respected at Kensington, are said not to have been on the most friendly footing; I forbear, however, to pursue the subject further, this week, my informant not being able to supply me with exact particulars.'

But, enough, sir. The inhabitant of Tattlesnivel who has taken pen in hand to expose this odious association of unprincipled men against a shining (local) character, turns from it with disgust and contempt. Let him in few words strip the remaining flimsy covering from the nude object of the conspirators, and his loathsome task is ended.

Sir, that object, he contends, is evidently twofold. First, to exhibit the London Correspondent of the Tattlesnivel Bleater in the light of a mischievous Blockhead who, by hiring himself out to tell what he cannot possibly know, is as great a public nuisance as a Blockhead in a corner can be. Second, to suggest to the men of Tattlesnivel that it does not improve their town to have so much Dry Rubbish shot there.

Now, sir, on both these points Tattlesnivel demands in accents of Thunder, Where is the Attorney General? Why doesn't the *Times* take it up? (Is the latter in the conspiracy? It never adopts his views, or quotes him, and incessantly contradicts him.) Tattlesnivel, sir, remembering that our forefathers contended with the Norman at Hastings, and bled at a variety of other places that will readily occur to you, demands that its birthright shall not be bartered away for a mess of pottage. Have a care, sir, have a care! Or Tattlesnivel (its idle Rifles piled in its scouted streets) may be seen ere long, advancing with its Bleater to the foot of the Throne, and demanding redress for this conspiracy, from the orbed and sceptred hands of Majesty itself!

THE YOUNG MAN FROM THE COUNTRY

[MARCH 1, 1862]

A SONG of the hour, now in course of being sung and whistled in every street, the other day reminded the writer of these words—as he chanced to pass a fag-end of the song for the twentieth time in a short London walk—that twenty years ago, a little book on the United States, entitled *American Notes*, was published by 'a Young Man from the Country,' who had just seen and left it.

This Young Man from the Country fell into a deal of trouble, by reason of having taken the liberty to believe that he perceived in America downward popular tendencies for which his young enthusiasm had been anything but prepared. It was in vain for the Young Man to offer in extenuation of his belief that no stranger could have set foot on those shores with a feeling of livelier interest in the country, and stronger faith in it, than he. Those were the days when the Tories had made their Ashburton Treaty, and when Whigs and Radicals must have no theory disturbed. All three parties waylaid and mauled the Young Man from the Country, and showed that he knew nothing about the country.

As the Young Man from the Country had observed in the Preface to his little book, that he 'could bide his time,' he took all this in silent part for eight years. Publishing then, a cheap edition of his book, he made no stronger protest than the following:

'My readers have opportunities of judging for themselves whether the influences and tendencies which I distrusted in America, have any existence but in my imagination. They can examine for themselves whether there has been anything in the public career of that country during these past eight years, or whether there is anything in its present position, at home or abroad, which suggests that those influences and tendencies really do exist. As they find the fact, they will judge me. If they discern any evidences of wrong-going, in any direction that I have indicated, they will acknowledge that I had reason in what I wrote. If they discern no such thing, they will consider me altogether mistaken.

THE YOUNG MAN FROM THE COUNTRY

I have nothing to defend, or to explain away. The truth is the truth; and neither childish absurdities, nor unscrupulous contradictions, can make it otherwise. The earth would still move round the sun, though the whole Catholic Church said No.'

Twelve more years having since passed away, it may, now at last, be simply just towards the Young Man from the Country, to compare what he originally wrote, with recent events and their plain motive powers. Treating of the House of Representatives at Washington, he wrote thus:

'Did I recognise in this assembly, a body of men, who, applying themselves in a new world to correct some of the falsehoods and vices of the old, purified the avenues to Public Life, paved the dirty ways to Place and Power, debated and made laws for the Common Good, and had no party but their Country?

'I saw in them, the wheels that move the meanest perversion of virtuous Political Machinery that the worst tools ever wrought. Despicable trickery at elections; under-handed tamperings with public officers; cowardly attacks upon opponents, with scurrilous newspapers for shields, and hired pens for daggers; shameful trucklings to mercenary knaves, whose claim to be considered, is, that every day and week they sow new crops of ruin with their venal types, which are the dragon's teeth of yore, in everything but sharpness; aidings and abettings of every bad inclination in the popular mind, and artful suppressions of all its good influences: such things as these, and in a word, Dishonest Faction in its most depraved and most unblushing form, stared out from every corner of the crowded hall.

'Did I see among them, the intelligence and refinement: the true, honest, patriotic heart of America? Here and there, were drops of its blood and life, but they scarcely coloured the stream of desperate adventurers which sets that way for profit and for pay. It is the game of these men, and of their profligate organs, to make the strife of politics so fierce and brutal, and so destructive of all self-respect in worthy men, that sensitive and delicate-minded persons shall be kept aloof, and they, and such as they, be left to battle out their selfish views unchecked. And thus this lowest of all scrambling fights goes on, and they who in other countries would,

219

from their intelligence and station, most aspire to make the laws, do here recoil the farthest from that degradation.

'That there are, among the representatives of the people in both Houses, and among all parties, some men of high character and great abilities, I need not say. The foremost among those politicians who are known in Europe, have been already described, and I see no reason to depart from the rule I have laid down for my guidance, of abstaining from all mention of individuals. It will be sufficient to add, that to the most favourable accounts that have been written of them, I fully and most heartily subscribe ; and that personal intercourse and free communication have bred within me, not the result predicted in the very doubtful proverb, but increased admiration and respect.'

Towards the end of his book, the Young Man from the Country thus expressed himself concerning its people :

'They are, by nature, frank, brave, cordial, hospitable, and affectionate. Cultivation and refinement seem but to enhance their warmth of heart and ardent enthusiasm ; and it is the possession of these latter qualities in a most remarkable degree, which renders an educated American one of the most endearing and most generous of friends. I never was so won upon, as by this class ; never yielded up my full confidence and esteem so readily and pleasurably, as to them ; never can make again, in half a year, so many friends for whom I seem to entertain the regard of half a life.

'These qualities are natural, I implicitly believe, to the whole people. That they are, however, sadly sapped and blighted in their growth among the mass ; and that there are influences at work which endanger them still more, and give but little present promise of their healthy restoration ; is a truth that ought to be told.

'It is an essential part of every national character to pique itself mightily upon its faults, and to deduce tokens of its virtue or its wisdom from their very exaggeration. One great blemish in the popular mind of America, and the prolific parent of an innumerable brood of evils, is Universal Distrust. Yet the American citizen plumes himself upon this spirit, even when he is sufficiently dispassionate to perceive the ruin it works ; and will often adduce it, in spite of his own reason, as an instance of the great

sagacity and acuteness of the people, and their superior shrewd-
ness and independence.

' " You carry," says the stranger, " this jealousy and distrust into
every transaction of public life. By repelling worthy men from your
legislative assemblies, it has bred up a class of candidates for the
suffrage, who, in their every act, disgrace your Institutions and your
people's choice. It has rendered you so fickle, and so given to
change, that your inconstancy has passed into a proverb ; for you no
sooner set up an idol firmly, than you are sure to pull it down and
dash it into fragments : and this, because directly you reward a
benefactor, or a public servant, you distrust him, merely because he
is rewarded ; and immediately apply yourselves to find out, either
that you have been too bountiful in your acknowledgments, or he
remiss in his deserts. Any man who attains a high place among
you, from the President downwards, may date his downfall from
that moment; for any printed lie that any notorious villain pens,
although it militate directly against the character and conduct of a
life, appeals at once to your distrust, and is believed. You will
strain at a gnat in the way of trustfulness and confidence, however
fairly won and well deserved ; but you will swallow a whole caravan
of camels, if they be laden with unworthy doubts and mean suspicions.
Is this well, think you, or likely to elevate the character of the
governors or the governed, among you ? "

' The answer is invariably the same : " There's freedom of opinion
here, you know. Every man thinks for himself, and we are not to
be easily overreached. That's how our people come to be suspicious."

' Another prominent feature is the love of " smart " dealing :
which gilds over many a swindle and gross breach of trust ; many a
defalcation, public and private ; and enables many a knave to hold
his head up with the best, who well deserves a halter : though it has
not been without its retributive operation, for this smartness has
done more in a few years to impair the public credit, and to cripple
the public resources, than dull honesty, however rash, could have
effected in a century. The merits of a broken speculation, or a
bankruptcy, or of a successful scoundrel, are not gauged by its or his
observance of the golden rule, " Do as you would be done by," but
are considered with reference to their smartness. I recollect, on
both occasions of our passing that ill-fated *Cairo* on the Mississippi,
remarking on the bad effects such gross deceits must have when they

exploded, in generating a want of confidence abroad, and discouraging foreign investment : but I was given to understand that this was a very smart scheme by which a deal of money had been made : and that its smartest feature was, that they forgot these things abroad, in a very short time, and speculated again, as freely as ever. The following dialogue I have held a hundred times : " Is it not a very disgraceful circumstance that such a man as So-and-so should be acquiring a large property by the most infamous and odious means, and notwithstanding all the crimes of which he has been guilty, should be tolerated and abetted by your citizens ? He is a public nuisance, is he not ? " " Yes, sir." " A convicted liar ? " " Yes, sir." " He has been kicked, and cuffed, and caned ? " " Yes, sir." " And he is utterly dishonourable, debased, and profligate ? " " Yes, sir." " In the name of wonder, then, what is his merit ? " " Well, sir, he is a smart man."

' But the foul growth of America has a more tangled root than this ; and it strikes its fibres, deep in its licentious Press.

' Schools may be erected, East, West, North, and South ; pupils be taught, and masters reared, by scores upon scores of thousands ; colleges may thrive, churches may be crammed, temperance may be diffused, and advancing knowledge in all other forms walk through the land with giant strides ; but while the newspaper press of America is in, or near, its present abject state, high moral improvement in that country is hopeless. Year by year, it must and will go back ; year by year, the tone of public opinion must sink lower down ; year by year, the Congress and the Senate must become of less account before all decent men ; and year by year, the memory of the Great Fathers of the Revolution must be outraged more and more, in the bad life of their degenerate child.

' Among the herd of journals which are published in the States, there are some, the reader scarcely need be told, of character and credit. From personal intercourse with accomplished gentlemen connected with publications of this class, I have derived both pleasure and profit. But the name of these is Few, and of the others Legion ; and the influence of the good, is powerless to counteract the moral poison of the bad.

' Among the gentry of America ; among the well-informed and moderate ; in the learned professions ; at the bar and on the bench ; there is, as there can be, but one opinion, in reference to the vicious character of these infamous journals. It is sometimes contended—I will not say strangely, for it is natural to seek excuses for such a disgrace—that their influence is not so great as a visitor would suppose. I must be pardoned for saying that there is no warrant for this plea, and that every fact and circumstance tends directly to the opposite conclusion.

'When any man, of any grade of desert in intellect or character, can climb to any public distinction, no matter what, in America, without first grovelling down upon the earth, and bending the knee before this monster of depravity ; when any private excellence is safe from its attacks ; when any social confidence is left unbroken by it, or any tie of social decency and honour is held in the least regard ; when any man in that Free Country has freedom of opinion, and presumes to think for himself, and speak for himself, without humble reference to a censorship which, for its rampant ignorance and base dishonesty, he utterly loaths and despises in his heart ; when those who most acutely feel its infamy and the reproach it casts upon the nation, and who most denounce it to each other, dare to set their heels upon, and crush it openly, in the sight of all men : then, I will believe that its influence is lessening, and men are returning to their manly senses. But while that Press has its evil eye in every house, and its black hand in every appointment in the state, from a president to a postman ; while, with ribald slander for its only stock in trade, it is the standard literature of an enormous class, who must find their reading in a newspaper, or they will not read at all ; so long must its odium be upon the country's head, and so long must the evil it works, be plainly visible in the Republic.'

The foregoing was written in the year eighteen hundred and forty-two. It rests with the reader to decide whether it has received any confirmation, or assumed any colour of truth, in or about the year eighteen hundred and sixty-two.

AN ENLIGHTENED CLERGYMAN

[MARCH 8, 1862]

AT various places in Suffolk (as elsewhere) penny readings take place
'for the instruction and amusement of the lower classes.' There is
a little town in Suffolk called Eye, where the subject of one of these
readings was a tale (by Mr. Wilkie Collins) from the last Christmas
Number of this Journal, entitled 'Picking up Waifs at Sea.' It
appears that the Eye gentility was shocked by the introduction of
this rude piece among the taste and musical glasses of that important town, on which the eyes of Europe are notoriously always
fixed. In particular, the feelings of the vicar's family were outraged; and a Local Organ (say, the Tattlesnivel Bleater) consequently doomed the said piece to everlasting oblivion, as being of an
'injurious tendency!'

When this fearful fact came to the knowledge of the unhappy
writer of the doomed tale in question, he covered his face with his
robe, previous to dying decently under the sharp steel of the
ecclesiastical gentility of the terrible town of Eye. But the
discovery that he was not alone in his gloomy glory, revived him,
and he still lives.

For, at Stowmarket, in the aforesaid county of Suffolk, at
another of those penny readings, it was announced that a certain
juvenile sketch, culled from a volume of sketches (by Boz) and
entitled 'The Bloomsbury Christening,' would be read. Hereupon,
the clergyman of that place took heart and pen, and addressed the
following terrific epistle to a gentleman bearing the very appropriate
name of Gudgeon :

STOWMARKET VICARAGE, *Feb. 25*, 1861.

SIR,—My attention has been directed to a piece called 'The Bloomsbury Christening' which you propose to read this evening. Without
presuming to claim any interference in the arrangement of the readings,
I would suggest to you whether you have on this occasion sufficiently
considered the character of the composition you have selected. I quite
appreciate the laudable motive of the promoters of the readings to
raise the moral tone amongst the working class of the town and to

RATHER A STRONG DOSE

direct this taste in a familiar and pleasant manner. 'The Bloomsbury Christening' cannot possibly do this. It trifles with a sacred ordinance, and the language and style, instead of improving the taste, has a direct tendency to lower it.

I appeal to your right feeling whether it is desirable to give publicity to that which must shock several of your audience, and create a smile amongst others, to be indulged in only by violating the conscientious scruples of their neighbours.

The ordinance which is here exposed to ridicule is one which is much misunderstood and neglected amongst many families belonging to the Church of England, and the mode in which it is treated in this chapter cannot fail to appear as giving a sanction to, or at least excusing, such neglect.

Although you are pledged to the public to give this subject, yet I cannot but believe that they would fully justify your substitution of it for another did they know the circumstances. An abridgment would only lessen the evil in a degree, as it is not only the style of the writing but the subject itself which is objectionable.

Excuse me for troubling you, but I felt that, in common with yourself, I have a grave responsibility in the matter, and I am most truly yours, T. S. COLES.

To Mr. J Gudgeon.

It is really necessary to explain that this is not a bad joke. It is simply a bad fact.

RATHER A STRONG DOSE

[MARCH 21, 1863]

'DOCTOR JOHN CAMPBELL, the minister of the Tabernacle Chapel, Finsbury, and editor of the *British Banner*, etc., with that massive vigour which distinguishes his style,' did, we are informed by Mr. Howitt, 'deliver a verdict in the *Banner*, for November, 1852,' of great importance and favour to the Table-rapping cause. We are not informed whether the Public, sitting in judgment on the question, reserved any point in this great verdict for subsequent consideration; but the verdict would seem to have been regarded by a perverse generation as not quite final, inasmuch as Mr. Howitt finds it necessary to re-open the case, a round ten years afterwards, in nine hundred and sixty-two stiff octavo pages, published by Messrs. Longman and Company.

Mr. Howitt is in such a bristling temper on the Supernatural subject, that we will not take the great liberty of arguing any point with him. But—with the view of assisting him to make converts— we will inform our readers, on his conclusive authority, what they are required to believe ; premising what may rather astonish them in connexion with their views of a certain historical trifle, called The Reformation, that their present state of unbelief is all the fault of Protestantism, and that 'it is high time, therefore, to protest against Protestantism.'

They will please to believe, by way of an easy beginning, all the stories of good and evil demons, ghosts, prophecies, communication with spirits, and practice of magic, that ever obtained, or are said to have ever obtained, in the North, in the South, in the East, in the West, from the earliest and darkest ages, as to which we have any hazy intelligence, real or supposititious, down to the yet unfinished displacement of the red men in North America. They will please to believe that nothing in this wise was changed by the fulfilment of Our Saviour's mission upon earth ; and further, that what Saint Paul did, can be done again, and has been done again. As this is not much to begin with, they will throw in at this point rejection of Faraday and Brewster, and 'poor Paley,' and implicit acceptance of those shining lights, the Reverend Charles Beecher, and the Reverend Henry Ward Beecher ('one of the most vigorous and eloquent preachers of America'), and the Reverend Adin Ballou.

Having thus cleared the way for a healthy exercise of faith, our advancing readers will next proceed especially to believe in the old story of the Drummer of Tedworth, in the inspiration of George Fox, in 'the spiritualism, prophecies, and prevision' of Huntington the coal-porter (him who prayed for the leather breeches which miraculously fitted him), and even in the Cock Lane Ghost. They will please wind up, before fetching their breath, with believing that there is a close analogy between rejection of any such plain and proved facts as those contained in the whole foregoing catalogue, and the opposition encountered by the inventors of railways, lighting by gas, microscopes and telescopes, and vaccination. This stinging consideration they will always carry rankling in their remorseful hearts as they advance.

RATHER A STRONG DOSE

As touching the Cock Lane Ghost, our conscience-stricken readers will please particularly to reproach themselves for having ever supposed that important spiritual manifestation to have been a gross imposture which was thoroughly detected. They will please to believe that Dr. Johnson believed in it, and that, in Mr. Howitt's words, he 'appears to have had excellent reasons for his belief.' With a view to this end, the faithful will be so good as to obliterate from their Boswells the following passage : 'Many of my readers, I am convinced, are to this hour under an impression that Johnson was thus foolishly deceived. It will therefore surprise them a good deal when they are informed upon undoubted authority that Johnson was one of those by whom the imposture was detected. The story had become so popular, that he thought it should be investigated, and in this research he was assisted by the Rev. Dr. Douglas, now Bishop of Salisbury, the great detector of impostures '— and therefore tremendously obnoxious to Mr. Howitt—' who informs me that after the gentlemen who went and examined into the evidence were satisfied of its falsity, Johnson wrote in their presence an account of it, which was published in the newspapers and *Gentleman's Magazine*, and undeceived the world.' But as there will still remain another highly inconvenient passage in the Boswells of the true believers, they must likewise be at the trouble of cancelling the following also, referring to a later time : 'He (Johnson) expressed great indignation at the imposture of the Cock Lane Ghost, and related with much satisfaction how he had assisted in detecting the cheat, and had published an account of it in the newspapers.'

They will next believe (if they be, in the words of Captain Bobadil, 'so generously minded ') in the transatlantic trance-speakers 'who professed to speak from direct inspiration,' Mrs. Cora Hatch, Mrs. Henderson, and Miss Emma Hardinge ; and they will believe in those eminent ladies having 'spoken on Sundays to five hundred thousand hearers '—small audiences, by the way, compared with the intelligent concourse recently assembled in the city of New York, to do honour to the Nuptials of General the Honourable T. Barnum Thumb. At about this stage of their spiritual education, they may take the opportunity of believing in ' letters from a distinguished gentleman of New York, in which the frequent appearance of the gentleman's deceased wife and of Dr. Franklin, to him and other well-known friends, are unquestionably unequalled in the annals of the marvellous.' Why these modest appearances should seem at all out of the common way to Mr. Howitt (who would be in a state of flaming indignation if we thought them so), we could not imagine, until we found on reading further, 'it is solemnly stated that the witnesses have not only seen but touched these spirits, and handled the clothes and hair of Franklin.' Without presuming to go Mr. Howitt's length of considering this by any means a marvellous experience, we yet venture to confess that it has awakened in our mind many interesting speculations touching the present whereabout in space, of the spirits of Mr. Howitt's own departed boots and hats.

The next articles of belief are Belief in the moderate figures of 'thirty thousand media in the United States in 1853'; and in two million five hundred thousand spiritualists in the same country of composed minds, in 1855, 'professing to have arrived at their convictions of spiritual communication from personal experience'; and in 'an average rate of increase of three hundred thousand per annum,' still in the same country of calm philosophers. Belief in spiritual knockings, in all manner of American places, and, among others, in the house of 'a Doctor Phelps at Stratford, Connecticut, a man of the highest character for intelligence,' says Mr. Howitt, and to whom we willingly concede the possession of far higher intelligence than was displayed by his spiritual knocker, in 'frequently cutting to pieces the clothes of one of his boys,' and in breaking 'seventy-one panes of glass'—unless, indeed, the knocker, when in the body, was connected with the tailoring and glazing interests. Belief in immaterial performers playing (in the dark though: they are obstinate about its being in the dark) on material instruments of wood, catgut, brass, tin, and parchment. Your belief is further requested in 'the Kentucky Jerks.' The spiritual achievements thus euphoniously denominated 'appear,' says Mr. Howitt, 'to have been of a very disorderly kind.' It appears that a certain Mr. Doke, a Presbyterian clergyman, 'was first seized by the jerks,' and the jerks laid hold of Mr. Doke in that unclerical way and with that scant respect for his cloth, that they 'twitched him about in a most extraordinary manner, often when in the pulpit, and caused him to shout aloud, and run out of the pulpit into the woods, screaming like a madman. When the fit was over, he returned calmly to his pulpit and finished the service.' The congregation having waited, we pre-

228

sume, and edified themselves with the distant bellowings of Doke in the woods, until he came back again, a little warm and hoarse, but otherwise in fine condition, 'People were often seized at hotels, and at table would, on lifting a glass to drink, jerk the liquor to the ceiling; ladies would at the breakfast-table suddenly be compelled to throw aloft their coffee, and frequently break the cup and saucer.' A certain venturesome clergyman vowed that he would preach down the Jerks, 'but he was seized in the midst of his attempt, and made so ridiculous that he withdrew himself from further notice'—an example much to be commended. That same favoured land of America has been particularly favoured in the development of 'innumerable mediums,' and Mr. Howitt orders you to believe in Daniel Dunglas Home, Andrew Davis Jackson, and Thomas L. Harris, as 'the three most remarkable, or most familiar, on this side of the Atlantic.' Concerning Mr. Home, the articles of belief (besides removal of furniture) are, That through him raps have been given and communications made from deceased friends. That 'his hand has been seized by spirit influence, and rapid communications written out, of a surprising character to those to whom they were addressed.' That at his bidding, 'spirit hands have appeared which have been seen, felt, and recognised frequently, by persons present, as those of deceased friends.' That he has been frequently lifted up and carried, floating 'as it were' through a room, near the ceiling. That in America, 'all these phenomena have displayed themselves in greater force than here'—which we have not the slightest doubt of. That he is 'the planter of spiritualism all over Europe.' That 'by circumstances that no man could have devised, he became the guest of the Emperor of the French, of the King of Holland, of the Czar of Russia, and of many lesser princes.' That he returned from 'this unpremeditated missionary tour,' 'endowed with compet-ence'; but not before, 'at the Tuileries, on one occasion when the emperor, empress, a distinguished lady, and himself only were sitting at table, a hand appeared, took up a pen, and wrote, in a strong and well-known character, the word Napoleon. The hand was then successively presented to the several personages of the party to kiss.' The stout believer, having disposed of Mr. Home, and rested a little, will then proceed to believe in Andrew Davis Jackson, or Andrew Jackson Davis (Mr. Howitt, having no Medium at hand to settle this difference and reveal the right name of the seer, calls him by both names), who merely ' beheld all the essential natures of things, saw the interior of men and animals, as perfectly as their exterior; and described them in language so correct, that the most able technologists could not surpass him. He pointed out the proper remedies for all the complaints, and the shops where they were to be obtained ';—in the latter respect appearing to hail from an advertising circle, as we conceive. It was also in this gentleman's limited department to ' see the metals in the earth,' and to have ' the most distant regions and their various productions present before him.' Having despatched this tough case, the believer will pass on to Thomas L. Harris, and will swallow *him* easily, together with ' whole epics ' of his composition ; a certain work ' of scarcely less than Miltonic grandeur, called The Lyric of the Golden Age—a lyric pretty nigh as long as one of Mr. Howitt's volumes—dictated by Mr. (not Mrs.) Harris to the publisher in ninety-four hours; and several extempore sermons, possessing the remarkably lucid property of being ' full, unforced, out-gushing, unstinted, and absorbing.' The candidate for examination in pure belief, will then pass on to the spirit-photography department ; this, again, will be found in so-favoured America, under the superintendence of Medium Mumler, a photographer of Boston : who was ' astonished ' (though, on Mr. Howitt's showing, he surely ought not to have been) ' on taking a photograph of himself, to find also by his side the figure of a young girl, which he immediately recognised as that of a deceased relative. The circumstance made a great excitement. Numbers of persons rushed to his rooms, and many have found deceased friends photographed with themselves.' (Perhaps Mr. Mumler, too, may become ' endowed with competence ' in time. Who knows ?) Finally, the true believers in the gospel according to Howitt, have, besides, but to pin their faith on ' ladies who see spirits habitually,' on ladies who *know* they have a tendency to soar in the air on sufficient provocation, and on a few other gnats to be taken after their camels, and they shall be pronounced by Mr. Howitt not of the stereotyped class of minds,' and not partakers of ' the astonishing ignorance of the press,' and shall receive a first-class certificate of merit.

But before they pass through this portal into the Temple of Serene Wisdom, we, halting blind and helpless on the steps, beg to suggest to them what they must at once and for ever disbelieve. They must disbelieve that in the dark times, when very few were

230

versed in what are now the mere recreations of Science, and when those few formed a priesthood-class apart, any marvels were wrought by the aid of concave mirrors and a knowledge of the properties of certain odours and gases, although the self-same marvels could be reproduced before their eyes at the Polytechnic Institution, Regent Street, London, any day in the year. They must by no means believe that Conjuring and Ventriloquism are old trades. They must disbelieve all Philosophical Transactions containing the records of painful and careful inquiry into now familiar disorders of the senses of seeing and hearing, and into the wonders of somnambulism, epilepsy, hysteria, miasmatic influence, vegetable poisons derived by whole communities from corrupted air, diseased imitation, and moral infection. They must disbelieve all such awkward leading cases as the case of the Woodstock Commissioners and their man, and the case of the identity of the Stockwell Ghost, with the maid-servant. They must disbelieve the vanishing of champion haunted houses (except, indeed, out of Mr. Howitt's book), represented to have been closed and ruined for years, before one day's inquiry by four gentlemen associated with this Journal, and one hour's reference to the Local Rate-books. They must disbelieve all possibility of a human creature on the last verge of the dark bridge from Life to Death, being mysteriously able, in occasional cases, so to influence the mind of one very near and dear, as vividly to impress that mind with some disturbed sense of the solemn change impending. They must disbelieve the possibility of the lawful existence of a class of intellects which, humbly conscious of the illimitable power of GOD and of their own weakness and ignorance, never deny that He can cause the souls of the dead to revisit the earth, or that He may have caused the souls of the dead to revisit the earth, or that He can cause any awful or wondrous thing to be ; but to deny the likelihood of apparitions or spirits coming here upon the stupidest of bootless errands, and producing credentials tantamount to a solicitation of our vote and interest and next proxy, to get them into the Asylum for Idiots. They must disbelieve the right of Christian people who do *not* protest against Protestantism, but who hold it to be a barrier against the darkest superstitions that can enslave the soul, to guard with jealousy all approaches tending down to Cock Lane Ghosts and suchlike infamous swindles, widely degrading when widely believed in ; and they must disbelieve that such people have the right to know,

231

and that it is their duty to know, wonder-workers by their fruits, and to test miracle-mongers by the tests of probability, analogy, and common sense. They must disbelieve all rational explanations of thoroughly proved experiences (only) which appear supernatural, derived from the average experience and study of the visible world. They must disbelieve the speciality of the Master and the Disciples, and that it is a monstrosity to test the wonders of show-folk by the same touchstone. Lastly, they must disbelieve that one of the best accredited chapters in the history of mankind is the chapter that records the astonishing deceits continually practised, with no object or purpose but the distorted pleasure of deceiving.

We have summed up a few—not nearly all—of the articles of belief and disbelief to which Mr. Howitt most arrogantly demands an implicit adherence. To uphold these, he uses a book as a Clown in a Pantomime does, and knocks everybody on the head with it who comes in his way. Moreover, he is an angrier personage than the Clown, and does not experimentally try the effect of his red-hot poker on your shins, but straightway runs you through the body and soul with it. He is always raging to tell you that if you are not Howitt, you are Atheist and Anti-Christ. He is the sans-culotte of the Spiritual Revolution, and will not hear of your accepting this point and rejecting that;—down your throat with them all, one and indivisible, at the point of the pike; No Liberty, Totality, Fraternity, or Death!

Without presuming to question that 'it is high time to protest against Protestantism' on such very substantial grounds as Mr. Howitt sets forth, we do presume to think that it is high time to protest against Mr. Howitt's spiritualism, as being a little in excess of the peculiar merit of Thomas L. Harris's sermons, and somewhat *too* 'full, out-gushing, unstinted, and absorbing.'

THE MARTYR MEDIUM

[April 4, 1863]

'After the valets, the master!' is Mr. Fechter's rallying cry in the picturesque romantic drama which attracts all London to the Lyceum Theatre. After the worshippers and puffers of Mr. Daniel Dunglas Home, the spirit medium, comes Mr. Daniel Dunglas Home himself, in one volume. And we must, for the honour of Literature, plainly express our great surprise and regret that he comes arm-in-arm with such good company as Messrs. Longman and Company.

We have already summed up Mr. Home's demands on the public capacity of swallowing, as sounded through the war-denouncing trumpet of Mr. Howitt, and it is not our intention to revive the strain as performed by Mr. Home on his own melodious instrument. We notice, by the way, that in that part of the Fantasia where the hand of the first Napoleon is supposed to be reproduced, recognised, and kissed, at the Tuileries, Mr. Home subdues the florid effects one might have expected after Mr. Howitt's execution, and brays in an extremely general manner. And yet we observe Mr. Home to be in other things very reliant on Mr. Howitt, of whom he entertains as gratifying an opinion as Mr. Howitt entertains of him : dwelling on his ' deep researches into this subject,' and of his ' great work now ready for the press,' and of his ' eloquent and forcible ' advocacy, and eke of his ' elaborate and almost exhaustive work,' which Mr. Home trusts will be ' extensively read.' But, indeed, it would seem to be the most reliable characteristic of the Dear Spirits, though very capricious in other particulars, that they always form their circles into what may be described, in worldly terms, as A Mutual Admiration and Complimentation Company (Limited).

Mr. Home's book is entitled *Incidents in My Life.* We will extract a dozen sample passages from it, as variations on and phrases of harmony in, the general strain for the Trumpet, which we have promised not to repeat.

1. MR. HOME IS SUPERNATURALLY NURSED

'I cannot remember when first I became subject to the curious phenomena which have now for so long attended me, but my aunt

233

and others have told me that when I was a baby my cradle was frequently rocked, as if some kind guardian spirit was attending me in my slumbers.'

2. DISRESPECTFUL CONDUCT OF MR. HOME'S AUNT NEVERTHELESS

'In her uncontrollable anger she seized a chair and threw it at me.'

3. PUNISHMENT OF MR. HOME'S AUNT

'Upon one occasion as the table was being thus moved about of itself, my aunt brought the family Bible, and placing it on the table, said, "There, that will soon drive the devils away"; but to her astonishment the table only moved in a more lively manner, as if pleased to bear such a burden.' (We believe this is constantly observed in pulpits and church reading desks, which are invariably lively.) 'Seeing this she was greatly incensed, and determined to stop it, she angrily placed her whole weight on the table, and was actually lifted up with it bodily from the floor.'

4. TRIUMPHANT EFFECT OF THIS DISCIPLINE ON MR. HOME'S AUNT

'And she felt it a duty that I should leave her house, and which I did.'

5. MR. HOME'S MISSION

It was communicated to him by the spirit of his mother, in the following terms: 'Daniel, fear not, my child, God is with you, and who shall be against you? Seek to do good: be truthful and truth-loving, and you will prosper, my child. Yours is a glorious mission—you will convince the infidel, cure the sick, and console the weeping.' It is a coincidence that another eminent man, with several missions, heard a voice from the Heavens blessing him, when he also was a youth, and saying, 'You will be rewarded, my son, in time.' This Medium was the celebrated Baron Munchausen, who relates the experience in the opening of the second chapter of the incidents in *his* life.

6. MODEST SUCCESS OF MR. HOME'S MISSION

'Certainly these phenomena, whether from Gòd or from the devil, have in ten years caused more converts to the great truths of immortality and angel communion, with all that flows from these

234

great facts, than all the sects in Christendom have made during the same period.'

7. WHAT THE FIRST COMPOSERS SAY OF THE SPIRIT-MUSIC, TO MR. HOME

' As to the music, it has been my good fortune to be on intimate terms with some of the first composers of the day, and more than one of them have said of such as they have heard, that it is such music as only angels could make, and no man could write it.'

These ' first composers ' are not more particularly named. We shall therefore be happy to receive and file at the office of this Journal, the testimonials in the foregoing terms of Dr. Sterndale Bennett, Mr. Balfe, Mr. Macfarren, Mr. Benedict, Mr. Vincent Wallace, Signor Costa, M. Auber, M. Gounod, Signor Rossini, and Signor Verdi. We shall also feel obliged to Mr. Alfred Mellon, who is no doubt constantly studying this wonderful music, under the Medium's auspices, if he will note on paper, from memory, say a single sheet of the same. Signor Giulio Regondi will then perform it, as correctly as a mere mortal can, on the Accordion, at the next ensuing concert of the Philharmonic Society ; on which occasion the before-mentioned testimonials will be conspicuously displayed in the front of the orchestra.

8. MR. HOME'S MIRACULOUS INFANT

'On the 26th April, old style, or 8th May, according to our style, at seven in the evening, and as the snow was fast falling, our little boy was born at the town house, situate on the Gagarines Quay, in St. Petersburg, where we were still staying. A few hours after his birth, his mother, the nurse, and I heard for several hours the warbling of a bird as if singing over him. Also that night, and for two or three nights afterwards, a bright starlike light, which was clearly visible from the partial darkness of the room, in which there was only a night-lamp burning, appeared several times directly over its head, where it remained for some moments, and then slowly moved in the direction of the door, where it disappeared. This was also seen by each of us at the same time. The light was more condensed than those which have been so often seen in my presence upon previous and subsequent occasions. It was brighter and more distinctly globular. I do not believe that it came through my mediumship, but rather through that of the child, who has manifested on several occasions the presence of the gift. I do not like to allude to such a matter, but as there are more strange things in Heaven and earth than are dreamt of, even in my philosophy, I do not feel myself at liberty to omit stating, that during the latter part of my wife's pregnancy, we thought it better that she should not join in Séances, because it was found that whenever the rappings occurred in the room, a simultaneous movement of the child was distinctly felt, perfectly in unison with the sounds. When there were three sounds, three movements were felt, and so on, and when five sounds were heard, which is generally the call for the alphabet, she felt the five internal movements, and she would frequently, when we were mistaken in the latter, correct us from what the child indicated.'

We should ask pardon of our readers for sullying our paper with this nauseous matter, if without it they could adequately understand what Mr. Home's book is.

9. CAGLIOSTRO'S SPIRIT CALLS ON MR. HOME

Prudently avoiding the disagreeable question of his giving himself, both in this state of existence and in his spiritual circle, a name to which he never had any pretensions whatever, and likewise prudently suppressing any reference to his amiable weaknesses as a swindler and an infamous trafficker in his own wife, the guileless Mr. Balsamo delivered, in a 'distinct voice,' this distinct celestial utterance—unquestionably punctuated in a supernatural manner: ' My power was that of a mesmerist, but all-misunderstood by those about me, my biographers have even done me injustice, but I care not for the untruths of earth.'

10. ORACULAR STATE OF MR. HOME

' After various manifestations, Mr. Home went into the trance, and addressing a person present, said, "You ask what good are such trivial manifestations, such as rapping, table-moving, etc.? God is a better judge than we are what is fitted for humanity, immense results may spring from trivial things. The steam from a kettle is a small thing, but look at the locomotive! The electric spark from the back of a cat is a small thing, but see the wonders of electricity! The raps are small things, but their results will

THE MARTYR MEDIUM

lead you to the Spirit-World, and to eternity! Why should great results spring from such small causes? Christ was born in a manger, he was not born a King. When you tell me why he was born in a manger, I will tell you why these manifestations, so trivial, so undignified as they appear to you, have been appointed to convince the world of the truth of spiritualism."'

Wonderful! Clearly direct Inspiration!—And yet, perhaps, hardly worth the trouble of going 'into the trance' for, either. Amazing as the revelation is, we seem to have heard something like it from more than one personage who was wide awake. A quack doctor, in an open barouche (attended by a barrel-organ and two footmen in brass helmets), delivered just such another address within our hearing, outside a gate of Paris, not two months ago.

11. THE TESTIMONY OF MR. HOME'S BOOTS

'The lady of the house turned to me and said abruptly, "Why, you are sitting in the air"; and on looking, we found that the chair remained in its place, but that I was elevated two or three inches above it, and my feet not touching the floor. This may show how utterly unconscious I am at times to the sensation of levitation. As is usual, when I had not got above the level of the heads of those about me, and when they change their position much—as they frequently do in looking wistfully at such a phenomenon—I came down again, but not till I had remained so raised about half a minute from the time of its being first seen. I was now impressed to leave the table, and was soon carried to the lofty ceiling. The Count de B—— left his place at the table, and coming under where I was, said, "Now, young Home, come and let me touch your feet." I told him I had no volition in the matter, but perhaps the spirits would kindly allow me to come down to him. They did so, by floating me down to him, and my feet were soon in his outstretched hands. He seized my boots, and now I was again elevated, he holding tightly, and pulling at my feet, till the boots I wore, which had elastic sides, came off and remained in his hands.'

12. THE UNCOMBATIVE NATURE OF MR. HOME

As there is a maudlin complaint in this book, about men of Science being hard upon 'the "Orphan" Home,' and as the 'gentle and uncombative nature' of this Medium in a martyred point of

237

view is pathetically commented on by the anonymous literary friend who supplies him with an introduction and appendix—rather at odds with Mr. Howitt, who is so mightily triumphant about the same Martyr's reception by crowned heads, and about the competence he has become endowed with—we cull from Mr. Home's book one or two little illustrative flowers. Sir David Brewster (a pestilent unbeliever) ' has come before the public in few matters which have brought more shame upon him than his conduct and assertions on this occasion, in which he manifested not only a disregard for truth, but also a disloyalty to scientific observation, and to the use of his own eyesight and natural faculties.' The same unhappy Sir David Brewster's ' character may be the better known, not only for his untruthful dealing with this subject, but also in his own domain of science in which the same unfaithfulness to truth will be seen to be the characteristic of his mind.' Again, he ' is really not a man over whom victory is any honour.' Again, ' not only he, but Professor Faraday have had time and ample leisure to regret that they should have so foolishly pledged themselves,' etc. A Faraday a fool in the sight of a Home! That unjust judge and whited wall, Lord Brougham, has his share of this Martyr Medium's uncombativeness. ' In order that he might not be compelled to deny Sir David's statements, he found it necessary that he should be silent, and I have some reason to complain that his Lordship preferred sacrificing me to his desire not to immolate his friend.' M. Arago also came off with very doubtful honours from a wrestle with the uncombative Martyr; who is perfectly clear (and so are we, let us add) that scientific men are not the men for his purpose. Of course, he is the butt of ' utter and acknowledged ignorance,' and of ' the most gross and foolish statements,' and of ' the unjust and dishonest,' and of ' the press-gang,' and of crowds of other alien and combative adjectives, participles, and substantives.

Nothing is without its use, and even this odious book may do some service. Not because it coolly claims for the writer and his disciples such powers as were wielded by the Saviour and the Apostles; not because it sees no difference between twelve table rappers in these days, and ' twelve fishermen ' in those; not because it appeals for precedents to statements extracted from the most ignorant and wretched of mankind, by cruel torture, and constantly withdrawn when the torture was withdrawn; not because it sets forth such a strange confusion of ideas as is presented by one of the faithful when, writing of a certain sprig of geranium handed by an invisible hand, he adds in ecstasies, '*which we have planted and it is growing, so that it is no delusion, no fairy money turned into dross or leaves*'—as if it followed that the conjuror's half-crowns really did become invisible and in that state fly, because he afterwards cuts them out of a real orange; or as if the conjuror's pigeon, being after the discharge of his gun, a real live pigeon fluttering on the target, must therefore conclusively be a pigeon, fired, whole, living and unshattered, out of the gun!—not because of the exposure of any of these weaknesses, or a thousand such, are these moving incidents in the life of the Martyr Medium, and similar productions, likely to prove useful, but because of their uniform abuse of those who go to test the reality of these alleged phenomena, and who come away incredulous. There is an old homely proverb concerning pitch and its adhesive character, which we hope this significant circumstance may impress on many minds. The writer of these lines has lately heard overmuch touching young men of promise in the imaginative arts, 'towards whom' Martyr Mediums assisting at evening parties feel themselves 'drawn.' It may be a hint to such young men to stick to their own drawing, as being of a much better kind, and to leave Martyr Mediums alone in their glory.

As there is a good deal in these books about 'lying spirits,' we will conclude by putting a hypothetical case. Supposing that a Medium (Martyr or otherwise) were established for a time in the house of an English gentleman abroad; say, somewhere in Italy. Supposing that the more marvellous the Medium became, the more suspicious of him the lady of the house became. Supposing that the lady, her distrust once aroused, were particularly struck by the Medium's exhibiting a persistent desire to commit her, somehow or other, to the disclosure of the manner of the death, to him unknown, of a certain person. Supposing that she at length resolved to test the Medium on this head, and, therefore, on a certain evening mentioned a wholly supposititious manner of death (which was not the real manner of death, nor anything at all like it) within the range of his listening ears. And supposing that a spirit presently afterwards rapped out its presence, claiming to be the spirit of that deceased person, and claiming to have departed this life in that

MISCELLANEOUS PAPERS

supposititious way. Would *that* be a lying spirit? Or would it be a something else, tainting all that Medium's statements and suppressions, even if they were not in themselves of a manifestly outrageous character?

THE LATE MR. STANFIELD

[JUNE 1, 1867]

EVERY Artist, be he writer, painter, musician, or actor, must bear his private sorrows as he best can, and must separate them from the exercise of his public pursuit. But it sometimes happens, in compensation, that his private loss of a dear friend represents a loss on the part of the whole community. Then he may, without obtrusion of his individuality, step forth to lay his little wreath upon that dear friend's grave.

On Saturday, the eighteenth of this present month, Clarkson Stanfield died. On the afternoon of that day, England lost the great marine painter of whom she will be boastful ages hence; the National Historian of her speciality, the Sea; the man famous in all countries for his marvellous rendering of the waves that break upon her shores, of her ships and seamen, of her coasts and skies, of her storms and sunshine, of the many marvels of the deep. He who holds the oceans in the hollow of His hand had given, associated with them, wonderful gifts into his keeping; he had used them well through threescore and fourteen years; and, on the afternoon of that spring day, relinquished them for ever.

It is superfluous to record that the painter of 'The Battle of Trafalgar,' of the '*Victory* being towed into Gibraltar with the body of Nelson on Board,' of 'The Morning after the Wreck,' of 'The Abandoned,' of fifty more such works, died in his seventy-fourth year, 'Mr.' Stanfield.—He was an Englishman.

Those grand pictures will proclaim his powers while paint and canvas last. But the writer of these words had been his friend for thirty years; and when, a short week or two before his death, he laid that once so skilful hand upon the writer's breast and told him they would meet again, 'but not here,' the thoughts of the latter turned, for the time, so little to his noble genius, and so much to his noble nature!

240

THE LATE MR. STANFIELD

He was the soul of frankness, generosity, and simplicity. The most genial, the most affectionate, the most loving, and the most lovable of men. Success had never for an instant spoiled him. His interest in the Theatre as an Institution—the best picturesqueness of which may be said to be wholly due to him—was faithful to the last. His belief in a Play, his delight in one, the ease with which it moved him to tears or to laughter, were most remarkable evidences of the heart he must have put into his old theatrical work, and of the thorough purpose and sincerity with which it must have been done. The writer was very intimately associated with him in some amateur plays ; and day after day, and night after night, there were the same unquenchable freshness, enthusiasm, and impressibility in him, though broken in health, even then.

No Artist can ever have stood by his art with a quieter dignity than he always did. Nothing would have induced him to lay it at the feet of any human creature. To fawn, or to toady, or to do undeserved homage to any one, was an absolute impossibility with him. And yet his character was so nicely balanced that he was the last man in the world to be suspected of self-assertion, and his modesty was one of his most special qualities.

He was a charitable, religious, gentle, truly good man. A genuine man, incapable of pretence or of concealment. He had been a sailor once ; and all the best characteristics that are popularly attributed to sailors, being his, and being in him refined by the influences of his Art, formed a whole not likely to be often seen. There is no smile that the writer can recall, like his ; no manner so naturally confiding and so cheerfully engaging. When the writer saw him for the last time on earth, the smile and the manner shone out once through the weakness, still : the bright unchanging Soul within the altered face and form.

No man was ever held in higher respect by his friends, and yet his intimate friends invariably addressed him and spoke of him by a pet name. It may need, perhaps, the writer's memory and associations to find in this a touching expression of his winning character, his playful smile, and pleasant ways. 'You know Mrs. Inchbald's story, Nature and Art?' wrote Thomas Hood, once, in a letter : 'What a fine Edition of Nature and Art is Stanfield !'

Gone ! And many and many a dear old day gone with him !

241

But their memories remain. And his memory will not soon fade out, for he has set his mark upon the restless waters, and his fame will long be sounded in the roar of the sea.

A SLIGHT QUESTION OF FACT

[FEBRUARY 13, 1869]

IT is never well for the public interest that the originator of any social reform should be soon forgotten. Further, it is neither wholesome nor right (being neither generous nor just) that the merit of his work should be gradually transferred elsewhere.

Some few weeks ago, our contemporary, the *Pall Mall Gazette*, in certain strictures on our Theatres which we are very far indeed from challenging, remarked on the first effectual discouragement of an outrage upon decency which the lobbies and upper-boxes of even our best Theatres habitually paraded within the last twenty or thirty years. From those remarks it might appear as though no such Manager of Covent Garden or Drury Lane as Mr. Macready had ever existed.

It is a fact beyond all possibility of question, that Mr. Macready, on assuming the management of Covent Garden Theatre in 1837, did instantly set himself, regardless of precedent and custom down to that hour obtaining, rigidly to suppress this shameful thing, and did rigidly suppress and crush it during his whole management of that theatre, and during his whole subsequent management of Drury Lane. That he did so, as certainly without favour as without fear; that he did so, against his own immediate interests; that he did so, against vexations and oppositions which might have cooled the ardour of a less earnest man, or a less devoted artist; can be better known to no one than the writer of the present words, whose name stands at the head of these pages.

LANDOR'S LIFE

[JULY 24, 1869]

PREFIXED to the second volume of Mr. Forster's admirable biography of Walter Savage Landor,[1] is an engraving from a portrait of that remarkable man when seventy-seven years of age, by Boxall. The writer of these lines can testify that the original picture is a singularly good likeness, the result of close and subtle observation on the part of the painter; but, for this very reason, the engraving gives a most inadequate idea of the merit of the picture and the character of the man.

From the engraving, the arms and hands are omitted. In the picture, they are, as they were in nature, indispensable to a correct reading of the vigorous face. The arms were very peculiar. They were rather short, and were curiously restrained and checked in their action at the elbows; in the action of the hands, even when separately clenched, there was the same kind of pause, and a noticeable tendency to relaxation on the part of the thumb. Let the face be never so intense or fierce, there was a commentary of gentleness in the hands, essential to be taken along with it. Like Hamlet, Landor would speak daggers but use none. In the expression of his hands, though angrily closed, there was always gentleness and tenderness; just as when they were open, and the handsome old gentleman would wave them with a little courtly flourish that sat well upon him, as he recalled some classic compliment that he had rendered to some reigning Beauty, there was a chivalrous grace about them such as pervades his softer verses. Thus, the fictitious Mr. Boythorn (to whom we may refer without impropriety in this connexion, as Mr. Forster does) declaims ' with unimaginable energy ' the while his bird is ' perched upon his thumb,' and he ' softly smooths its feathers with his forefinger.'

From the spirit of Mr. Forster's Biography these characteristic hands are never omitted, and hence (apart from its literary merits) its great value. As the same masterly writer's *Life and Times of Oliver Goldsmith* is a generous and yet conscientious picture of a

[1] *Walter Savage Landor*: a Biography, by John Forster, 2 vols. Chapman and Hall.

period, so this is a not less generous and yet conscientious picture of one life; of a life, with all its aspirations, achievements, and disappointments; all its capabilities, opportunities, and irretrievable mistakes. It is essentially a sad book, and herein lies proof of its truth and worth. The life of almost any man possessing great gifts, would be a sad book to himself; and this book enables us not only to see its subject, but to be its subject, if we will.

Mr. Forster is of opinion that 'Landor's fame very surely awaits him.' This point admitted or doubted, the value of the book remains the same. It needs not to know his works (otherwise than through his biographer's exposition), it needs not to have known himself, to find a deep interest in these pages. More or less of their warning is in every conscience; and some admiration of a fine genius, and of a great, wild, generous nature, incapable of mean self-extenuation or dissimulation—if unhappily incapable of self-repression too—should be in every breast. 'There may be still living many persons,' Walter Landor's brother, Robert, writes to Mr. Forster of this book, 'who would contradict any narrative of yours in which the best qualities were remembered, the worst forgotten.' Mr. Forster's comment is: 'I had not waited for this appeal to resolve, that, if this memoir were written at all, it should contain, as far as might lie within my power, a fair statement of the truth.' And this eloquent passage of truth immediately follows: 'Few of his infirmities are without something kindly or generous about them; and we are not long in discovering there is nothing so wildly incredible that he will not himself in perfect good faith believe. When he published his first book of poems on quitting Oxford, the profits were to be reserved for a distressed clergyman. When he published his Latin poems, the poor of Leipzig were to have the sum they realised. When his comedy was ready to be acted, a Spaniard who had sheltered him at Castro was to be made richer by it. When he competed for the prize of the Academy of Stockholm, it was to go to the poor of Sweden. If nobody got anything from any one of these enterprises, the fault at all events was not his. With his extraordinary power of forgetting disappointments, he was prepared at each successive failure to start afresh, as if each had been a triumph. I shall have to delineate this peculiarity as strongly in the last half as in the first half of his life, and it was certainly an amiable one. He was ready at all times to set aside, out of his own possessions, something for somebody who might please him for the time; and when frailties of temper and tongue are noted, this other eccentricity should not be omitted. He desired eagerly the love as well as the good opinion of those whom for the time he esteemed, and no one was more affectionate while under such influences. It is not a small virtue to feel such genuine pleasure, as he always did in giving and receiving pleasure. His generosity, too, was bestowed chiefly on those who could make small acknowledgment in thanks and no return in kind.'

Some of his earlier contemporaries may have thought him a vain man. Most assuredly he was not, in the common acceptation of the term. A vain man has little or no admiration to bestow upon competitors. Landor had an inexhaustible fund. He thought well of his writings, or he would not have preserved them. He said and wrote that he thought well of them, because that was his mind about them, and he said and wrote his mind. He was one of the few men of whom you might always know the whole: of whom you might always know the worst, as well as the best. He had no reservations or duplicities. ' No, by Heaven ! ' he would say (' with unimaginable energy '), if any good adjective were coupled with him which he did not deserve: 'I am nothing of the kind. I wish I were ; but I don't deserve the attribute, and I never did, and I never shall ! ' His intense consciousness of himself never led to his poorly excusing himself, and seldom to his violently asserting himself. When he told some little story of his bygone social experiences, in Florence, or where not, as he was fond of doing, it took the innocent form of making all the interlocutors, Landors. It was observable, too, that they always called him ' Mr. Landor '—rather ceremoniously and submissively. There was a certain ' Caro Pádre Abáte Marina '—invariably so addressed in these anecdotes—who figured through a great many of them, and who always expressed himself in this deferential tone.

Mr. Forster writes of Landor's character thus :

' A man must be judged, at first, by what he says and does. But with him such extravagance as I have referred to was little more than the habitual indulgence (on such themes) of passionate feelings and language, indecent indeed but utterly purposeless ; the mere explosion of wrath provoked by tyranny or cruelty ; the irregularities of an overheated steam-engine too weak for its own vapour. It is very certain that no one could detest oppression more truly than Landor did in all seasons and times; and if no one expressed that scorn, that abhorrence of tyranny and fraud, more hastily or more intemperately, all his fire and fury signified really little else than ill-temper too easily provoked. Not to justify or excuse such language, but to explain it, this consideration is urged. If not uniformly placable, Landor was always compassionate. He was tender-hearted rather than bloody-minded at all times, and upon only the most partial acquaintance with his writings could other opinion be formed. A completer knowledge of them would satisfy any one that he had as little real disposition to kill a king as to kill a mouse. In fact there is not a more marked peculiarity in his genius than the union with its strength of a most uncommon gentleness, and in the personal ways of the man this was equally manifest.'—Vol. i. p. 496.

Of his works, thus :

' Though his mind was cast in the antique mould, it had opened itself to every kind of impression through a long and varied life; he has written with equal excellence in both poetry and prose, which can hardly be said of any of his contemporaries; and perhaps the single epithet by which his books would be best described is that reserved exclusively for books not characterised only by genius, but also by special individuality. They are unique. Having possessed them, we should miss them. Their place would be supplied by no others. They have that about them, moreover, which renders it almost certain that they will frequently be resorted to in future time. There are none in the language more quotable. Even where impulsiveness and want of patience have left them most fragmentary, this rich compensation is offered to the reader. There is hardly a conceivable subject, in life or literature, which they do not illustrate by striking aphorisms, by concise and profound observations, by wisdom ever applicable to the needs of men, and by wit as available for their enjoyment. Nor, above all, will there anywhere be found a more pervading passion for liberty, a fiercer hatred of the base, a wider sympathy with the wronged and the oppressed, or help more ready at all times for those who fight at odds and disadvantage against the powerful and the fortunate, than in the writings of Walter Savage Landor.'—*Last page of second volume.*

The impression was strong upon the present writer's mind, as on

LANDOR'S LIFE

Mr. Forster's, during years of close friendship with the subject of this biography, that his animosities were chiefly referable to the singular inability in him to dissociate other people's ways of thinking from his own. He had, to the last, a ludicrous grievance (both Mr. Forster and the writer have often amused themselves with it), against a good-natured nobleman, doubtless perfectly unconscious of having ever given him offence. The offence was, that on the occasion of some dinner party in another nobleman's house, many years before, this innocent lord (then a commoner) had passed in to dinner, through some door, before him, as he himself was about to pass in through that same door with a lady on his arm. Now, Landor was a gentleman of most scrupulous politeness, and in his carriage of himself towards ladies there was a certain mixture of stateliness and deference, belonging to quite another time, and, as Mr. Pepys would observe, ' mighty pretty to see.' If he could by any effort imagine himself committing such a high crime and misdemeanour as that in question, he could only imagine himself as doing it of a set purpose, under the sting of some vast injury, to inflict a great affront. A deliberately designed affront on the part of another man, it therefore remained to the end of his days. The manner in which, as time went on, he permeated the unfortunate lord's ancestry with this offence, was whimsically characteristic of Landor. The writer remembers very well, when only the individual himself was held responsible in the story for the breach of good breeding ; but in another ten years or so, it began to appear that his father had always been remarkable for ill manners ; and in yet another ten years or so, his grandfather developed into quite a prodigy of coarse behaviour.

Mr. Boythorn—if he may again be quoted—said of his adversary, Sir Leicester Dedlock : ' That fellow is, *and his father was, and his grandfather was,* the most stiff-necked, arrogant, imbecile, pig-headed numskull, ever, by some inexplicable mistake of Nature, born in any station of life but a walking-stick's ! '

The strength of some of Mr. Landor's most captivating kind qualities was traceable to the same source. Knowing how keenly he himself would feel the being at any small social disadvantage, or the being unconsciously placed in any ridiculous light, he was wonderfully considerate of shy people, or of such as might be below the level of his usual conversation, or otherwise out of their element. The writer once observed him in the keenest distress of mind in behalf of a modest young stranger who came into a drawing-room with a glove on his head. An expressive commentary on this sympathetic condition, and on the delicacy with which he advanced to the young stranger's rescue, was afterwards furnished by himself at a friendly dinner at Gore House, when it was the most delightful of houses. His dress—say, his cravat or shirt-collar—had become slightly disarranged on a hot evening, and Count D'Orsay laughingly called his attention to the circumstance as we rose from table. Landor became flushed, and greatly agitated : ' My dear Count D'Orsay, I thank you ! My dear Count D'Orsay, I thank you from my soul for pointing out to me the abominable condition to which I am reduced ! If I had entered the Drawing-room, and presented myself before Lady Blessington in so absurd a light, I would have instantly gone home, put a pistol to my head, and blown my brains out ! '

Mr. Forster tells a similar story of his keeping a company waiting dinner, through losing his way; and of his seeing no remedy for that breach of politeness but cutting his throat, or drowning himself, unless a countryman whom he met could direct him by a short road to the house where the party were assembled. Surely these are expressive notes on the gravity and reality of his explosive inclinations to kill kings !

His manner towards boys was charming, and the earnestness of his wish to be on equal terms with them and to win their confidence was quite touching. Few, reading Mr. Forster's book, can fail to see in this, his pensive remembrance of that ' studious wilful boy at once shy and impetuous,' who had not many intimacies at Rugby, but who was ' generally popular and respected, and used his influence often to save the younger boys from undue harshness or violence.' The impulsive yearnings of his passionate heart towards his own boy, on their meeting at Bath, after years of separation, likewise burn through this phase of his character.

But a more spiritual, softened, and unselfish aspect of it, was to be derived from his respectful belief in happiness which he himself had missed. His marriage had not been a felicitous one—it may be fairly assumed for either side—but no trace of bitterness or distrust concerning other marriages was in his mind. He was never more serene than in the midst of a domestic circle, and was invariably

248

remarkable for a perfectly benignant interest in young couples and young lovers. That, in his ever-fresh fancy, he conceived in this association innumerable histories of himself involving far more unlikely events that never happened than Isaac D'Israeli ever imagined, is hardly to be doubted ; but as to this part of his real history he was mute, or revealed his nobleness in an impulse to be generously just. We verge on delicate ground, but a slight remembrance rises in the writer which can grate nowhere. Mr. Forster relates how a certain friend, being in Florence, sent him home a leaf from the garden of his old house at Fiesole. That friend had first asked him what he should send him home, and he had stipulated for this gift— found by Mr. Forster among his papers after his death. The friend, on coming back to England, related to Landor that he had been much embarrassed, on going in search of the leaf, by his driver's suddenly stopping his horses in a narrow lane, and presenting him (the friend) to ' La Signora Landora.' The lady was walking alone on a bright Italian-winter-day ; and the man, having been told to drive to the Villa Landora, inferred that he must be conveying a guest or visitor. ' I pulled off my hat,' said the friend, ' apologised for the coachman's mistake, and drove on. The lady was walking with a rapid and firm step, had bright eyes, a fine fresh colour, and looked animated and agreeable.' Landor checked off each clause of the description, with a stately nod of more than ready assent, and replied, with all his tremendous energy concentrated into the sentence : ' And the Lord forbid that I should do otherwise than declare that she always WAS agreeable—to every one but *me* !'

Mr. Forster step by step builds up the evidence on which he writes this life and states this character. In like manner, he gives the evidence for his high estimation of Landor's works, and—it may be added—for their recompense against some neglect, in finding so sympathetic, acute, and devoted a champion. Nothing in the book is more remarkable than his examination of each of Landor's successive pieces of writing, his delicate discernment of their beauties, and his strong desire to impart his own perceptions in this wise to the great audience that is yet to come. It rarely befalls an author to have such a commentator : to become the subject of so much artistic skill and knowledge, combined with such infinite and loving pains. Alike as a piece of Biography, and as a commentary upon the beauties of a great writer, the book is a massive book ; as the man and the writer were massive too. Sometimes, when the balance held by Mr. Forster has seemed for a moment to turn a little heavily against the infirmities of temperament of a grand old friend, we have felt something of a shock; but we have not once been able to gainsay the justice of the scales. This feeling, too, has only fluttered out of the detail, here or there, and has vanished before the whole. We fully agree with Mr. Forster that 'Judgment has been passed'—as it should be—'with an equal desire to be only just on all the qualities of his temperament which affected necessarily not his own life only. But, now that the story is told, no one will have difficulty in striking the balance between its good and ill; and what was really imperishable in Landor's genius will not be treasured less, or less understood, for the more perfect knowledge of his character.'

Mr. Forster's second volume gives a facsimile of Landor's writing at seventy-five. It may be interesting to those who are curious in caligraphy, to know that its resemblance to the recent handwriting of that great genius, M. Victor Hugo, is singularly strong.

In a military burial-ground in India, the name of Walter Landor is associated with the present writer's, over the grave of a young officer. No name could stand there, more inseparably associated in the writer's mind with the dignity of generosity: with a noble scorn of all littleness, all cruelty, oppression, fraud, and false pretence.

PLAYS

THE STRANGE GENTLEMAN
A COMIC BURLETTA
IN TWO ACTS
[1836]

CAST OF THE CHARACTERS

At St. James's Theatre, September 29, 1836

Mr. Owen Overton (*Mayor of a small town on the road to Gretna, and useful at the St. James's Arms*) . Mr. Hollingsworth.

John Johnson (*detained at the St. James's Arms*) . Mr. Sidney.

The Strange Gentleman (*just arrived at the St. James's Arms*) . . . . . . Mr. Harley.

Charles Tomkins (*incognito at the St. James's Arms*) Mr. Forester.

Tom Sparks (*a one-eyed 'Boots' at the St. James's Arms*) Mr. Gardner.

John ⎫
Tom ⎬ *Waiters at the St. James's Arms*
Will ⎭

Mr. Williamson.
Mr. May.
Mr. Coulson.

Julia Dobbs (*looking for a husband at the St. James's Arms*) . . . . . . Madame Sala.

Fanny Wilson (*with an appointment at the St. James's Arms*) . . . . . . Miss Smith.

Mary Wilson (*her sister, awkwardly situated at the St. James's Arms*) . . . . Miss Julia Smith.

Mrs. Noakes (*the Landlady at the St. James's Arms*) . Mrs. W. Penson.

Chambermaid (*at the St. James's Arms*) . . . Miss Stuart.

Miss Smith and Miss Julia Smith will sing the duet of
'*I know a Bank,*' *in* '*The Strange Gentleman.*'

COSTUME

Mr. Owen Overton.—*Black smalls, and high black boots. A blue body coat, rather long in the waist, with yellow buttons, buttoned close up to the chin. A white stock; ditto gloves. A broad-brimmed low-crowned white hat.*

Strange Gentleman.—*A light blue plaid French-cut trousers and vest. A brown cloth frock coat, with full skirts, scarcely covering the hips. A light blue kerchief, and eccentric low-crowned broad-brimmed white hat. Boots.*

John Johnson.—*White fashionable trousers, boots, light vest, frock coat, black hat, gloves, etc.*

Charles Tomkins.—*Shepherd's plaid French-cut trousers; boots; mohair fashionable frock coat, buttoned up; black hat, gloves, etc.*

Tom Sparks.—*Leather smalls, striped stockings, and lace-up half boots, red vest, and a Holland stable jacket; coloured kerchief, and red wig.*

The Waiters.—*All in black trousers, black stockings and shoes, white vests, striped jackets, and white kerchiefs.*

Mary Wilson.—*Fashionable walking dress, white silk stockings; shoes and gloves.*

Fanny Wilson.—*Precisely the same as Mary.*

Julia Dobbs.—*A handsome white travelling dress, cashmere shawl, white silk stockings; shoes and gloves. A bonnet to correspond.*

Mrs. Noakes.—*A chintz gown, rather of a dark pattern, French apron, and handsome cap.*

SCENE.—A SMALL TOWN, ON THE ROAD TO GRETNA.
TIME.—PART OF A DAY AND NIGHT.
Time in acting.—One hour and twenty minutes.

254

THE STRANGE GENTLEMAN

ACT I

SCENE I.—*A Room at the St. James's Arms; Door in Centre, with a Bolt on it. A Table with Cover, and two Chairs,* R. H.

Enter MRS. NOAKES, C. DOOR.

MRS. NOAKES. Bless us, what a coachful! Four inside—twelve out; and the guard blowing the key-bugle in the fore-boot, for fear the informers should see that they have got one over the number. Post-chaise and a gig besides.—We shall be filled to the very attics. Now, look alive, there—bustle about.

Enter FIRST WAITER, *running,* C. DOOR.

Now, John.

FIRST WAITER (*coming down* L. H.). Single lady, inside the stage, wants a private room, ma'am.

MRS. NOAKES (R. H.). Much luggage?

FIRST WAITER. Four trunks, two bonnet-boxes, six brown-paper parcels, and a basket.

MRS. NOAKES. Give her a private room, directly. No. 1, on the first floor.

FIRST WAITER. Yes, ma'am. [*Exit* FIRST WAITER, *running,* C. DOOR.

Enter SECOND WAITER, *running,* C. DOOR.

Now, Tom.

SECOND WAITER (*coming down* R. H.). Two young ladies and one gentleman, in a post-chaise, want a private sitting-room d'rectly, ma'am.

MRS. NOAKES. Brother and sisters, Tom?

SECOND WAITER. Ladies are something alike, ma'am. Gentleman like neither of 'em.

MRS. NOAKES. Husband and wife and wife's sister, perhaps. Eh, Tom?

SECOND WAITER. Can't be husband and wife, ma'am, because I saw the gentleman kiss one of the ladies.

MRS. NOAKES. Kissing one of the ladies! Put them in the small sitting-room behind the bar, Tom, that I may have an eye on

255

them through the little window, and see that nothing improper goes forward.

SECOND WAITER. Yes, ma'am. (*Going.*)

MRS. NOAKES. And Tom! (*Crossing to* L. H.)

SECOND WAITER (*coming down* R. H.). Yes, ma'am.

MRS. NOAKES. Tell Cook to put together all the bones and pieces that were left on the plates at the great dinner yesterday, and make some nice soup to feed the stage-coach passengers with.

SECOND WAITER. Very well, ma'am. [*Exit* SECOND WAITER, C. DOOR.

Enter THIRD WAITER, *running*, C. DOOR.

Now, Will.

THIRD WAITER (*coming down* L. H.). A strange gentleman in a gig, ma'am, wants a private sitting-room.

MRS. NOAKES. Much luggage, Will?

THIRD WAITER. One portmanteau, and a great-coat.

MRS. NOAKES. Oh! nonsense!—Tell him to go into the commercial room.

THIRD WAITER. I told him so, ma'am, but the Strange Gentleman says he *will* have a private apartment, and that it's as much as his life is worth, to sit in a public room.

MRS. NOAKES. As much as his life is worth?

THIRD WAITER. Yes, ma'am.—Gentleman says he doesn't care if it's a dark closet; but a private room of some kind he must and will have.

MRS. NOAKES. Very odd.—Did you ever see him before, Will?

THIRD WAITER. No, ma'am; he's quite a stranger here.—He's a wonderful man to talk, ma'am—keeps on like a steam engine. Here he is, ma'am.

STRANGE GENTLEMAN (*without*). Now don't tell me, because that's all gammon and nonsense; and gammoned I never was, and never will be, by any waiter that ever drew the breath of life, or a cork.— And just have the goodness to leave my portmanteau alone, because I can carry it very well myself; and show me a private room without further delay; for a private room I must and will have.—Damme, do you think I'm going to be murdered!—

Enter the three Waiters, C. DOOR—*they form down* L. H., *the* STRANGE GENTLEMAN *following, carrying his portmanteau and great-coat.*

There—this room will do capitally well. Quite the thing,—just the fit.—How are you, ma'am? I suppose you are the landlady of this place? Just order those very attentive young fellows out, will you, and I'll order dinner.

Mrs. Noakes (*to Waiters*). You may leave the room.

Strange Gentleman. Hear that?—You may leave the room. Make yourselves scarce. Evaporate—disappear—come.

[*Exeunt Waiters*, c. door.

That's right. And now, madam, while we're talking over this important matter of dinner, I'll just secure us effectually against further intrusion. (*Bolts the door.*)

Mrs. Noakes. Lor, sir! Bolting the door, and *me* in the room!

Strange Gentleman. Don't be afraid—I won't hurt you. I have no designs against you, my dear ma'am : but *I must be private*. (*Sits on the portmanteau,* r. h.)

Mrs. Noakes. Well, sir—I have no objection to break through our rules for once; but it is not our way, when we're full, to give private rooms to solitary gentlemen, who come in a gig, and bring only one portmanteau. You're quite a stranger *here*, sir. If I'm not mistaken, it's your first appearance in this house.

Strange Gentleman. You're right, ma'am. It *is* my first, my very first—but not my last, I can tell you.

Mrs. Noakes. No?

Strange Gentleman. No (*looking round him*). I like the look of this place. Snug and comfortable—neat and lively. You'll very often find me at the St. James's Arms, I can tell you, ma'am.

Mrs. Noakes (*aside*). A civil gentleman. Are you a stranger in this town, sir?

Strange Gentleman. Stranger! Bless you, no. I have been here for many years past, in the season.

Mrs. Noakes. Indeed!

Strange Gentleman. Oh, yes. Put up at the Royal Hotel regularly for a long time , but I was obliged to leave it at last.

Mrs. Noakes. I have heard a good many complaints of it.

Strange Gentleman. O! terrible! such a noisy house.

Mrs. Noakes. Ah!

Strange Gentleman. Shocking! Din, din, din—Drum, drum, drum, all night. Nothing but noise, glare, and nonsense. I bore it a long time for old acquaintance sake; but what do you think they did at last, ma'am?

257

Mrs. Noakes. I can't guess.

Strange Gentleman. Turned the fine Old Assembly Room into a stable, and took to keeping horses. I tried that too, but I found I couldn't stand it; so I came away, ma'am, and—and—here I am. (*Rises.*)

Mrs. Noakes. And I'll be bound to say, sir, that you will have no cause to complain of the exchange.

Strange Gentleman. I'm sure not, ma'am; I know it—I feel it, already.

Mrs. Noakes. About dinner, sir; what would you like to take?

Strange Gentleman. Let me see; will you be good enough to suggest something, ma'am?

Mrs. Noakes. Why, a broiled fowl and mushrooms is a very nice dish.

Strange Gentleman. You are right, ma'am; a broiled fowl and mushrooms form a very delightful and harmless amusement, either for one or two persons. Broiled fowl and mushrooms let it be, ma'am.

Mrs. Noakes. In about an hour, I suppose, sir?

Strange Gentleman. For the second time, ma'am, you have anticipated my feelings.

Mrs. Noakes. You'll want a bed to-night, I suppose, sir; perhaps you'd like to see it? Step this way, sir, and—(*going* L. H.).

Strange Gentleman. No, no, never mind. (*Aside.*) This is a plot to get me out of the room. She's bribed by somebody who wants to identify me. I must be careful; I am exposed to nothing but artifice and stratagem. Never mind, ma'am, never mind.

Mrs. Noakes. If you'll give me your portmanteau, sir, the Boots will carry it into the next room for you.

Strange Gentleman (*aside*). Here's diabolical ingenuity; she thinks it's got the name upon it. (*To her.*) I'm very much obliged to the Boots for his disinterested attention, ma'am, but with your kind permission this portmanteau will remain just exactly where it is; consequently, ma'am, (*with great warmth,*) if the aforesaid Boots wishes to succeed in removing this portmanteau, he must previously remove *me*, ma'am, *me*; and it will take a *pair* of very stout Boots to do that, ma'am, I promise you.

Mrs. Noakes. Dear me, sir, you needn't fear for your portmanteau in this house; I dare say nobody wants it.

Strange Gentleman. I hope not, ma'am, because in that case nobody

258

will be disappointed. (*Aside.*) How she fixes her old eyes on me!

MRS. NOAKES (*aside*). I never saw such an extraordinary person in all my life. What can he be? (*Looks at him very hard.*)

[*Exit* MRS. NOAKES, C. DOOR.

STRANGE GENTLEMAN. She's gone at last! Now let me commune with my own dreadful thoughts, and reflect on the best means of escaping from my horrible position. (*Takes a letter from his pocket.*) Here's an illegal death-warrant; a pressing invitation to be slaughtered; a polite request just to step out and be killed, thrust into my hand by some disguised assassin in a dirty black calico jacket, the very instant I got out of the gig at the door. I know the hand; there's a ferocious recklessness in the cross to this 'T,' and a baleful malignity in the dot of that 'I,' which warns me that it comes from my desperate rival. (*Opens it, and reads.*) 'Mr. Horatio Tinkles'—that's him—'presents his compliments to his enemy' —that's me—'and requests the pleasure of his company to-morrow morning, under the clump of trees, on Corpse Common,' —Corpse Common!—'to which any of the town's people will direct him, and where he hopes to have the satisfaction of giving him his gruel.'—Giving him his gruel! Ironical cut-throat!—'His punctuality will be esteemed a personal favour, as it will save Mr. Tinkles the trouble and inconvenience of calling with a horsewhip in his pocket. Mr. Tinkles has ordered breakfast at the Royal for *one*. It is paid for. The individual who returns alive can eat it. Pistols—half-past five—precisely.'—Bloodthirsty miscreant! *The* individual who returns alive! I have seen him hit the painted man at the shooting-gallery regularly every time in his centre shirt plait, except when he varied the entertainments, by lodging the ball playfully in his left eye. Breakfast! I shall want nothing beyond the gruel. What's to be done? Escape! I can't escape; concealment's of no use, he knows I am here. He has dodged me all the way from London, and will dodge me all the way to the residence of Miss Emily Brown, whom my respected, but swine-headed parents have picked out for my future wife. A pretty figure I should cut before the old people, whom I have never beheld more than once in my life, and Miss Emily Brown, whom I have never seen at all, if I went down there, pursued by this Sala-mander, who, I suppose, is her accepted lover! What is to be done? I can't go back again; father would be furious. What can be done? nothing! (*Sinks into a chair*.) I must undergo this fiery ordeal, and submit to be packed up, and carried back to my weeping parents, like an unfortunate buck, with a flat piece of lead in my head, and a brief epitaph on my breast, 'Killed on Wednesday morning.' No, I won't (*starting up, and walking about*). I won't submit to it; I'll accept the challenge, but first I'll write an anonymous letter to the local authorities, giving them information of this intended duel, and desiring them to place me under immediate restraint. That's feasible; on further consideration, it's capital. My character will be saved—I shall be bound over—he'll be bound over—I shall resume my journey—reach the house—marry the girl—pocket the fortune, and laugh at him. No time to be lost; it shall be done forthwith. (*Goes to table and writes*.) There; the challenge accepted, with a bold defiance, that'll look very brave when it comes to be printed. Now for the other. (*Writes*.) 'To the Mayor—Sir—A strange Gentleman at the St. James's Arms, whose name is unknown to the writer of this communication, is bent upon committing a rash and sanguinary act, at an early hour to-morrow morning. As you value human life, secure the amiable youth, without delay. Think, I implore you, sir, think what would be the feelings of those to whom he is nearest and dearest, if any mischance befall the interesting young man. Do not neglect this solemn warning; the number of his room is seventeen.' There—(*folding it up*). Now if I can find any one who will deliver it secretly.—

Tom Sparks, *with a pair of boots in his hand, peeps in at the* c. d.

Tom. Are these here your'n?

Strange Gentleman. No.

Tom. Oh! (*going back*).

Strange Gentleman. Hallo! stop, are you the Boots?

Tom (*still at the door*). I'm the head o' that branch o' the establishment. There's another man under me, as brushes the dirt off, and puts the blacking on. The fancy work's my department; I do the polishing, nothing else.

Strange Gentleman. You are the upper Boots, then?

Tom. Yes, I'm the reg'lar; t'other one's only the deputy; top boots and half boots, I calls us.

STRANGE GENTLEMAN. You 're a sharp fellow.

TOM. Ah! I 'd better cut then (*going*).

STRANGE GENTLEMAN. Don't hurry, Boots—don't hurry; I want you. (*Rises, and comes forward*, R. H.)

TOM (*coming forward*, L. H.). Well!

STRANGE GENTLEMAN. Can—can—you be secret, Boots?

TOM. That depends entirely on accompanying circumstances;—see the point?

STRANGE GENTLEMAN. I think I comprehend your meaning, Boots. You insinuate that you could be secret (*putting his hand in his pocket*) if you had—five shillings for instance—isn't that it, Boots?

TOM. That 's the line o' argument I should take up; but that an't exactly my meaning.

STRANGE GENTLEMAN. No!

TOM. No.   A secret 's a thing as is always a rising to one's lips.   It requires an astonishing weight to keep one on 'em down.

STRANGE GENTLEMAN. Ah!

TOM. Yes; I don't think I could keep one snug—reg'lar snug, you know——

STRANGE GENTLEMAN. Yes, regularly snug, of course.

TOM. —If it had a less weight a-top on it, than ten shillins.

STRANGE GENTLEMAN. You don't think three half-crowns would do it?

TOM. It might, I won't say it wouldn't, but I couldn't warrant it.

STRANGE GENTLEMAN. You could the other!

TOM. Yes.

STRANGE GENTLEMAN. Then there it is.   (*Gives him four half-crowns.*) You see these letters?

TOM. Yes, I can manage that without my spectacles.

STRANGE GENTLEMAN. Well; that 's to be left at the Royal Hotel. This, *this*, is an anonymous one; and I want it to be delivered at the Mayor's house, without his knowing from whom it came, or seeing who delivered it.

TOM (*taking the letters*). I say—you 're a rum 'un, you are.

STRANGE GENTLEMAN. Think so! Ha, ha! so are you.

TOM. Ay, but you 're a rummer one than me.

STRANGE GENTLEMAN. No, no, that 's your modesty.

TOM. No it an't.   I say, how vell you did them last hay-stacks. How do you contrive that ere now, if it 's a fair question.   Is it done with a pipe, or do you use them Lucifer boxes?

261

STRANGE GENTLEMAN. Pipe—Lucifer boxes—hay-stacks! Why, what do you mean?

TOM (*looking cautiously round*). I know your name, old 'un.

STRANGE GENTLEMAN. You know my name! (*Aside.*) Now how the devil has he got hold of that, I wonder!

TOM. Yes, I know it. It begins with a 'S.'

STRANGE GENTLEMAN. Begins with an S!

TOM. And ends with a 'G' (*winking*). We 've all heard talk of *Swing* down here.

STRANGE GENTLEMAN. Heard talk of Swing! Here 's a situation! Damme, d' ye think I 'm a walking carbois of vitriol, and burn everything I touch?—Will you go upon the errand you 're paid for?

TOM. Oh, I 'm going—I 'm going. It 's nothing to me, you know; I don't care. I 'll only just give these boots to the deputy, to take them to whoever they belong to, and then I 'll pitch this here letter in at the Mayor's office-window, in no time.

STRANGE GENTLEMAN. Will you be off?

TOM. Oh, I 'm going, I 'm going. Close, you knows, close!

[*Exit* TOM, C. DOOR.

STRANGE GENTLEMAN. In five minutes more the letter will be delivered; in another half hour, if the Mayor does his duty, I shall be in custody, and secure from the vengeance of this infuriated monster. I wonder whether they 'll take me away? Egad! I may as well be provided with a clean shirt and a night-cap in case. Let 's see, she said the next room was my bedroom, and as I have accepted the challenge, I may venture so far now. (*Shouldering the portmanteau.*) What a capital notion it is; there 'll be all the correspondence in large letters, in the county paper, and my name figuring away in roman capitals, with a long story, how I was such a desperate dragon, and so bent upon fighting, that it took four constables to carry me to the Mayor, and one boy to carry my hat. It 's a capital plan—must be done—the only way I have of escaping unpursued from this place, unless I could put myself in the General Post, and direct myself to a friend in town. And then it 's a chance whether they 'd take me in, being so much over weight. [*Exit* STRANGE GENTLEMAN, *with portmanteau*, L. H.

MRS. NOAKES, *peeping in* C. DOOR, *then entering*.

MRS. NOAKES. This is the room, ladies, but the gentleman has stepped out somewhere, he won't be long, I dare say. Pray come in, Miss.

Enter MARY *and* FANNY WILSON, C. DOOR.

MARY (C.). This is the Strange Gentleman's apartment, is it?

MRS. NOAKES (R.). Yes, Miss; shall I see if I can find him, ladies, and tell him you are here?

MARY. No; we should prefer waiting till he returns, if you please.

MRS. NOAKES. Very well, ma'am. He'll be back directly, I dare say; for it's very near his dinner time. [*Exit* MRS. NOAKES, C. DOOR.

MARY. Come, Fanny, dear; don't give way to these feelings of depression. Take pattern by me—I feel the absurdity of our situation acutely; but you see that I keep up, nevertheless.

FANNY. It is easy for you to do so. *Your* situation is neither so embarrassing, nor so painful a one as mine.

MARY. Well, my dear, it *may* not be, certainly; but the circumstances which render it less so are, I own, somewhat incomprehensible to me. My harebrained, mad-cap swain, John Johnson, implores me to leave my guardian's house, and accompany him on an expedition to Gretna Green. I with immense reluctance, and after considerable pressing——

FANNY. Yield a very willing consent.

MARY. Well, we won't quarrel about terms; at all events I *do* consent. He bears me off, and when we get exactly half-way, discovers that his money is all gone, and that we must stop at this Inn, until he can procure a remittance from London, by post. I think, my dear, you'll own that *this* is rather an embarrassing position.

FANNY. Compare it with mine. Taking advantage of your flight, I send express to *my* admirer, Charles Tomkins, to say that I have accompanied you; first, because I should have been miserable if left behind with a peevish old man alone; secondly, because I thought it proper that your sister should accompany you——

MARY. And, thirdly, because you knew that he would immediately comply with this indirect assent to his entreaties of three months' duration, and follow you without delay, on the same errand. Eh, my dear?

FANNY. It by no means follows that such was my intention, or that I knew he would pursue such a course, but supposing he *has* done so; supposing this Strange Gentleman should be himself——

263

MARY. *Supposing!*—Why, you know it is. You told him not to disclose his name, on any account ; and the *Strange Gentleman* is not a very common travelling name, I should imagine ; besides the hasty note, in which he said he should join you here.

FANNY. Well, granted that it is he. In what a situation am I placed. You tell me, for the first time, that *my* violent intended must on no account be beheld by *your* violent intended, just now, because of some old quarrel between them, of long standing, which has never been adjusted to this day. What an appearance this will have ! How am I to explain it, or relate your present situation ? I should sink into the earth with shame and confusion.

MARY. Leave it to me. It arises from my heedlessness. I will take it all upon myself, and see him alone. But tell me, my dear —as you got up this love affair with so much secrecy and expedition during the four months you spent at Aunt Martha's, I have never yet seen Mr. Tomkins, you know. Is he so very handsome ?

FANNY. See him, and judge for yourself.

MARY. Well, I will ; and you may retire, till I have paved the way for your appearance. But just assist me first, dear, in making a little noise to attract his attention, if he really be in the next room, or I may wait here all day.

DUET—*At end of which exit* FANNY, C. DOOR. MARY *retires up* R. H.

Enter STRANGE GENTLEMAN, L. H.

STRANGE GENTLEMAN. There ; now with a clean shirt in one pocket and a night-cap in the other, I 'm ready to be carried magnanimously to my dungeon in the cause of love.

MARY (*aside*). He says, he 's ready to be carried magnanimously to a dungeon in the cause of love. I thought it was Mr. Tomkins ! Hem ! (*Coming down* L. H.)

STRANGE GENTLEMAN (*seeing her*). Hallo ! Who 's this ! Not a disguised peace officer in petticoats. Beg your pardon, ma'am. (*Advancing towards her.*) What—did—you——

MARY. Oh, Sir ; I feel the delicacy of my situation.

STRANGE GENTLEMAN (*aside*). Feels the delicacy of her situation ; Lord bless us, what 's the matter ! Permit me to offer you a seat, ma'am, if you 're in a delicate situation. (*He places chairs ; they sit.*)

MARY. You are very good, Sir. You are surprised to see me here, Sir?

STRANGE GENTLEMAN. No, no, at least not very; rather, perhaps—rather. (*Aside.*) Never was more astonished in all my life!

MARY (*aside*). His politeness, and the extraordinary tale I have to tell him, overpower me. I must summon up courage. Hem!

STRANGE GENTLEMAN. Hem!

MARY. Sir!

STRANGE GENTLEMAN. Ma'am!

MARY. You have arrived at this house in pursuit of a young lady, if I mistake not?

STRANGE GENTLEMAN. You are quite right, ma'am. (*Aside.*) Mysterious female!

MARY. If you *are* the gentleman I'm in search of, you wrote a hasty note a short time since, stating that you would be found here this afternoon.

STRANGE GENTLEMAN (*drawing back his chair*). I—I—wrote a note, ma'am!

MARY. You need keep nothing secret from me, Sir.   I know all.

STRANGE GENTLEMAN (*aside*). That villain, Boots, has betrayed me! Know all, ma'am?

MARY. Everything.

STRANGE GENTLEMAN (*aside*). It must be so. She's a constable's wife.

MARY. You *are* the writer of that letter, Sir? I think I am not mistaken.

STRANGE GENTLEMAN. You are not, ma'am; I confess I did write it. What was I to do, ma'am? Consider the situation in which I was placed.

MARY. In your situation, you had, as it appears to me, only one course to pursue.

STRANGE GENTLEMAN. You mean the course I adopted?

MARY. Undoubtedly.

STRANGE GENTLEMAN. I am very happy to hear you say so, though of course I should like it to be kept a secret.

MARY. Oh, of course.

STRANGE GENTLEMAN (*drawing his chair close to her, and speaking very softly*). Will you allow me to ask you, whether the constables are downstairs?

MARY (*surprised*). The constables!

STRANGE GENTLEMAN. Because if I am to be apprehended, I should like to have it over. I am quite ready, if it must be done.

MARY. No legal interference has been attempted. There is nothing to prevent your continuing your journey to-night.

STRANGE GENTLEMAN. But will not the other party follow?

MARY (*looking down*). The other party, I am compelled to inform you, is detained here by—by want of funds.

STRANGE GENTLEMAN (*starting up*). Detained here by want of funds! Hurrah! Hurrah! I have caged him at last. I'm revenged for all his blustering and bullying This is a glorious triumph, ha, ha, ha! I have nailed him—nailed him to the spot!

MARY (*rising indignantly*). This exulting over a fallen foe, Sir, is mean and pitiful. In my presence, too, it is an additional insult.

STRANGE GENTLEMAN. Insult! I wouldn't insult you for the world, after the joyful intelligence you have brought me—I could hug you in my arms!—One kiss, my little constable's deputy. (*Seizing her.*)

MARY (*struggling with him*). Help! help!

Enter JOHN JOHNSON, C. DOOR.

JOHN. What the devil do I see! (*Seizes* STRANGE GENTLEMAN *by the collar.*)

MARY (L. H.). John, and Mr. Tomkins, met together! They'll kill each other.—Here, help! help! [*Exit* MARY, *running*, C. DOOR.

JOHN (*shaking him*). What do you mean by that, scoundrel?

STRANGE GENTLEMAN. Come, none of your nonsense—there's no harm done.

JOHN. No harm done.—How dare you offer to salute that lady?

STRANGE GENTLEMAN. What did you send her here for?

JOHN. *I* send her here!

STRANGE GENTLEMAN. Yes, *you*; you gave her instructions, I suppose. (*Aside.*) Her husband, the constable, evidently.

JOHN. That lady, Sir, is attached to me.

STRANGE GENTLEMAN. Well, I know she is; and a very useful little person she must be, to be attached to anybody,—it's a pity she can't be legally sworn in.

JOHN. *Legally* sworn in! Sir, that is an insolent reflection upon the temporary embarrassment which prevents our taking the marriage vows. How dare you to insinuate——

266

STRANGE GENTLEMAN. Pooh! pooh!—don't talk about daring to insinuate; it doesn't become a man in your station of life——

JOHN. My station of life!

STRANGE GENTLEMAN. But as you have managed this matter very quietly, and say you 're in temporary embarrassment—here—here 's five shillings for you. (*Offers it.*)

JOHN. Five shillings! (*Raises his cane.*)

STRANGE GENTLEMAN (*flourishing a chair*). Keep off, sir!

Enter MARY, TOM SPARKS, *and two Waiters.*

MARY. Separate them, or there 'll be murder! (TOM *clasps* STRANGE GENTLEMAN *round the waist—the Waiters seize* JOHN JOHNSON).

TOM. Come, none o' that 'ere, Mr. S. We don't let private rooms for such games as these.—If you want to try it on wery partickler, we don't mind making a ring for you in the yard, but you mustn't do it here.

JOHN. Let me get at him. Let me go; waiters—Mary, don't hold me. I insist on your letting me go.

STRANGE GENTLEMAN. Hold him fast.—Call yourself a *peace* officer, you prize-fighter!

JOHN (*struggling*). Let me go, I say!

STRANGE GENTLEMAN. Hold him fast! Hold him fast!

[TOM *takes* STRANGE GENTLEMAN *off*, R. H. *Waiters take* JOHN *off*, L. H., MARY *following.*

SCENE II.—*Another Room in the Inn.*

Enter JULIA DOBBS *and* OVERTON, L. H.

JULIA. You seem surprised, Overton.

OVERTON. Surprised, Miss Dobbs! Well I may be, when, after seeing nothing of you for three years and more, you come down here without any previous notice, for the express purpose of running away—positively running away, with a young man. I am astonished, Miss Dobbs!

JULIA. You would have had better reason to be astonished if I had come down here with any notion of positively running away with an old one, Overton.

OVERTON. Old or young, it would matter little to me, if you had not

267

conceived the preposterous idea of entangling me—*me*, an attorney, and mayor of the town, in so ridiculous a scheme.—Miss Dobbs, I can't do it.—I really cannot consent to mix myself up with such an affair.

JULIA. Very well, Overton, very well. You recollect that in the lifetime of that poor old dear, Mr. Woolley, who——

OVERTON. —Who would have married you, if he hadn't died; and who, as it was, left you his property, free from all incumbrances, the incumbrance of himself, as a husband, not being among the least.

JULIA. Well, you may recollect, that in the poor old dear's lifetime, sundry advances of money were made to you, at my persuasion, which still remain unpaid. Oblige me by forwarding them to my agent in the course of the week, and I free you from any inter-ference in this little matter. (*Crosses to* L. H. *and is going.*)

OVERTON. Stay, Miss Dobbs, stay. As you say, we *are* old ac-quaintances, and there certainly *were* some small sums of money, which—which——

JULIA. Which certainly *are* still outstanding.

OVERTON. Just so, just so; and which, perhaps, you would be likely to forget, if you had a husband—eh, Miss Dobbs, eh?

JULIA. I have little doubt that I should. If I gained one through your assistance, indeed—I can safely say I should forget all about them.

OVERTON. My dear Miss Dobbs, we perfectly understand each other. —Pray proceed.

JULIA. Well—dear Lord Peter——

OVERTON. That's the young man you're going to run away with, I presume?

JULIA. That's the young *nobleman* who's going to run away with me, Mr. Overton.

OVERTON. Yes, just so.—I beg your pardon—pray go on.

JULIA. Dear Lord Peter is young and wild, and the fact is, his friends do not consider him very sagacious or strong-minded. To prevent their interference, our marriage is to be a secret one. In fact, he is stopping now at a friend's hunting seat in the neighbourhood; he is to join me here; and we are to be married at Gretna.

OVERTON. Just so.—A matter, as it seems to me, which you can conclude without my interference.

JULIA. Wait an instant. To avoid suspicion, and prevent our being recognised and followed, I settled with him that you should give

268

out in this house that he was a lunatic, and that I—his aunt—was going to convey him in a chaise, to-night, to a private asylum at Berwick. I have ordered the chaise at half-past one in the morning. You can see him, and make our final arrangements. It will avert all suspicion, if I have no communication with him, till we start. You can say to the people of the house that the sight of me makes him furious.

OVERTON. Where shall I find him?—Is he here?

JULIA. You know best.

OVERTON. I!

JULIA. I desired him, immediately on his arrival, to write you some mysterious nonsense, acquainting you with the number of his room.

OVERTON (*producing a letter*). Dear me, he has arrived, Miss Dobbs.

JULIA. No!

OVERTON. Yes—see here—a most mysterious and extraordinary composition, which was thrown in at my office window this morning, and which I could make neither head nor tail of. Is that his handwriting? (*Giving her the letter.*)

JULIA (*taking letter*). I never saw it more than once, but I know he writes very large and straggling.—(*Looks at letter.*) Ha, ha, ha! This is capital, isn't it?

OVERTON. Excellent!—Ha, ha, ha!—So mysterious

JULIA. Ha, ha, ha!—So very good.—' Rash act.'

OVERTON. Yes. Ha, ha!

JULIA. 'Interesting young man.'

OVERTON. Yes.—Very good.

JULIA. 'Amiable youth!'

OVERTON. Capital!

JULIA. 'Solemn warning!'

OVERTON. Yes.—That's best of all. (*They both laugh.*)

JULIA. Number seventeen, he says. See him at once, that's a good creature. (*Returning the letter.*)

OVERTON (*taking letter*). I will. (*He crosses to* L. H. *and rings a bell.*)

Enter WAITER, L. H.

Who is there in number seventeen, waiter?

WAITER. Number seventeen, sir?—Oh!—the strange gentleman, sir.

OVERTON. Show me the room. [*Exit* WAITER, L. H.

269

(*Looking at* JULIA, *and pointing to the letter.*) 'The Strange Gentleman.'—Ha, ha, ha! Very good—very good indeed.—Excellent notion! (*They both laugh.*)   [*Exeunt severally.*

SCENE III.—*Same as the first.—A small table, with wine, dessert, and lights on it,* R. H. *of* C. DOOR ; *two chairs.*

STRANGE GENTLEMAN *discovered seated at table.*

STRANGE GENTLEMAN. 'The other party is detained here, by want of funds.' Ha, ha, ha! I can finish my wine at my leisure, order my gig when I please, and drive on to Brown's in perfect security. I 'll drink the other party's good health, and long may he be detained here. (*Fills a glass.*) Ha, ha, ha! The other party ; and long may he—(*A knock at* C. DOOR.) Hallo! I hope *this* isn't the other party. Talk of the—(*A knock at* C. DOOR.) Well—(*setting down his glass*)—this is the most extraordinary private room that was ever invented. I am continually disturbed by unaccountable knockings. (*A gentle tap at* C. DOOR.) There 's another ; that was a gentle rap—a persuasive tap—like a friend's fore-finger on one's coat-sleeve. It *can't* be Tinkles with the gruel. —Come in.

OVERTON *peeping in at* C. DOOR.

OVERTON. Are you alone, my Lord?

STRANGE GENTLEMAN (*amazed*). Eh!

OVERTON. Are you alone, my Lord?

STRANGE GENTLEMAN. My Lord!

OVERTON (*stepping in, and closing the door*). You are right, sir, we cannot be too cautious, for we do not know who may be within hearing. You are very right, sir.

STRANGE GENTLEMAN (*rising from table, and coming forward,* R. H.). It strikes me, sir, that you are very wrong.

OVERTON. Very good, very good ; I like this caution ; it shows me you are wide awake.

STRANGE GENTLEMAN. Wide awake!—damme, I begin to think I am fast asleep, and have been for the last two hours.

OVERTON (*whispering*). I—am—the mayor.

STRANGE GENTLEMAN (*in the same tone*). Oh!

OVERTON. This is your letter? (*Shows it ;* STRANGE GENTLEMAN *nods assent solemnly.*) It will be necessary for you to leave here

270

to-night, at half-past one o'clock, in a postchaise and four; and the higher you bribe the postboys to drive at their utmost speed, the better.

STRANGE GENTLEMAN. You don't say so?

OVERTON. I do indeed.   You are not safe from pursuit here.

STRANGE GENTLEMAN. Bless my soul, can such dreadful things happen in a civilised community, Mr. Mayor?

OVERTON. It certainly does at first sight appear rather a hard case that people cannot marry whom they please, without being hunted down in this way.

STRANGE GENTLEMAN. To be sure.   To be hunted down, and killed as if one was game, you know.

OVERTON. Certainly; and you *an't* game, you know.

STRANGE GENTLEMAN. Of course not.   But can't you prevent it? can't you save me by the interposition of your power?

OVERTON. My power can do nothing in such a case.

STRANGE GENTLEMAN. Can't it, though?

OVERTON. Nothing whatever.

STRANGE GENTLEMAN. I never heard of such dreadful revenge, never! Mr. Mayor, I am a victim, I am the unhappy victim of parental obstinacy.

OVERTON. Oh, no; don't say that.   You may escape yet.

STRANGE GENTLEMAN (*grasping his hand*). Do you think I may? Do you think I may, Mr. Mayor?

OVERTON. Certainly! certainly!   I have little doubt of it, if you manage properly.

STRANGE GENTLEMAN. I thought I *was* managing properly.   I understood the other party was detained here, by want of funds.

OVERTON. Want of funds!—There's no want of funds in that quarter, I can tell you.

STRANGE GENTLEMAN. An't there, though?

OVERTON. Bless you, no.   Three thousand a year!—But who told you there was a want of funds?

STRANGE GENTLEMAN. Why, she did.

OVERTON. *She!* you *have* seen her then?   She told me you had not.

STRANGE GENTLEMAN. Nonsense; don't believe her.   She was in this very room half an hour ago.

OVERTON. Then I must have misunderstood her, and you must have misunderstood her too.—But to return to business.   Don't you

271

think it would keep up appearances if I had you put under some restraint.

STRANGE GENTLEMAN. I think it would. I am very much obliged to you. (*Aside.*) This regard for my character in an utter stranger, and in a Mayor too, is quite affecting.

OVERTON. I'll send somebody up, to mount guard over you.

STRANGE GENTLEMAN. Thank 'ee, my dear friend, thank 'ee.

OVERTON. And if you make a little resistance, when we take you upstairs to your bedroom, or away in the chaise, it will be keeping up the character, you know.

STRANGE GENTLEMAN. To be sure.—So it will.—I'll do it.

OVERTON. Very well, then. I shall see your Lordship again by and by.—For the present, my Lord, good evening. (*Going.*)

STRANGE GENTLEMAN. Lord!—Lordship!—Mr. Mayor!

OVERTON. Eh?—Oh!—I see. (*Comes forward.*) Practising the lunatic, my Lord. Ah, very good—very vacant look indeed.— Admirable, my Lord, admirable!—I say, my Lord—(*pointing to letter*)—'Amiable youth!'—'Interesting young man.'—'Strange Gentleman.'—Eh? Ha, ha, ha! Knowing trick indeed, my Lord, very! [*Exit* OVERTON, C. D.

STRANGE GENTLEMAN. That mayor is either in the very last stage of mystified intoxication, or in the most hopeless state of incurable insanity.—I have no doubt of it. A little touched here (*tapping his forehead*). Never mind, he is sufficiently sane to understand my business at all events. (*Goes to table and takes a glass.*) Poor fellow!—I'll drink his health, and speedy recovery. (*A knock at* C. DOOR.) It is a most extraordinary thing, now, that every time I propose a toast to myself, some confounded fellow raps at that door, as if he were receiving it with the utmost enthusiasm. Private room!—I might as well be sitting behind the little shutter of a Two-penny Post Office, where all the letters put in were to be post-paid. (*A knock at* C. DOOR.) Perhaps it's the guard! I shall feel a great deal safer if it is. Come in. (*He has brought a chair forward, and sits* L. H.)

Enter TOM SPARKS, C. DOOR, *very slowly, with an enormous stick. He closes the door, and, after looking at the* STRANGE GENTLE-MAN *very steadily, brings a chair down* L. H., *and sits opposite him.*

STRANGE GENTLEMAN. Are you sent by the mayor of this place, to mount guard over me ?

TOM. Yes, yes.—It's all right.

STRANGE GENTLEMAN (*aside*). It's all right—I'm safe.   (*To* TOM, *with affected indignation*.) Now mind, I have been insulted by receiving this challenge, and I want to fight the man who gave it me. I protest against being kept here. I denounce this treatment as an outrage.

TOM. Ay, ay.   Anything you please—poor creature ; don't put yourself in a passion.   It'll only make you worse.   (*Whistles.*)

STRANGE GENTLEMAN. This is most extraordinary behaviour.—I don't understand it.—What d'ye mean by behaving in this manner ?   (*Rising.*)

TOM (*aside*). He's a getting wiolent.   I must frighten him with a steady look.—I say, young fellow, do you see this here eye ? (*Staring at him, and pointing at his own eye.*)

STRANGE GENTLEMAN (*aside*). Do I see his eye ! — What can he mean by glaring upon me, with that large round optic !—Ha ! a terrible light flashes upon me.—He thought I was 'Swing' this morning.   It was an insane delusion.—That eye is an insane eye. —He's a madman !

TOM. Madman ! Damme, I think he is a madman with a wengeance.

STRANGE GENTLEMAN. He acknowledges it.   He is sensible of his misfortune !—Go away—leave the room instantly, and tell them to send somebody else.—Go away !

TOM. Oh, you unhappy lunatic !

STRANGE GENTLEMAN. What a dreadful situation !—I shall be attacked, strangled, smothered, and mangled, by a madman ! Where's the bell ?

TOM (*advancing and brandishing his stick*). Leave that 'ere bell alone—leave that 'ere bell alone—and come here !

STRANGE GENTLEMAN. Certainly, Mr. Boots, certainly.—He's going to strangle me.   (*Going towards table.*) Let me pour you out a glass of wine, Mr. Boots—pray do !   (*Aside.*) If he said 'Yes,' I'd throw the decanter at his temple.

TOM. None o' your nonsense.—Sit down there.   (*Forces him into a chair,* L. H.) I'll sit here.   (*Opposite him,* R. H.) Look me full in the face, and I won't hurt you.   Move hand, foot, or eye, and you'll never want to move either of 'em again.

273

STRANGE GENTLEMAN. I'm paralysed with terror.

TOM. Ha! (*raising his stick in a threatening attitude*).

STRANGE GENTLEMAN. I'm dumb, Mr. Boots—dumb, sir.

> *They sit gazing intently on each other; TOM with the stick raised, as the Act Drop slowly descends.*

END OF ACT FIRST

FIRST ACT FIFTY MINUTES.

ACT II

SCENE I.—*The same as* SCENE III. ACT I.

TOM SPARKS *discovered in the same attitude watching the* STRANGE GENTLEMAN, *who has fallen asleep with his head over the back of his Chair.*

TOM. He's asleep; poor unhappy wretch! How very mad he looks with his mouth wide open and his eyes shut! (STRANGE GENTLE-MAN *snores*.) Ah! there's a wacant snore; no meaning in it at all. I cou'd ha' told he was out of his senses from the very tone of it. (*He snores again.*) That's a wery insane snore. I should say he was melancholly mad from the sound of it.

Enter, through C. DOOR, OVERTON, MRS. NOAKES, *a Chambermaid, and two Waiters;* MRS. NOAKES *with a warming-pan, the Maid with a light.* STRANGE GENTLEMAN *starts up, greatly exhausted.*

TOM (*starting up in* C.). Hallo!—Hallo! keep quiet, young fellow. Keep quiet!

STRANGE GENTLEMAN (L. H.). Out of the way, you savage maniac. Mr. Mayor (*crossing to him*, R. H.), the person you sent to keep guard over me is a madman, sir. What do you mean by shutting me up with a madman?—what do you mean, sir, I ask?

OVERTON, R. H. C. (*aside to* STRANGE GENTLEMAN). Bravo! bravo! very good indeed—excellent!

STRANGE GENTLEMAN. Excellent, sir!—It's horrible!—The bare re-collection of what I have endured, makes me shudder, down to my very toe-nails.

MRS. NOAKES (R. H.). Poor dear!—Mad people always think other people mad.

STRANGE GENTLEMAN. Poor dear! Ma'am! What the devil do you mean by 'Poor dear?' How dare you have a madman here, ma'am, to assault and terrify the visitors to your establishment?

MRS. NOAKES. Ah! terrify indeed! I'll never have another, to please anybody, you may depend upon that, Mr. Overton. (*To* STRANGE GENTLEMAN.) There, there.—Don't exert yourself, there's a dear.

STRANGE GENTLEMAN (C.). Exert myself!—Damme! it's a mercy I have any life left to exert myself with. It's a special miracle, ma'am, that my existence has not long ago fallen a sacrifice to that sanguinary monster in the leather smalls.

OVERTON, R. C. (*aside to* STRANGE GENTLEMAN). I never saw any passion more real in my life. Keep it up, it's an admirable joke.

STRANGE GENTLEMAN. Joke!—joke!—Peril a precious life, and call it a joke,—you, a man with a sleek head and a broad-brimmed hat, who ought to know better, calling it a joke.—Are you mad too, sir,—are you mad? (*Confronting* OVERTON.)

TOM, L. H. (*very loud*). Keep your hands off. Would you murder the wery mayor, himself, you mis-rable being?

STRANGE GENTLEMAN. Mr. Mayor, I call upon you to issue your warrant for the instant confinement of that one-eyed Orson in some place of security.

OVERTON (*aside, advancing a little*). He reminds me that he had better be removed to his bedroom. He is right.—Waiters, carry the gentleman upstairs.—Boots, you will continue to watch him in his bedroom.

STRANGE GENTLEMAN. *He* continue!—What, am I to be boxed up again with this infuriated animal, and killed off, when he has done playing with me?—I won't go—I won't go—help there, help! (*The Waiters cross from* R. H. *to behind him.*)

Enter JOHN JOHNSON *hastily*, C. DOOR.

JOHN (*coming forward* L. H.). What on earth is the meaning of this dreadful outcry, which disturbs the whole house?

MRS. NOAKES. Don't be alarmed, sir, I beg.—They're only going to carry an unfortunate gentleman, as is out of his senses, to his bedroom.

STRANGE GENTLEMAN, C. (*to* JOHN). Constable — constable — do your duty—apprehend these persons—every one of them. Do you hear, officer, do you hear?—(*The Waiters seize him by the arms.*)—

275

Here—here—you see this. You've seen the assault committed. Take them into custody—off with them.

MRS. NOAKES. Poor creature!—He thinks you are a constable, sir.

JOHN. Unfortunate man! It is the second time to-day that he has been the victim of this strange delusion.

STRANGE GENTLEMAN (*breaking from Waiters and going to* JOHN). L. H. Unfortunate man!—What, do *you* think I am mad?

JOHN. Poor fellow! His hopeless condition is pitiable indeed. (*Goes up.*)

STRANGE GENTLEMAN (*returning to* C.). They're all mad!—Every one of 'em!

MRS. NOAKES. Come now, come to bed — there's a dear young man, do.

STRANGE GENTLEMAN. Who are you, you shameless old ghost, standing there before company, with a large warming-pan, and asking me to come to bed?—Are *you* mad?

MRS. NOAKES. Oh! he's getting shocking now. Take him away.— Take him away.

OVERTON. Ah, you had better remove him to his bedroom at once. (*The Waiters take him up by the feet and shoulders.*)

STRANGE GENTLEMAN. Mind, if I survive this, I'll bring an action of false imprisonment against every one of you. Mark my words— especially against that villainous old mayor.—Mind, I'll do it! (*They bear him off, struggling and talking—the others crowding round, and assisting.*)

OVERTON (*following*). How well he does it!   [*Exeunt* L. H. *1st* E.

Enter a Waiter, showing in CHARLES TOMKINS *in a travelling coat*, C. DOOR.

WAITER (L. H.). This room is disengaged now, sir. There *was* a gentleman in it, but he has just left it.

CHARLES. Very well, this will do. I may want a bed here to-night, perhaps, waiter.

WAITER. Yes, sir.—Shall I take your card to the bar, sir?

CHARLES. My card!—No, never mind.

WAITER. No name, sir?

CHARLES. No—it doesn't matter.

WAITER (*aside, as going out*). *Another* Strange Gentleman!

[*Exit Waiter*, C. DOOR.

CHARLES. Ah!—(*Takes off coat.*)—The sun and dust on this long ride have been almost suffocating.   I wonder whether Fanny has arrived ?   If she has—the sooner we start forward on our journey further North the better.   Let me see ; she would be accompanied by her sister, she said in her note—and they would both be on the look-out for me.   Then the best thing I can do is to ask no questions, for the present at all events, and to be on the look-out for them.   (*Looking towards* C. DOOR.)   Why here she comes, walking slowly down the long passage, straight towards this room—she can't have seen me yet.—Poor girl, how melancholy she looks ! I'll keep in the background for an instant, and give her a joyful surprise.   (*He goes up* R. H.)

Enter FANNY, C. DOOR.

FANNY (L. H.).   Was ever unhappy girl placed in so dreadful a situation !—Friendless, and almost alone, in a strange place—my dear, dear Charles a victim to an attack of mental derangement, and I unable to avow my interest in him, or express my anxious sympathy and solicitude for his sufferings !   I cannot bear this dreadful torture of agonising suspense.   I must and will see him, let the cost be what it may.   (*She is going* L. H.)

CHARLES (*coming forward* R. H.).   Hist ! Fanny !

FANNY (*starting and repressing a scream*).   Ch—Charles—here in this room !

CHARLES.   Bodily present, my dear, in this very room.   My darling Fanny, let me strain you to my bosom.   (*Advancing.*)

FANNY (*shrinking back*).   N—n—no, dearest Charles, no, not now.— (*Aside.*)—How flushed he is !

CHARLES.   No !—Fanny, this cold reception is a very different one to what I looked forward to meeting with, from you.

FANNY (*advancing, and offering the tip of her finger*).   N—n—no— not cold, Charles ; not cold.   I do not mean it to be so, indeed.— How is your head, now, dear ?

CHARLES.   How is my head !   After days and weeks of suspense and anxiety, when half our dangerous journey is gained, and I meet you here, to bear you whither you can be made mine for life, you greet me with the tip of your longest finger, and inquire after my head,—Fanny, what can you mean ?

277

FANNY. You—you have startled me rather, Charles.—I thought you had gone to bed.

CHARLES. Gone to bed!—Why I have but this moment arrived.

FANNY (*aside*). Poor, poor Charles!

CHARLES. Miss Wilson, what am I to——

FANNY. No, no; pray, pray, do not suffer yourself to be excited——

CHARLES. Suffer myself to be excited!—Can I possibly avoid it? can I do aught but wonder at this extraordinary and sudden change in your whole demeanour?—Excited! But five minutes since, I arrived here, brimful of the hope and expectation which had buoyed up my spirits during my long journey. I find you cold, reserved, and embarrassed—everything but what I expected to find you—and then you tell me not to be excited.

FANNY (*aside*). He is wandering again. The fever is evidently upon him.

CHARLES. This altered manner and ill-disguised confusion all convince me of what you would fain conceal. Miss Wilson, you repent of your former determination, and love another!

FANNY. Poor fellow!

CHARLES. Poor fellow!—What, am I pitied?

FANNY. Oh, Charles, do not give way to this. Consider how much depends upon your being composed.

CHARLES. I see how much depends upon my being composed, ma'am —well, very well.—A husband depends upon it, ma'am. Your new lover is in this house, and if he overhears my reproaches he will become suspicious of the woman who has jilted *another*, and may jilt *him*. That's it, madam—a great deal depends, as you say, upon my being composed.—A great deal, ma'am.

FANNY. Alas! these are indeed the ravings of frenzy!

CHARLES. Upon my word, ma'am, you must form a very modest estimate of your own power, if you imagine that disappointment has impaired my senses. Ha, ha, ha!—I am delighted. I am delighted to have escaped you, ma'am. I am glad, ma'am— damn'd glad! (*Kicks a chair over.*)

FANNY (*aside*). I must call for assistance. He grows more incoherent and furious every instant.

CHARLES. I leave you, ma'am. — I am unwilling to interrupt the tender *tête-à-tête* with the other gentleman, to which you are, no doubt, anxiously looking forward.—To you I have no more to say.

To *him* I must beg to offer a few rather unexpected congratulations on his approaching marriage.   [*Exit* Charles *hastily*, c. door.

Fanny. Alas! it is but too true.   His senses have entirely left him.
                                                                [*Exit* l. h.

Scene Second and Last.—*A Gallery in the Inn, leading to the Bedrooms.   Four Doors in the Flat, and one at each of the upper Entrances, numbered from 20 to 25, beginning at the* r. h.   *A pair of boots at the door of 23.*

Enter Chambermaid with two lights; and Charles Tomkins, r. h. *1st* e.

Maid. This is your room, sir, No. 21.   (*Opening the door.*)

Charles. Very well.   Call me at seven in the morning.

Maid. Yes, sir.   (*Gives him a light, and*
                                                    [*Exit Chambermaid*, r. h. 1*st* e.

Charles. And at nine, if I can previously obtain a few words of explanation with this unknown rival, I will just return to the place from whence I came, in the same coach that brought me down here.   I wonder who he is and where he sleeps.   (*Looking round.*)   I have a lurking suspicion of those boots.   (*Pointing to No. 23.*)   They are an ill-looking, underhanded sort of pair, and an undefinable instinct tells me that they have clothed the feet of the rascal I am in search of.   Besides myself, the owner of those ugly articles is the only person who has yet come up to bed.   I will keep my eyes open for half an hour or so ; and my ears too.
                                                    [*Exit* Charles *into No. 21.*

Enter r. h. *1st* e. Mrs. Noakes *with two lights,
        followed by* Mary *and* Fanny.

Mrs. Noakes. Take care of the last step, ladies.   This way, ma'am, if you please.   No. 20 is your room, ladies : nice large double-bedded room, with coals and a rushlight.

Fanny, r. h. (*aside to* Mary). I must ask which is his room.   I cannot rest unless I know he has at length sunk into the slumber he so much needs.   (*Crosses to* Mrs. Noakes, *who is* l. h.)   Which is the room in which the Strange Gentleman sleeps?

Mrs. Noakes. No. 23, ma'am.   There's his boots outside the door.   Don't be frightened of him, ladies.   He's very quiet now, and our Boots is a watching him.

279

FANNY. Oh, no—we are not afraid of him. (*Aside*.) Poor Charles!

MRS. NOAKES (*going to door No. 20, which is 3rd E. R. H.*). This way, if you please ; you 'll find everything very comfortable, and there 's a bell-rope at the head of the bed, if you want anything in the morning. Good night, ladies.

As MARY *and* FANNY *pass* MRS. NOAKES, FANNY *takes a light.*
[*Exeunt* FANNY *and* MARY *into No.* 20.

MRS. NOAKES (*tapping at No. 23*). Tom—Tom—

Enter TOM *from No. 23.*

TOM (*coming forward, L. H.*). Is that you, missis ?

MRS. NOAKES (R. H.). Yes.—How 's the Strange Gentleman, Tom ?

TOM. He was wery boisterous half an hour ago, but I punched his head a little, and now he 's uncommon comfortable. He 's fallen asleep, but his snores is still wery incoherent.

MRS. NOAKES. Mind you take care of him, Tom. They 'll take him away in half an hour's time. It 's very nearly one o'clock now.

TOM. I 'll pay ev'ry possible attention to him. If he offers to call out, I shall whop him again. [*Exit* TOM *into No.* 23.

MRS. NOAKES (*looking off* R. H.). This way, ma'am, if you please. Up these stairs.

Enter JULIA DOBBS *with a light*, R. H. 1*st* E.

JULIA. Which did you say was the room in which I could arrange my dress for travelling ?

MRS. NOAKES. No. 22, ma'am ; the next room to your nephew's. Poor dear—he 's fallen asleep, ma'am, and I dare say you 'll be able to take him away very quietly by and by.

JULIA (*aside*). Not so quietly as you imagine, if he plays his part half as well as Overton reports he does. (*To* MRS. NOAKES.) Thank you.—For the present, good night. [*Exit* JULIA *into No.* 22.

MRS. NOAKES. Wish you good night, ma'am. There.—Now I think I may go downstairs again, and see if Mr. Overton wants any more negus. Why who 's this ? (*Looking off* R. H.) Oh, I forgot —No. 24 an't a-bed yet.—It 's him.

Enter JOHN JOHNSON *with a light*, R. H. 1*st* E.

MRS. NOAKES. No. 24, sir, if you please.

JOHN. Yes, yes, I know. The same room I slept in last night. (*Crossing* L. H.)

Mrs. Noakes. Yes, sir.—Wish you good night, sir.

[*Exit* Mrs. Noakes, R. H. 1*st* E.

John. Good night, ma'am. The same room I slept in last night, indeed, and the same room I may sleep in to-morrow night, and the next night, and the night after that, and just as many more nights as I can get credit here, unless this remittance arrives. I could raise the money to prosecute my journey without difficulty were I on the spot; but my confounded thoughtless liberality to the post-boys has left me absolutely penniless. Well, we shall see what to-morrow brings forth. (*He goes into No. 24, but immediately returns and places his boots outside his room door, leaving it ajar.*)   [*Exit* John *into No. 24.*

Charles *peeping from No. 21, and putting out his boots.*

Charles. There's another pair of boots. Now I wonder which of these two fellows is the man. I can't help thinking it's No. 23. —Hallo! (*He goes in and closes his door.*)

The door of No. 20 opens; Fanny *comes out with a light in a night shade. No. 23 opens. She retires into No. 20.*

Enter Tom Sparks, *with a stable lantern from No. 23.*

Tom (*closing the door gently*). Fast asleep still. I may as vell go my rounds, and glean for the deputy. (*Pulls out a piece of chalk from his pocket, and takes up boots from No. 23.*) Twenty-three. It's difficult to tell what a fellow is ven he han't got his senses, but I think this here twenty-three's a timorious faint-hearted genus. (*Examines the boots.*) You want new soleing, No. 23. (*Goes to No. 24, takes up boots and looks at them.*) Hallo! here's a *bust*: and there's been a piece put on in the corner.—I must let my missis know. The bill's always doubtful ven there's any mending. (*Goes to No. 21, takes up boots.*) French calf Vellingtons.—All's right here. These here French calves always comes it strong— light vines, and all that 'ere. (*Looking round.*) Werry happy to see there an't no high-lows—they never drinks nothing but gin- and-vater. Them and the cloth boots is the vurst customers an inn has.—The cloth boots is always obstemious, only drinks sherry vine and vater, and never eats no suppers. (*He chalks the No. of the room on each pair of boots as he takes them up.*) Lucky for you,

281

my French calves, that you an't done with the patent polish, or you'd ha' been witrioled in no time. I don't like to put oil o' witriol on a well-made pair of boots; but ven they're rubbed vith that 'ere polish, it must be done, or the profession's ruined.

[*Exit* Tom *with boots*, R. H. 1*st* E.

Enter Fanny *from No.* 20, *with light as before.*

Fanny. I tremble at the idea of going into his room, but surely at a moment like this, when he is left to be attended by rude and uninterested strangers, the strict rules of propriety which regulate our ordinary proceedings may be dispensed with. I will but satisfy myself that he sleeps, and has those comforts which his melancholy situation demands, and return immediately. (*Goes to No.* 23, *and knocks.*)

Charles Tomkins *peeping from No.* 21.

Charles. I'll swear I heard a knock.—A woman! Fanny Wilson— and at that door at this hour of the night!

Fanny *comes forward.*

Why what an ass I must have been ever to have loved that girl.— It *is* No. 23, though.—I'll throttle him presently. The next room-door open—I'll watch there. (*He crosses to No.* 24, *and goes in.*)

Fanny *returns to No.* 23, *and knocks — the door opens and the* Strange Gentleman *appears, night-cap on his head and a light in his hand.*—Fanny *screams and runs back into No.* 20.

Strange Gentleman (*coming forward*). Well, of all the wonderful and extraordinary houses that ever did exist, this particular tenement is the most extraordinary. I've got rid of the madman at last—and it's almost time for that vile old mayor to remove me. But where?—I'm lost, bewildered, confused, and actually begin to think I am mad. Half these things I've seen to-day must be visions of fancy—they never could have really happened. No, no, I'm clearly mad!—I've not the least doubt of it now. I've caught it from that horrid Boots. He has inoculated the whole establishment. We're all mad together.—(*Looking off* R. H.) Lights coming upstairs!—Some more lunatics.

[*Exit* Strange Gentleman *in No.* 23.

Enter R. H. 1*st* E. OVERTON *with a cloak*, MRS. NOAKES, TOM SPARKS
*with lantern, and three Waiters with lights. The Waiters range
up* R. H. *side.* TOM *is in* R. H. *corner and* MRS. NOAKES *next to him.*

OVERTON. Remain there till I call for your assistance. (*Goes up to
No. 23 and knocks.*)

Enter STRANGE GENTLEMAN *from No. 23.*

Now, the chaise is ready.—Muffle yourself up in this cloak. (*Puts
it on the* STRANGE GENTLEMAN.—*They come forward.*)

STRANGE GENTLEMAN (L. H.). Yes.

OVERTON (C.). Make a little noise when we take you away, you know.

STRANGE GENTLEMAN. Yes—yes.—I say, what a queer room this is of
mine.   Somebody has been tapping at the wall for the last half
hour, like a whole forest of woodpeckers.

OVERTON. Don't you know who that was?

STRANGE GENTLEMAN. No.

OVERTON. The other party.

STRANGE GENTLEMAN (*alarmed*). The other party!

OVERTON. To be sure.—The other party is going with you.

STRANGE GENTLEMAN. Going with me!—In the same chaise!

OVERTON. Of course.—Hush! (*Goes to No. 22.   Knocks.*)

Enter JULIA DOBBS *from No. 22, wrapped up in a large cloak.*

Look here! (*Bringing her forward.* JULIA *is next to* MRS. NOAKES.)

STRANGE GENTLEMAN (*starting into* L. H. CORNER). I won't go—I won't
go.   This is a plot—a conspiracy.   I won't go, I tell you.   I shall
be assassinated.—I shall be murdered!

FANNY *and* MARY *appear at No. 20,* JOHNSON *and* TOMKINS *at 24.*

JOHN (*at the door*).   I told you he was mad.

CHARLES (*at the door*). I see—I see—poor fellow!

JULIA (*crossing to* STRANGE GENTLEMAN *and taking his arm*).   Come,
dear, come.

MRS. NOAKES. Yes, do go, there's a good soul.   Go with your affectionate aunt.

STRANGE GENTLEMAN (*breaking from her*). My affectionate aunt!

JULIA *returns to her former position.*

TOM. He don't deserve no affection.   I niver see such an un-fectionate
fellow to his relations.

283

STRANGE GENTLEMAN (L. H.). Take that wretch away, and smother him between two feather beds. Take him away, and make a sandwich of him directly.

JULIA (*to* OVERTON, *who is in* C.). What voice was that?—It was not Lord Peter's. (*Throwing off her cloak.*)

OVERTON. Nonsense — nonsense.— Look at him. (*Pulls cloak off* STRANGE GENTLEMAN.)

STRANGE GENTLEMAN (*turning round*). A woman!

JULIA. A stranger!

OVERTON. A stranger! What, an't he your husband that is to—your mad nephew, I mean?

JULIA. No!

ALL. No!

STRANGE GENTLEMAN. No!—no, I'll be damned if I am. I an't anybody's nephew.—My aunt's dead, and I never had an uncle.

MRS. NOAKES. And an't he mad, ma'am?

JULIA. No.

STRANGE GENTLEMAN. Oh, I'm *not* mad.—I was mistaken just now.

OVERTON. And isn't he going away with you?

JULIA. No.

MARY (*coming forward* R. H., *next to* MRS. NOAKES). And isn't his name Tomkins?

STRANGE GENTLEMAN (*very loud*). No!

(*All these questions and answers should be very rapid.* JOHNSON *and* TOMKINS *advance to the ladies, and they all retire up.*)

MRS. NOAKES. What *is* his name? (*Producing a letter.*) It an't Mr. Walker Trott, is it? (*She advances a little towards him.*)

STRANGE GENTLEMAN. Something so remarkably like it, ma'am, that, with your permission, I'll open that epistle. (*Taking letter.*)

All go up, but JULIA *and* STRANGE GENTLEMAN.

(*Opening letter.*) Tinkle's hand. (*Reads.*) 'The challenge was a *ruse*. By this time I shall have been united at Gretna Green to the charming Emily Brown.'—Then, through a horror of duels, I have lost a wife!

JULIA (R. H. *with her handkerchief to her eyes*). And through Lord Peter's negligence, I have lost a husband!

STRANGE GENTLEMAN. Eh! (*Regards her a moment, then beckons*

284

OVERTON, *who comes forward,* L. H.)   I say, didn't you say something about three thousand a year this morning?

OVERTON. I did.

STRANGE GENTLEMAN. You alluded to that party? (*Nodding towards* JULIA.)

OVERTON. I did.

STRANGE GENTLEMAN. Hem! (*Puts* OVERTON *back.*) Permit me, ma'am (*going to her*), to sympathise most respectfully with your deep distress.

JULIA. Oh, sir! your kindness penetrates to my very heart.

STRANGE GENTLEMAN (*aside*). Penetrates to her heart!—It's taking the right direction.—If I understand your sorrowing murmur, ma'am, you contemplated taking a destined husband away with you, in the chaise at the door?

JULIA. Oh! sir,—spare my feelings—I did.—The horses were ordered and paid for; and everything was ready. (*Weeps.*)

STRANGE GENTLEMAN (*aside*). She weeps.——Expensive thing, posting, ma'am.

JULIA. Very, sir.

STRANGE GENTLEMAN. Eighteen-pence a mile, ma'am, not including the boys.

JULIA. Yes, sir.

STRANGE GENTLEMAN. *You've* lost a husband, ma'am—*I* have lost a wife.—Marriages are made above—I'm quite certain ours is booked. —Pity to have all this expense for nothing—let's go together.

JULIA (*drying her eyes*). The suddenness of this proposal, sir——

STRANGE GENTLEMAN. Requires a sudden answer, ma'am.—You don't say no—you mean yes. Permit me to—(*kisses her*).—All right! Old one (*to* OVERTON, *who comes down* L. H.), I've done it.—Mrs. Noakes (*she comes down* R. H.), don't countermand the chaise.— We're off directly.

CHARLES (*who with* FANNY *comes down* L. H. C.).   So are we.

JOHN (*who with* MARY *comes down* R. H. C.). So are we, thanks to a negotiated loan, and an explanation as hasty as the quarrel that gave rise to it.

STRANGE GENTLEMAN. Three post-chaises and four, on to Gretna, directly.   [*Exeunt Waiters,* R. H. 1*st* E.

I say—we'll stop here as we come back?

JOHN *and* CHARLES. Certainly.

STRANGE GENTLEMAN. But before I go, as I fear I have given a great deal of trouble here to-night—permit me to inquire whether you will view my mistakes and perils with an indulgent eye, and consent to receive '*The Strange Gentleman*' again to-morrow.

JOHN. JULIA. STRANGE GENTLEMAN.

MARY.   FANNY.

MRS. NOAKES.   CHARLES.

TOM.   OVERTON.

R. H.   L. H.

CURTAIN

THE END

SECOND ACT THIRTY MINUTES.

THE VILLAGE COQUETTES
A COMIC OPERA
IN TWO ACTS
(Music by John Hullah)
[1836]

DEDICATION

To J. P. HARLEY, ESQ.

MY DEAR SIR,

My dramatic bantlings are no sooner born, than you father them. You have made my 'Strange Gentleman' exclusively your own; you have adopted Martin Stokes with equal readiness; and you still profess your willingness to do the same kind office for all future scions of the same stock.

I dedicate to you the first play I ever published; and you made for me the first play I ever produced :—the balance is in your favour, and I am afraid it will remain so.

That you may long contribute to the amusement of the public, and long be spared to shed a lustre, by the honour and integrity of your private life, on the profession which for many years you have done so much to uphold, is the sincere and earnest wish of, my dear Sir,

Yours most faithfully,

CHARLES DICKENS.

December 15th, 1836

PREFACE

'EITHER the Honourable Gentleman is in the right, or he is not,' is a phrase in very common use within the walls of Parliament. This drama may have a plot, or it may not; and the songs may be poetry, or they may not; and the whole affair, from beginning to end, may be great nonsense, or it may not, just as the honourable gentleman or lady who reads it may happen to think. So, retaining his own private and particular opinion upon the subject (an opinion which he formed upwards of a year ago, when he wrote the piece), the Author leaves every such gentleman or lady, to form his or hers, as he or she may think proper, without saying one word to influence or conciliate them.

All he wishes to say is this;—That he hopes MR. BRAHAM, and all the performers who assisted in the representation of this opera, will accept his warmest thanks for the interest they evinced in it, from its very first rehearsal, and for their zealous efforts in his behalf—efforts which have crowned it with a degree of success far exceeding his most sanguine anticipations; and of which no form of words could speak his acknowledgment.

It is needless to add that the *libretto* of an opera must be, to a certain extent, a mere vehicle for the music; and that it is scarcely fair or reasonable to judge it by those strict rules of criticism which would be justly applicable to a five-act tragedy, or a finished comedy.

DRAMATIS PERSONÆ

At St. James's Theatre, December 6, 1836

Squire Norton	Mr. Braham.
The Hon. Sparkins Flam (*his friend*) . .	Mr. Forester.
Old Benson (*a small farmer*) . . .	Mr. Strickland.
Mr. Martin Stokes (*a very small farmer with a very large circle of particular friends*) . .	Mr. Harley.
George Edmunds (*betrothed to Lucy*) . .	Mr. Bennett.
Young Benson	Mr. J. Parry.
John Maddox (*attached to Rose*) . . .	Mr. Gardner.
Lucy Benson	Miss Rainforth.
Rose (*her cousin*)	Miss J. Smith.

Time occupied in Representation.—Two hours and a half.

PERIOD.—THE AUTUMN OF 1729.

SCENE.—AN ENGLISH VILLAGE.

The Passages marked with inverted commas were omitted in the representation.

THE VILLAGE COQUETTES

ACT I

SCENE I.—*A Rick-yard, with a cart laden with corn-sheaves.* JOHN
MADDOX, *and labourers, unloading it. Implements of husbandry,
etc., lie scattered about. A gate on one side.* JOHN MADDOX *is
in the cart, and dismounts at the conclusion of the Chorus.*

Round.

Hail to the merry Autumn days, when yellow cornfields shine,
Far brighter than the costly cup that holds the monarch's wine!
Hail to the merry harvest time, the gayest of the year,
The time of rich and bounteous crops, rejoicing, and good cheer!

'Tis pleasant on a fine Spring morn to see the buds expand,
'Tis pleasant in the Summer time to view the teeming land;
'Tis pleasant on a Winter's night to crouch around the blaze,—
But what are joys like these, my boys, to Autumn's merry days!

Then hail to merry Autumn days, when yellow corn-fields shine,
Far brighter than the costly cup that holds the monarch's wine!
And hail to merry harvest time, the gayest of the year,
The time of rich and bounteous crops, rejoicing, and good cheer!

JOHN. Well done, my lads; a good day's work, and a warm one.
Here, Tom (*to Villager*), run into the house, and ask Miss Rose
to send out some beer for the men, and a jug for Master Maddox;
and d'ye hear, Tom, tell Miss Rose it's a fine evening, and that
if she'll step out herself, it'll do her good, and do me good into
the bargain. (*Exit Villager.*) That's right, my lads, stow
these sheaves away, before the sun goes down. Let's begin fresh
in the morning, without any leavings of to-day. By this time
to-morrow the last load will have been carried, and then for our
Harvest-Home!

293

VILLAGERS. Hurrah! Hurrah!

(*First four lines of Round repeated.*)

Enter MARTIN STOKES.

MARTIN. Very good! very good, indeed!—always sing while you work—capital custom! I always do when I work, and I never work at all when I can help it;—another capital custom. John, old fellow, how are you?—give us your hand,—hearty squeeze,—good shake,—capital custom number three. Fine dry weather for the harvest, John. Talking of that, I'm dry too: you always give away plenty of beer, here;—capital custom number four. Trouble you for the loan of that can, John.

JOHN (*taking it from the cart*). Here's the can, but as to there being anything good in it it's as dry as the weather, and as empty as you. Hoo! hoo! (*laughing boisterously, is suddenly checked by a look from* MARTIN).

MARTIN. Hallo, John, hallo! I have often told you before, Mr. Maddox, that I don't consider you in a situation of life which entitles you to make jokes, far less to laugh at 'em. If you must make a joke, do it solemnly, and respectfully. If *I* laugh, that's quite enough, and it must be far more gratifying to your feelings than any contortions of that enormous mouth of yours.

JOHN. Well, perhaps, as you say, I oughtn't to make jokes till I arrive, like you, at the dignity of a small piece of ground and a cottage; but I must laugh at a joke, sometimes.

MARTIN. Must, must you!—Rather presuming fellow, this Maddox. (*Aside.*)

JOHN. Why, when you make one of them rum jokes of yours,—'cod, I must laugh then!

MARTIN. Oh! ah! you may laugh then, John; always laugh at my jokes,—capital custom number five; no harm in that, because you can't help it, you know. — Knowing fellow, though. (*Aside*).

JOHN. Remember that joke about the old cow, as you made five years ago?—'cod, that was a joke! Hoo! hoo! hoo!—I never shall forget that joke. I never see a cow, to this day, without laughing.

MARTIN. Ha! ha! ha! very good, very good!—Devilish clever

294

fellow this! (*Aside.*) Well, Jack, you behave yourself well, all the evening, and perhaps I may make that joke again before the day 's out.

JOHN Thank 'ee, that 's very kind.

MARTIN. Don't mention it, don't mention it; but I say, John, I called to speak to you about more important matters.—Something wrong here, an't there? (*Mysteriously.*)

JOHN. Wrong! you 're always fancying something wrong.

MARTIN. Fancying,—come, I like that. I say, why don't you keep your harvest-home at home, to-morrow night? Why are we all to go up to the Squire's, as if we couldn't be merry in Benson's barn? And why is the Squire always coming down here, looking after some people, and cutting out other people?—an't that wrong? Where 's George Edmunds—old Benson 's so fond of, and that Lucy *was* fond of too, once upon a time,—eh? An't that wrong? Where 's your sweetheart, Rose?—An't her walkings, and gigglings, and whisperings, and simperings, with the Squire's friend, Mr. Sparkins Flam, the talk of the whole place? Nothing wrong there,—eh? (MADDOX *goes up.*) Had him there; I knew there was something wrong. I 'll keep a sharp eye upon these doings, for I don't like these new-fangled customs. It was all very well in the old time, to see the Squire's father come riding among the people on his bay cob, nodding to the common folks, shaking hands with me, and all that sort of thing; but when you change the old country-gentleman into a dashing fop from London, and the steady old steward into Mr. Sparkins Flam, the case is very different. We shall see,—but if I might tell Miss Lucy Benson a bit of my mind, I should say, 'Stick to an independent young fellow, like George Edmunds, and depend upon it you will be happier than you would with all the show and glitter of a squire's lady.' And I should say to Rose, very solemn, 'Rose——'

ROSE *enters unperceived, with beer.*

'Rose——'

ROSE (*starting*). Lord bless us! What a hollow voice!—Why, it 's Mr. Stokes!—What on earth is the matter with him?

MARTIN (*not seeing her*). Rose,—if you would be happy and contented, if you would escape destruction, shield yourself from dangerous peril, and save yourself from horrid ruin!—

ROSE. What dreadful words!—

MARTIN. You will at once, and without delay, bestow your hand on John Maddox; or if you would aspire to a higher rank in life, and a loftier station in society, you will cultivate the affections of Mr. Stokes,—Mr. Martin Stokes,—a young gentleman of great mental attractions, and very considerable personal charms; leaving the false and fatal Flam to the ignominious fate which——

ROSE. Why, Mr. Stokes.—

MARTIN. Ignominious fate which——

ROSE. Dear, he must be in a fit! Mr. Stokes!

MARTIN. Eh?—Ah! Miss Rose,—It's you, is it?

ROSE. Me! Yes, and here have I been waiting all this time, while you were talking nonsense to yourself. Here, I have brought you some beer.

MARTIN. Oh! Miss Rose, if you go on in this way, you'll bring us to our bier, instead of bringing our beer to us. (*Looking round.*) You may laugh, if you want to, very much, John.

JOHN. Hoo! hoo! hoo!

ROSE. Be quiet, oaf! And pray, sir (*to* MARTIN), to what may your most humorous observation refer?

MARTIN. Why, my dear Miss Rose, you know my way,—always friendly,—always thinking of the welfare of those I like best, and very seldom receiving any gratitude in return.

ROSE. I know you very seldom deserve any.

MARTIN. Ah! that's exactly my meaning; that's the way, you see. The moment I begin to throw out a hint to one of my dear friends, out comes some unkind and rude remark. But I bear it all for their sakes. I won't allow you to raise my ill nature,—you shan't stop me. I was going to say,—don't you think—now *don't* you think—that you—don't be angry—make rather—don't colour up,—*rather* too free with Mr. Sparkins Flam?

ROSE. *I* make free with Mr. Sparkins Flam! Why you odious, insolent creature!

MARTIN. Ah, of course—always the way—I told you so—I knew you'd say that.

ROSE. And you, John, you mean-spirited scarecrow; will you stand there, and see me insulted by an officious, impertinent——

MARTIN. Go on, go on! (*A gun fired.*) Hallo! (*Looking off.*) Here they are, the Squire and Mr. Sparkins Flam.

ROSE (*hastily adjusting her dress*). My goodness !   Mr. Spar——
run, John, run, there's a dear !

JOHN (*not moving*). Very dear, I dare say.

ROSE. Run, and tell my uncle and Lucy, that Mr. Spar——I mean
that the Squire's coming.

JOHN. I wouldn't ha' gone anyhow ; but nobody need go now, for
here they are.   Now, I'm extinguished for the rest of the day.

Enter through the gate SQUIRE NORTON *and* MR. SPARKINS FLAM,
*dressed for sporting, with guns, etc., and two Gamekeepers.
On the other side, Old* BENSON *and* LUCY.   MARTIN, *during
the whole scene, thrusts himself in the* SQUIRE'S *way, to be taken
notice of.*

SQUIRE (*to Gamekeeper, and putting down his gun*). Take the birds
into the house.   Benson, we have had a good day's sport, but a
tiring one ; and as the load is heavy for my fellows, you'll let
our game remain where it is.   I could not offer it to a better
friend.

BENSON. Your honour's very good, but——

SQUIRE. Nay, you make a merit of receiving the smallest favour.

BENSON. Not a merit of receiving, nor a boast of refusing it; but a
man in humble station should be cautious how he receives favours
from those above him, which he never asks, and can never return.
I have had too many such favours forced upon me by your honour,
lately, and would rather not increase the number.

SQUIRE. But such a trifle——

BENSON. A trifle from an equal, but a condescension from a superior.
Let your men carry your birds up to the Hall, sir, or, if they
are tired, mine shall do it for them, and welcome.   (*Retires up.*)

FLAM (*aside*). Swine and independence !   Leather breeches and
liberty !

SQUIRE. At least I may be permitted to leave a few brace, as a
present to the ladies.   Lucy, I hope, will not object.   (*Crosses
to her.*)

LUCY. I feel much flattered by your honour's politeness—and—and—
and——

ROSE. My cousin means to say, sir, that we're very much obliged to
your honour and Mr. Flam for your politeness, and that we are
very willing to accept of anything, your honour.

FLAM (*aside*). Condescending little savage!

SQUIRE. You have spoken well, both for yourself and your cousin. Flam, this is Rose—the pretty little Rose, you know.

FLAM. Know! can I ever forget the charming Rose—the beautiful —the—the—(*aside*) the Cabbage Rose!

SQUIRE (*aside*). Keep that girl engaged, while I talk to the other one.

ROSE. Oh, Mr. Flam!

FLAM. Oh, Miss Rose! (*He salutes her.*)

BENSON. Your honour will not object to taste our ale, after your day's sport. The afternoon is fresh and cool, and 'twill be pleasant here in the air. Here, Ben, Thomas, bring mugs here —quick—quick—and a seat for his honour.

[*Exeunt* BENSON, MADDOX, *etc.*

SQUIRE. It will be delightful—won't it, Flam?

FLAM. Inexpressibly charming! (*Aside.*) An amateur tea-garden. (*He retires a little up with* ROSE—*she coquetting.*)

SQUIRE (*to* LUCY). And in such society, how much the pleasure will be enhanced!

LUCY. Your honour knows I ought not to listen to you—George Edmunds would——

SQUIRE. Edmunds! a rustic!—you cannot love that Edmunds, Lucy. Forget him—remember your own worth.

LUCY. I wish I could, sir. My heart will tell me though, weak and silly as I am, that I cannot better show the consciousness of my own worth, than by remaining true to my first and early love. Your honour rouses my foolish pride; but real true love is not to be forgotten easily.

Song.—LUCY.

> Love is not a feeling to pass away,
> Like the balmy breath of a summer day;
> It is not—it cannot be—laid aside;
> It is not a thing to forget or hide.
> It clings to the heart, ah, woe is me!
> As the ivy clings to the old oak tree.
>
> Love is not a passion of earthly mould,
> As a thirst for honour, or fame, or gold:
> For when all these wishes have died away,
> The deep strong love of a brighter day,

298

Though nourish'd in secret, consumes the more,
As the slow rust eats to the iron's core.

Re-enter OLD BENSON, JOHN MADDOX, *and Villagers, with jugs,
seats, etc.*; SQUIRE NORTON *seats himself next* LUCY, *and* ROSE
contrives to sit next MR. SPARKINS FLAM, *which* MARTIN *and*
MADDOX *in vain endeavour to prevent.*

SQUIRE. Flam, you know these honest people? all tenants of my own.

FLAM. Oh, yes, I know 'em—pleasant fellows! This—this is—
what's his name?

BENSON. Martin, sir,—Martin Stokes.

MARTIN (*starting forward*). A—a—*Mr.* Stokes, at your service, sir,
—how do you do, sir? (*shaking* FLAM *by the hand, while speaking*).
I hope you are quite well, sir; I am delighted to see you looking
so well, sir. I hope your majestic father, and your fashionable
mother, are in the enjoyment of good health, sir. I should have
spoken to you before, sir, only you have been so very much
engaged, that I couldn't succeed in catching your honourable eye;
—very happy to see you, sir.

FLAM. Ah. Pleasant fellow, this Martin!—agreeable manners,—no
reserve about him.

MARTIN. Sir, you do me a great deal of honour. Mr. Norton, sir, I
have the honour of drinking your remarkably good health,—I
admire you, sir.

SQUIRE (*laughing*). Sir, I feel highly gratified, I'm sure.

MARTIN (*aside*). He's gratified!—I flatter myself I have produced a
slight impression here. (*Drinks.*)

FLAM (*turns round, sees* MADDOX). Ah, Ox!

JOHN. *Ox!* Who do you call Ox? Maddox is my name.

FLAM. Oh, mad Ox! true; I forgot the lunacy:—your health, mad
Ox.

SQUIRE (*rising and coming forward*). Come, Flam, another glass.
Here, friends, is success to our Harvest-Home!

MARTIN. Hear, hear! a most appropriate toast, most eloquently
given,—a charming sentiment, delightfully expressed. Gentlemen
(*to Villagers*), allow me to have the pleasure of proposing Mr.
Norton, if you please. Take your time from me. (*He gives the
time, and they all cheer.*) Mr. Norton, sir, I beg to call upon you
for a song.

299

Song.—SQUIRE NORTON.

That very wise head, old Æsop, said,
   The bow should be sometimes loose ;
Keep it tight for ever, the string you sever :—
   Let 's turn his old moral to use.
The world forget, and let us yet,
   The glass our spirits buoying,
Revel to-night in those moments bright
   Which make life worth enjoying.
The cares of the day, old moralists say,
   Are quite enough to perplex one ;
Then drive to-day's sorrow away till to-morrow,
   And then put it off till the next one.
      Chorus.—The cares of the day, etc.

Some plodding old crones, the heartless drones !
   Appeal to my cool reflection,
And ask me whether such nights can ever
   Charm sober recollection.
Yes, yes ! I cry, I 'll grieve and die,
   When those I love forsake me ;
But while friends so dear surround me here,
   Let Care, if he can, o'ertake me.
      Chorus.—The cares of the day, etc.

(*During the Chorus,* SQUIRE NORTON *and* FLAM *resume their guns, and go up the stage, followed by the various characters. The Chorus concludes as the Scene closes.*)

SCENE II.—*An open spot near the village, with stile and path-way leading to the church, which is seen in the distance.*

GEORGE EDMUNDS *enters, with a stick in his hand.*

EDMUNDS. How thickly the fallen leaves lie scattered at the feet of that old row of elm-trees ! When I first met Lucy on this spot, it was a fine spring day, and those same leaves were trembling in the sunshine, as green and bright as if their beauty would last for ever. What a contrast they present now, and how true an emblem of my own lost happiness !

300

Song.—GEORGE EDMUNDS.

Autumn leaves, autumn leaves, lie strewn around me here;
Autumn leaves, autumn leaves, how sad, how cold, how drear!
    How like the hopes of childhood's day,
      Thick clustering on the bough!
    How like those hopes is their decay,—
      How faded are they now!
Autumn leaves, autumn leaves, lie strewn around me here;
Autumn leaves, autumn leaves, how sad, how cold, how drear!

Wither'd leaves, wither'd leaves, that fly before the gale;
Wither'd leaves, wither'd leaves, ye tell a mournful tale,
    Of love once true, and friends once kind,
      And happy moments fled:
    Dispersed by every breath of wind,
      Forgotten, changed, or dead!
Autumn leaves, autumn leaves, lie strewn around me here;
Autumn leaves, autumn leaves, how sad, how cold, how drear!

An hour past the old time, and still no Lucy! 'Tis useless lingering
here: I'll wait no longer.   A female crossing the meadow!—'Tis
Rose, the bearer of a letter or a message perhaps.

Enter ROSE.   (*She avoids him.*)

No! Then I will see Lucy at once, without a moment's delay.
(*Going.*)

ROSE. No, no, you can't.   (*Aside.*) There'll certainly be bloodshed!
I am quite certain Mr. Flam will kill him.   He offered me, with
the most insinuating speeches, to cut John's throat at a moment's
notice: and when the Squire complimented him on being a good
shot, he said he should like to 'bag' the whole male population
of the village.   (*To him.*)   You can't see her.

EDMUNDS. Not see her, and she at home!   Were you instructed to
say this, Rose?

ROSE. I say it, because I know you can't see her. She is not well;
and—and——

EDMUNDS. And Mr. Norton is there, you would say.

ROSE. Mr. Norton!

EDMUNDS. Yes, Mr. Norton.   Was he not there last evening?   Was
he not there the evening before?   Is he not there at this moment?

Enter JOHN MADDOX.

JOHN. There at this moment?—of course he is.

ROSE (*aside*). John here!

JOHN. Of course he is; of course he was there last night; and of course he was there the evening before. He's always there, and so is his bosom friend and confidential demon, Mr. Sparkins Flam. Oh! George, we're injured men, both of us.

EDMUNDS. Heartless girl! (*Retires up.*)

JOHN (*to* ROSE). Faithless person!

ROSE. Don't call me a person.

JOHN. You *are* a person, perjured, treacherous, and deceiving! Oh! George, if you had seen what I have seen to-day. Soft whisperings and loving smiles, gentle looks and encouraging sighs,—such looks and sighs as used once upon a time to be bestowed on us, George! If you had seen the Squire making up to Lucy, and Rose making up to Flam:—but I am very glad you did not see it, George, very. It would have broken your heart, as it has broken mine! Oh, Rose! could you break my heart?

ROSE. I could break your head with the greatest pleasure, you mischief-making booby; and if you don't make haste to wherever you're going, somebody that I know of will certainly do so, very quickly.

JOHN. Will he, will he?—your friend, Mr. Flam, I suppose! Let him—that's all; let him! (*Retires up.*)

ROSE. Oh! I'll let him: you needn't be afraid of my interfering. Dear, dear, I wish Mr. Flam would come, for I will own, notwithstanding what graver people may say, that I enjoy a little flirtation as much as any one.

Song.—ROSE.

Some folks who have grown old and sour
Say love does nothing but annoy.
The fact is, they have had their hour,
So envy what they can't enjoy.
I like the glance—I like the sigh—
That does of ardent passion tell!
If some folks were as young as I,
I'm sure they'd like it quite as well.

302

Old maiden aunts so hate the men,
So well know how wives are harried,
It makes them sad—not jealous—when
They see their poor dear nieces married.
All men are fair and false, they know,
And with deep sighs they assail 'em,
It's so long since they tried men, though,
I rather think their memories fail 'em.

—Here comes Mr. Flam. You'd better go, John. I know you'll be murdered.

JOHN. Here I shall stop; let him touch me, and he shall feel the weight of my indignation.

Enter FLAM.

FLAM. Ah, my charmer! Punctual to my time, you see, my sweet little Damask Rose!

JOHN (*coming down*). A great deal more like a monthly one,—constantly changing, and gone the moment you wear it.

ROSE. Impertinent creature!

FLAM. Who is this poetical cauliflower?

JOHN. Don't pretend not to know me. You know who I am, well enough.

FLAM. As I live, it's the Ox!—retire, Ox, to your pasture, and don't rudely disturb the cooing of the doves. Go and graze, Ox!

JOHN. Suppose I choose to remain here, what then?

FLAM. Why then you must be driven off, mad Ox. (*To* ROSE.) Who is that other grasshopper?

ROSE. Hush, hush! for Heaven's sake don't let him hear you! It's young Edmunds.

FLAM. Young Edmunds? And who the devil is young Edmunds? For beyond the natural inference that young Edmunds is the son of old Edmunds, curse me if the fame of young Edmunds has ever reached my ears.

ROSE (*in a low tone*). It's Lucy's former lover, whom she has given up for the squire.

FLAM. The rejected cultivator?

ROSE. The same.

FLAM. Ah! I guessed as much from his earthy appearance. But, my darling Rose, I must speak with you,—I must—(*putting his arm round her waist, sees* JOHN).   Good-bye, Ox!

JOHN. Good-bye!

FLAM. Pleasant walk to you, Ox!

JOHN (*not moving*).   Thank 'ee;—same to you!

FLAM. That other clodpole must not stay here either.

ROSE. Yes, yes! he neither sees nor hears us.   Pray let him remain.

FLAM (*to* JOHN). You understand, Ox, that it is my wish that you forthwith retire and graze,—or in other words, that you at once, and without delay, betake yourself to the farm, or the devil, or any other place where you are in your element, and won't be in the way.

JOHN. Oh yes, I understand that.

FLAM. Very well; then the sooner you create a scarcity of such animals in this market, the better.   Now, my dear Rose (*puts his arm round her waist again*).   Are you gone, Ox?

JOHN. No.

FLAM. Are you going?

JOHN. By no means.

FLAM. This insolence is not to be borne.

ROSE. Oh, pray don't hurt him,—pray don't.   Go away, you stupid creature, if you don't want to be ruined.

JOHN. That's just the very advice I would give you, Rose; do *you* go away, if you don't want to be ruined.   As for me, this is a public place, and here I'll remain just as long as I think proper.

FLAM (*quitting* ROSE, *and advancing towards him*).   You will?

JOHN. I will.

ROSE. Oh, dear, dear! I knew he'd be murdered all along.   I was quite certain of it.

JOHN. Don't frown and scowl at me,—it won't do,—it only makes me smile; and when you talk of insolence and put my blood up, I tell you at once, that I am not to be bullied.

FLAM. Bullied?

JOHN. Ay, bullied was the word,—bullied by a coward, if you like that better.

FLAM. Coward! (*Seizes his gun by the barrel, and aims a blow at him, with the butt-end;* EDMUNDS *rushes forward, and strikes it up with his stick.*)

EDMUNDS. Hold your hand, sir,—hold your hand, or I'll fell you to

the ground. Maddox, leave this place directly : take the opposite
path, and I 'll follow you. (*Exit* MADDOX.) As for you, sir, who
by the way of vindicating yourself from the charge of cowardice,
raise your gun against an unarmed man, tell your protector, the
Squire, from me, that he and his companions might content
themselves with turning the heads of our farmers' daughters, and
endeavouring to corrupt their hearts, without wantonly insulting
the men they have most injured. Let this be a lesson to you, sir,
—although you were armed, you would have had the worst of a
scuffle, and you may not have the benefit of a third person's interference at so critical a moment, another time ;—remember this
warning, sir, and benefit by it.   [*Exit.*

FLAM (*aside*). If Norton does not take a dear revenge for this
insult, I have lost my influence with him. Bully ! coward !
They shall rue it.

ROSE (*with her apron to her eyes*). Oh, Mr. Flam ! I can't bear to
think that you should have suffered all this, on my account.

FLAM (*aside*). On her account !—a little vanity ! (*To her.*) Suffered !
Why, my dear, it was the drollest and most humorous affair that
ever happened. Here stand I,—the Honourable Sparkins Flam,
—on this second day of September, one thousand seven hundred
and twenty-nine ; and positively and solemnly declare that all
the coffee-houses, play-houses, faro-tables, brag-tables, assemblies,
drums and routs of a whole season put together, could not furnish
such a splendid piece of exquisite drollery. The idea is admirable.
My affecting to quarrel with a ploughman, and submitting to be
lectured by another caterpillar, whom I suffer to burst into a
butterfly importance !

ROSE. Then you were not really quarrelling ?

FLAM. Bless you, no ! I was only acting.

ROSE. Lor' ! how well you do act, to be sure.

FLAM. Come, let us retire into the house, or after this joke we shall
be the gaze of all the animated potatoes that are planted in this
hole of a village. Why do you hesitate, Damask ?

ROSE. Why, I have just been thinking that if you go to all these
coffee-houses, and play-houses, and fairs, and brags, and keep playing drums, and routing people about, you 'll forget me, when you
go back to London.

FLAM (*aside*). More than probable. (*To her.*) Never fear ; you

305

will be generally known as Rose the lovely, and I shall be universally denominated Flam the constant.

Duet.—ROSE *and* SPARKINS FLAM.

FLAM.　　　　'Tis true I'm caress'd by the witty,
　　　　　　　The envy of all the fine beaux,
　　　　　　　The pet of the court and the city,
　　　　　　　But still I'm the lover of Rose.

ROSE.　　　　Country sweethearts, oh, how I despise!
　　　　　　　And oh! how delighted I am
　　　　　　　To think that I shine in the eyes
　　　　　　　Of the elegant—sweet—Mr. Flam.

FLAM. Allow me (*offers to kiss her*).
ROSE.　　　　Pray don't be so bold, sir.　(*Kisses her.*)
FLAM.　　　　What sweets on that honey'd lip hang!
ROSE.　　　　Your presumption, I know, I should scold, sir,
　　　　　　　But I really *can't* scold Mr. Flam.

BOTH.　　　　Then let us be happy together,
　　　　　　　Content with the world as it goes,
　　　　　　　An unchangeable couple for ever,
　　　　　　　Mr. Flam and his beautiful Rose.　　　[*Exeunt.*

SCENE III.—*The Farmer's Kitchen.　A table and chairs.*

Enter OLD BENSON *and* MARTIN.

BENSON. Well, Stokes. Now you have the opportunity you have
　　desired, and we are alone, I am ready to listen to the information
　　which you wished to communicate to my private ear.
MARTIN. Exactly;—you said information, I think?
BENSON. *You* said information, or I have forgotten.
MARTIN. Just so, exactly; I said information. I *did* say informa-
　　tion, why should I deny it?
BENSON. I see no necessity for your doing so, certainly. Pray go on.
MARTIN. Why, you see, my dear Mr. Benson, the fact is—won't you
　　be seated? Pray sit down (*brings forward two chairs;—they sit*).
　　There, now,—let me see,—where was I?
BENSON. You were going to begin, I think.

306

MARTIN. Oh,—ah!—so I was;—I hadn't begun, had I?

BENSON. No, no! Pray begin again, if you had.

MARTIN. Well, then, what I have got to say is not so much information, as a kind of advice, or suggestion, or hint, or something of
that kind; and it relates to—eh?—(*looking very mysterious*).

BENSON. What?

MARTIN. Yes (*nodding*). Don't you think there's something wrong
there?

BENSON. Where?

MARTIN. In that quarter.

BENSON. In what quarter? Speak more plainly, sir.

MARTIN. You know what a friendly feeling I entertain to your
family. You know what a very particular friend of mine you are.
You know how anxious I always am to prevent anything going
wrong.

BENSON. Well! (*abruptly*).

MARTIN. Yes, I see you're very sensible of it, but I'll take it for
granted: you needn't bounce and fizz about, in that way, because
it makes one nervous. Don't you think, now, *don't* you think,
that ill-natured people may say;—don't be angry, you know,
because if I wasn't a very particular friend of the family, I
wouldn't mention the subject on any account;—don't you think
that ill-natured people may say there's something wrong in the
frequency of the Squire's visits here?

BENSON (*starting up furiously*). What!

MARTIN (*aside*). Here he goes again!

BENSON. Who dares suspect my child?

MARTIN. Ah, to be sure, that's exactly what I say. Who dares?
Damme, I should like to see 'em!

BENSON. Is it you?

MARTIN. I! Bless you, no, not for the world! I!—Come, that's a
good one. I only say what other people say, you know; that's all.

BENSON. And what are these tales, that idle busy fools prate of with
delight, among themselves, caring not whose ears they reach, so
long as they are kept from the old man, whose blindness—the
blindness of a fond and doting father—is subject for their rude
and brutal jeering. What are they?

MARTIN. Dear me, Mr. Benson, you keep me in a state of perpetual
excitement.

307

BENSON. Tell me, without equivocation, what do they say?

MARTIN. Why, they say they think it—not exactly wrong, perhaps; don't fly out, now—but among those remarkable coincidences which do occur sometimes, that whenever you go out of your house, the Squire and his friend should come into it; that Miss Lucy and Miss Rose, in the long walks they take every day, should be met and walked home with by the same gentlemen; that long after you have gone to bed at night, the Squire and Mr. Sparkins Flam should still be seen hovering about the lane and meadow; and that one of the lattice windows should be always open, at that hour.

BENSON. This is all?

MARTIN. Ye—yes,—yes, that's all.

BENSON. Nothing beside?

MARTIN. Eh?

BENSON. Nothing beside?

MARTIN. Why, there *is* something else, but I know you'll begin to bounce about again, if I tell it you.

BENSON. No, no! let me hear it all.

MARTIN. Why, then, they do say that the Squire has been heard to boast that he had practised on Lucy's mind—that when he bid her, she would leave her father and her home, and follow him over the world.

BENSON. They lie! Her breast is pure and innocent! Her soul is free from guilt; her mind from blemish. They lie! I'll not believe it. Are they mad? Do they think that I stand tamely by, and look upon my child's disgrace? Heaven! do they know of what a father's heart is made?

MARTIN. My dear Mr. Benson, if you——

BENSON. This coarse and brutal boast shall be disowned. (*Going*; MARTIN *stops him*.)

MARTIN. My dear Mr. Benson, you know it may not have been made after all,—my dear sir,——

BENSON (*struggling*). Unhand me, Martin! Made or not made, it has gone abroad, fixing an infamous notoriety on me and mine. I'll hear its truth or falsehood from himself. (*Breaks from him and exit.*)

MARTIN (*solus*). There'll be something decidedly wrong here presently. Hallo! here's another very particular friend in a fume.

308

Enter YOUNG BENSON *hastily.*

MARTIN. Ah! my dear fellow, how——

YOUNG BENSON. Where is Lucy?

MARTIN. I don't know, unless she has walked out with the Squire.

YOUNG BENSON. The Squire!

MARTIN. To be sure; she very often walks out with the Squire. Very pleasant recreation walking out with the Squire;—capital custom, an't it?

YOUNG BENSON. Where's my father?

MARTIN. Why, upon my word, I am unable to satisfy your curiosity in that particular either. All I know of him is that he whisked out of this room in a rather boisterous and turbulent manner for an individual at his time of life, some few seconds before you whisked in. But what's the matter?—you seem excited. Nothing wrong, is there?

YOUNG BENSON (*aside*). This treatment of Edmunds, and Lucy's altered behaviour to him, confirm my worst fears. Where is Mr. Norton?

MARTIN (*calling off*). Ah! to be sure,—where is Mr. Norton?

Enter SQUIRE.

SQUIRE. Mr. Norton is here. Who wishes to see him?

MARTIN. To be sure, sir. Mr. Norton is here: who wishes to see him?

YOUNG BENSON. I do.

MARTIN. I don't. Old fellow, good-bye! Mr. Norton, good evening! (*Aside.*) There'll be something wrong here, in a minute. [*Exit.*

SQUIRE. Well, young man?

YOUNG BENSON. If you contemplate treachery here, Mr. Norton, look to yourself. My father is an old man; the chief prop of his declining years is his child,—my sister. For your actions here, sir, you shall render a dear account to me.

SQUIRE. To *you*, peasant!

YOUNG BENSON. To me, sir. One other scene like that enacted by your creature, at your command, to-night, may terminate more seriously to him. For your behaviour here you are responsible to me.

SQUIRE. Indeed! Anything more, sir?

Young Benson. Simply this :—after injuring the old man beyond reparation, and embittering the last moments of his life, you may possibly attempt to shield yourself under the paltry excuse, that, as a gentleman, you cannot descend to take the consequences from my hand. You *shall* take them from me, sir, if I strike you to the earth first.   [*Exit.*

Squire. Fiery and valorous, indeed! As the suspicions of the family are aroused, no time is to be lost : the girl must be carried off to-night, if possible. With Flam's assistance and management, she may be speedily removed from within the reach of these rustic sparks. In my cooler moments, the reflection of the misery I may inflict upon the old man makes my conduct appear base and dishonourable, even to myself. Pshaw! hundreds have done the same thing before me, who have been lauded and blazoned forth as men of honour. Honour in such cases,—an idle tale!—a by-word! Honour! There is much to be gleaned from old tales; and the legend of the child and the old man speaks but too truly.

Song.—Squire Norton.

The child and the old man sat alone
    In the quiet peaceful shade
Of the old green boughs, that had richly grown
    In the deep thick forest glade.
It was a soft and pleasant sound,
    That rustling of the oak ;
And the gentle breeze play'd lightly round,
    As thus the fair boy spoke :—

' Dear father, what can honour be,
    Of which I hear men rave ?
Field, cell and cloister, land and sea,
    The tempest and the grave :—
It lives in all, 'tis sought in each,
    'Tis never heard or seen :
Now tell me, father, I beseech,
    What can this honour mean ? '

' It is a name,—a name, my child,—
    It lived in other days,
When men were rude, their passions wild,
    Their sport, thick battle-frays.

310

When in armour bright, the warrior bold,
    Knelt to his lady's eyes:
Beneath the abbey-pavement old
    That warrior's dust now lies.

'The iron hearts of that old day
    Have moulder'd in the grave;
And chivalry has pass'd away,
    With knights so true and brave;
The honour, which to them was life,
    Throbs in no bosom now;
It only gilds the gambler's strife,
    Or decks the worthless vow.'[1]

Enter LUCY.

SQUIRE. Lucy, dear Lucy.

LUCY. Let me entreat you not to stay here, sir! you will be exposed to nothing but insult and attack. Edmunds and my brother have both returned, irritated at something that has passed with my cousin Rose:—for my sake,—for my sake, Mr. Norton, spare me the pain of witnessing what will ensue, if they find you here. You little know what I have borne already.

SQUIRE. For your sake, Lucy, I would do much; but why should I leave you to encounter the passion and ill-will, from which you would have me fly?

LUCY. Oh, I can bear it, sir; I deserve it but too well.

SQUIRE. Deserve it!—you do yourself an injustice, Lucy. No; rather let me remove you from a house where you will suffer nothing but persecution, and confer upon you a title which the proudest lady in the land might wear. Here—here, on my knees (*he bends on his knee, and seizes her hand*).

Enter FLAM.

'SQUIRE (*rising*). Flam here!

'FLAM (*aside*). Upon my word!—I thought we had been getting on 'pretty well in the open air, but they're beating us hollow here, 'under cover.

---

[1] In John Hullah's music to this song, the last two lines are printed as follows:—

    'The name adorns the gambler's strife,
    Or gilds the worthless vow.'—ED.

'SQUIRE. Lucy, but one word, and I understand your decision.

'LUCY. I—I cannot subdue the feelings of uneasiness and distrust
'which the great difference between your honour's rank and mine
'awakens in my mind.

'SQUIRE. Difference! Hundreds of such cases happen every day.

'LUCY. Indeed!

'SQUIRE. Oh, 'tis a matter of general notoriety,—isn't it, Flam?

'FLAM. No doubt of it. (*Aside.*) Don't exactly know yet what
'they are talking about, though.

'SQUIRE. A relation of my own, a man of exalted rank, courted a
'girl far his inferior in station, but only beneath him in that
'respect. In all others she was on a footing of equality with
'himself, if not far above him.

'LUCY. And were they married?

'FLAM (*aside*). Rather an important circumstance in the case. I *do*
'remember that.

'SQUIRE. They were,—after a time, when the resentment of his
'friends, occasioned by his forming such an attachment, had sub-
'sided, and he was able to acknowledge her, without involving the
'ruin of both.

'LUCY. They were married privately at first, then?

'FLAM (*aside*). I must put in a word here. Oh, yes, it was all
'comfortably arranged to everybody's satisfaction, — wasn't it,
'Norton?

'SQUIRE. Certainly. And a happy couple they were, weren't they,
'Flam?

'FLAM. Happiest of the happy. As happy as (*aside*)—a separation
'could make them.

'SQUIRE. Hundreds of great people have formed similar attachments,
'—haven't they, Flam?

'FLAM. Undoubtedly. There was the Right Honourable Augustus
'Frederick Charles Thomson Camharado, and the German Baron
'Hyfenstyfenlooberhausen, and they were both married—(*aside*) to
'somebody else, first. Not to mention Damask and I, who are
'models of constancy. By the bye, I have lost sight of her, and I
'am interrupting you. (*Aside to* SQUIRE, *as he goes out.*) I came to
'tell you that she is ripe for an elopement, if you urge her strongly.
'Edmunds has been reproaching her to my knowledge. She 'll
'consent while her passion lasts.   [*Exit.*

312

SQUIRE. Lucy, I wait your answer. One word from you, and a few hours will place you far beyond the reach of those who would fetter your choice and control your inclinations. You hesitate. Come, decide. The Squire's lady, or the wife of Edmunds!

Duet.—LUCY *and* SQUIRE NORTON.

SQUIRE.   In rich and lofty station shine,
                        Before his jealous eyes :
                   In golden splendour, lady mine,
                        This peasant youth despise.

LUCY (*apart : the* SQUIRE *regarding her attentively*).
                   Oh! it would be revenge indeed
                        With scorn his glance to meet.
                   I, I, his humble pleading heed !
                        I'd spurn him from my feet.

SQUIRE.   With love and rage her bosom's torn,
                        And rash the choice will be ;
LUCY.   With love and rage my bosom's torn,
                        And rash the choice will be.

SQUIRE.   From hence she quickly must be borne,
                        Her home, her home, she'll flee.
LUCY.   Oh ! long shall I have cause to mourn
                        My home, my home, for thee !

Enter OLD BENSON.

BENSON. What do I see ! The Squire and Lucy.

SQUIRE. Listen. A chaise and four fleet horses, under the direction of a trusty friend of mine, will be in waiting on the high road, at the corner of the Elm-Tree avenue, to-night, at ten o'clock. They shall bear you whither we can be safe, and in secret, by the first light of morning.

LUCY. His cruel harshness;—it would be revenge, indeed. But my father—my poor old father !

SQUIRE. Your father is prejudiced in Edmunds' favour ; and so long as he thinks there is any chance of your being his, he will oppose your holding communication with me. Situated as you are now, you only stand in the way of his wealth and advancement. Once

313

' fly with me, and in four-and-twenty hours you will be his pride,
' his boast, his support.

OLD BENSON coming forward.

BENSON. It is a lie, a base lie!—(LUCY *shrieks and throws herself at his feet.*) My pride! my boast! She would be my disgrace, my shame: an outcast from her father's roof, and from the world. Support!—support *me* with the gold coined in her infamy and guilt! Heaven help me! Have I cherished her for this!

LUCY (*clinging to him*). Father!—dear, dear father!

SQUIRE. Hear me speak, Benson. Be calm.

BENSON. Calm!—Do you know that from infancy I have almost worshipped her, fancying that I saw in her young mind the virtues of a mother, to whom the anguish of this one hour would have been worse than death! Calm!—do you know that I have a heart and soul within me; or do you believe that because I am of lower station, I am a being of a different order from yourself, and that Nature has denied me thought and feeling! Calm! Man, do you know that I am this girl's father?

SQUIRE. Benson, if you will not hear me, at least do not, by hastily exposing this matter, deprive me of the inclination of making you some reparation.

BENSON. Reparation! You need be thankful, sir, for the grasp she has upon my arm. Money! If she were dying for want, and the smallest coin from you could restore her to life and health, sooner than she should take it from your hand, I would cast her from a sick bed to perish on the road-side.

SQUIRE. Benson, a word.

BENSON. Do not, I caution you; do not talk to me, sir. I am an old man, but I do not know what passion may make me do.

SQUIRE. These are high words, Benson. A farmer!

BENSON. Yes, sir; a farmer, one of the men on whom you, and such as you, depend for the money they squander in profligacy and idleness. A farmer, sir! I care not for your long pedigree of ancestors,—my forefathers made them all. Here, neighbours, friends! (ROSE, MADDOX, STOKES, *Villagers, etc., crowd on the stage.*) Hear this, hear this! your landlord, a high-born gentleman, entering the houses of your humble farmers, and tempting their daughters to destruction!

314

Enter YOUNG BENSON *and* GEORGE EDMUNDS.

YOUNG BENSON. What's that I hear? (*rushing towards the* SQUIRE, STOKES *interposes*).

MARTIN. Hallo, hallo! Take hold of the other one, John. (MADDOX *and he remove them to opposite sides of the stage.*) Hold him tight, John, hold him tight. Stand still, there's a good fellow. Keep back, Squire. Knew there'd be something wrong,—ready to come in at the nick of time,—captital custom.

FLAM *enters and stands next the* SQUIRE.

SQUIRE. Exposed, baited! Benson, are you mad? Within the last few hours my friend here has been attacked and insulted on the very land you hold, by a person in your employ and young Edmunds there. I, too, have been threatened and insulted in the presence of my tenantry and workmen. Take care you do not drive me to extremities. Remember—the lease of this farm for seventy years, which your father took of mine, expires to-morrow; and that I have the power to refuse its renewal. Again I ask you, are you mad?

BENSON. Quit my house, villain!

SQUIRE. Villain! quit *my* house, then. This farm is mine: and you and yours shall depart from under its roof, before the sun has set to-morrow. (BENSON *sinks into a chair in centre, and covers his face with his hands.*)

Sestet and Chorus.

LUCY—ROSE—EDMUNDS—SQUIRE NORTON—FLAM—
YOUNG BENSON—*and Chorus.*

YOUNG BENSON. Turn him from the farm! From his home will you cast
    The old man who has till'd it for years?
Every tree, every flower, is link'd with the past,
    And a friend of his childhood appears.
Turn *him* from the farm! O'er its grassy hill-side,
    A gay boy he once loved to range;
His boyhood has fled, and its dear friends are dead,
    But these meadows have never known change.

EDMUNDS.   Oppressor, hear me.
LUCY.   On my knees I implore
SQUIRE.   I command it, and you will obey.

Rose.   Rise, dear Lucy, rise; you shall not kneel before
            The tyrant who drives us away.

Squire.   Your sorrows are useless, your prayers are in vain;
            I command it and you will begone.
            I 'll hear no more.

Edmunds.   No, they shall not beg again,
            Of a man whom I view with deep scorn.

Flam. Do not yield.

Young Benson.
Squire.   } Leave the farm!
Lucy.
Rose.

Edmunds.   Your power I despise.

Squire. And your threats, boy, I disregard, too.

Flam. Do not yield.

Young Benson.
Squire.   } Leave the farm!
Lucy.
Rose.

Rose.   If he leaves it, he dies.

Edmunds. This base act, proud man, you shall rue.

Young Benson. Turn him from the farm!   From his home will you
            cast
            The old man who has till'd it for years?
            Every tree, every flower, is link'd with the past,
            And a friend of his childhood appears!

Squire.   Yes, yes, leave the farm!   From his home I will cast
            The old man who has till'd it for years;
            Though each tree and flower is link'd with the past,
            And a friend of his childhood appears.

Chorus.

He has turn'd from his farm, from his home he has cast
    The old man who has till'd it for years;
Though each tree and flower is link'd with the past,
    And a friend of his childhood appears.

END OF THE FIRST ACT

316

ACT II

SCENE I.—*An Apartment in the Hall. A breakfast-table, with urn and tea-service. A Livery Servant arranging it.* FLAM, *in a morning gown and slippers, reclining on the sofa.*

FLAM. Is the Squire out of bed yet?

SERVANT. Yes, sir, he will be down directly.

FLAM. Any letters from London?

SERVANT. One for your honour, that the man brought over from the market-town, this morning.

FLAM. Give it me, blockhead! (*Servant gives it, and exit.*) Never like the look of a great official-folded letter, with a large seal, 'it's always an unpleasant one. Talk of discovering a man's 'character from his handwriting!—I'll back myself against any 'odds to form a very close guess at the contents of a letter from 'the form into which it is folded. This, now, I should say, is a 'decidedly hostile fold.' Let us see—'King's Bench Walk— September 1st, 1729. Sir, I am instructed by my client, Mr. Edward Montague, to apply to you—(the old story—for the immediate payment, I suppose—what's this?)—to apply to you for the instant restitution of the sum of two hundred and fifty pounds, his son lost to you at play; and to acquaint you, that unless it is immediately forwarded to my office, as above, the circumstances of the transaction will be made known; and the unfair and fraudulent means by which you deprived the young man of his money, publicly advertised.—I am, Sir, your obedient Servant, John Ellis.' The devil! 'who would believe now, that 'such a trifling circumstance as the mere insinuation of a small 'piece of gold into the corner of two dice would influence a man's 'destiny!' What's to be done? If, by some dextrous stroke, I could manage to curry favour with Norton, and procure some handsome present in return for services rendered,—for, 'work and labour done and performed,' as my obedient servant, John Ellis, would say, I might keep my head above water yet. I have it! He shall have a joyful surprise. I'll carry this girl off for him, and he shall know nothing of the enterprise until it is completed, or at least till she is fairly off. I have been well rewarded for

317

similar services before, and may securely calculate on his gratitude in the present instance. He is here. (*Puts up the letter.*)

Enter SQUIRE NORTON.

SQUIRE (*seating himself at table*). Has any application for permission to remain on the farm been made from Benson, this morning, Flam?

FLAM. None.

SQUIRE. I am very sorry for it, although I admire the old man's independent spirit. I am very sorry for it. Wrong as I know I have been, I would rather that the first concession came from him.

FLAM. Concession!

SQUIRE. The more I reflect upon the occurrences of yesterday, Flam, the more I regret that, under the influence of momentary passion and excitement, I should have used so uncalled-for a threat against my father's oldest tenant. It is an act of baseness to which I look back with abhorrence.

FLAM (*aside*). What weathercock morality is this!

SQUIRE. It was unnecessary violence.

FLAM. Unnecessary! Oh, certainly; no doubt you could have attained your object without it, and can still. There is no occasion to punish the old man.

SQUIRE. Nor will I. He shall not leave the farm, if I myself implore, and beg him to remain.

Enter Servant.

SERVANT. Two young women to speak with your honour.

Enter LUCY *and* ROSE.

SQUIRE. Lucy!

FLAM (*aside*). She must be carried off to-night, or she certainly will save me the trouble, and I shall lose the money.

LUCY. Your honour may be well surprised to see me here, after the events of yesterday. It has cost me no trifling struggle to take this step, but I hope my better feelings have at length prevailed, and conquered my pride and weakness. I wish to speak to your honour, with nobody by.

FLAM (*aside*). Nobody by! I rather suspect I'm not particularly wanted here. (*To them.*) Pray allow us to retire for a few moments. Rose, my dear.

ROSE. Well!

318

FLAM. Come along.

LUCY. Rose will remain here, I brought her for that purpose.

FLAM. Bless me! that's very odd. As you please, of course, but I really think you'll find her very much in the way. (*Aside*.) Acting propriety! So much the better for my purpose; a little coyness will enhance the value of the prize. [*Exit* FLAM.

LUCY. Mr. Norton, I come here to throw myself upon your honourable feelings, as a man and as a gentleman. Oh, sir! now that my eyes are opened to the misery into which I have plunged myself, by my own ingratitude and treachery, do not—do not add to it the reflection that I have driven my father in his old age from the house where he was born, and in which he hoped to have died.

SQUIRE. Be calm, Lucy; your father shall continue to hold the farm; the lease shall be renewed.

LUCY. I have more to say to your honour still, and what I have to add may even induce your honour to retract the promise you have just now made me.

SQUIRE. Lucy! what can you mean?

LUCY. Oh, sir! call me coquette, faithless, treacherous, deceitful, what you will; I deserve it all;—but believe me, I speak the truth when I make the humiliating avowal. A weak, despicable vanity induced me to listen with a ready ear to your honour's addresses, and to cast away the best and noblest heart that ever woman won.

SQUIRE. Lucy, 'twas but last night you told me that your love for Edmunds had vanished into air; that you hated and despised him.

LUCY. I know it, sir, too well. He laid bare my own guilt, and showed me the ruin which impended over me. He spoke the truth. Your honour more than confirmed him.

SQUIRE (*after a pause*). Even the avowal you have just made, unexpected as it is, shall not disturb my resolution. Your father shall not leave the farm.

Quartet.

LUCY—ROSE—SQUIRE NORTON, *and afterwards* YOUNG BENSON.

SQUIRE. Hear me, when I swear that the farm is your own
        Through all changes Fortune may make;
    The base charge of falsehood I never have known;
        This promise I never will break.

319

ROSE *and* LUCY. Hear him, when he swears that the farm is our own
      Through all changes Fortune may make ;
      The base charge of falsehood he never has known ;
      This promise he never will break.

Enter YOUNG BENSON.

YOUNG BENSON. My sister here !   Lucy ! begone, I command.

SQUIRE. To your home I restore you again.

YOUNG BENSON. No boon I 'll accept from that treacherous hand
      As the price of my sister's fair fame.

SQUIRE. To your home !

YOUNG BENSON (*to* LUCY). Hence away !

LUCY.   Brother dear, I obey.

SQUIRE. I restore.

YOUNG BENSON.   Hence away !

YOUNG BENSON, ROSE, *and* LUCY.   Let us leave.

LUCY. He swears it, dear brother.

SQUIRE.   I swear it.

YOUNG BENSON.   Away !

SQUIRE. I swear it.

YOUNG BENSON.   You swear to deceive.

SQUIRE. Hear me, when I swear that the farm is your own
      Through all changes Fortune may make.

LUCY *and* ROSE. Hear him when he swears that the farm is our own
      Through all changes Fortune may make.

YOUNG BENSON. Hear him swear, hear him swear, that the farm is
      our own
      Through all changes Fortune may make.

SQUIRE. The base charge of falsehood I never have known,
      This promise I never will break.

LUCY *and* ROSE. The base charge of falsehood he never has known,
      This promise he never will break.

YOUNG BENSON. The base charge of falsehood he often has known,
      This promise he surely will break.

                       [*Exeunt omnes.*

Re-enter FLAM, *in a walking-dress.*

FLAM. The coast is clear at last.   What on earth the conversation
can have been, at which Rose *was* wanted, and I was not, I confess

320

my inability to comprehend; but away with speculation, and now
to business.—(*Rings.*)

Enter Servant.

Pen and ink.

SERVANT. Yes, sir.   [*Exit Servant.*

FLAM (*solus*). Nearly all the tenantry will be assembled here at the
ball to-night; and if the father of this rustic Dulcinea is reinstated
in his farm, he and his people will no doubt be among the number.
It will be easy enough to entice the girl into the garden, through
the window opening on the lawn; a chaise can be waiting in the
quiet lane at the side, and some trusty fellow can slip a hasty
note into Norton's hands informing him of the flight, and naming
the place at which he can join us. (*Re-enter Servant with pen,
ink, taper, and two sheets of notepaper; he places them on the table
and exit.*) I may as well reply to my friend Mr. John Ellis's
obliging favour now, too, by promising that the money shall be
forwarded in the course of three days' post. (*Takes the letter from
his pocket, and lays it on the table.*) Lie you there. First, for
Norton's note.—' Dear Norton,—knowing your wishes—seized the
girl—no blame attach to you. Join us as soon as people have
dispersed in search of her in all directions but the right one,—
fifteen miles off.' (*Folds it ready for an envelope and lays it by the
side of the other letter.*) Now for John Ellis. Why, what does
the rascal mean by bringing but two sheets of paper? No matter:
that affair will keep cool till to-morrow, when I have less business
on my hands, and more money in my pockets, I hope. (*Crumples
the letter he has just written, hastily up, thrusts it into his pocket,
and folds the wrong one in the envelope. As he is sealing it*

Enter MARTIN, *very cautiously.*

MARTIN (*peeping*). There he is, hatching some mysterious and diabolical plot. If I can only get to the bottom of these dreadful
designs, I shall immortalise myself. What a lucky dog I am, to be
such a successful gleaner of news, and such a confidential person
into the bargain, as to be the first to hear that he wanted some
trustworthy person. All comes of talking to everybody I meet,
and drawing out everything they hear. Capital custom! He don't
see me. Hem! (*Coughs very loud, and when* FLAM *looks round,
nods familiarly.*) How are you again?

321

FLAM. How am I again ! Who the devil are you ?—and what do you want here ?

MARTIN. Hush !

FLAM. Eh ?

MARTIN. Hush ! I 'm the man.

FLAM. *The* man !

MARTIN. Yes, the man that you asked the ostler at the George to recommend you ; the trustworthy man that knows all the by-roads well, and can keep a secret ; the man that you wanted to lend you a hand in a job that——

FLAM. Hush, hush !

MARTIN. Oh ! you 're beginning to hush now, are you ?

FLAM. Haven't I seen your face before ?

MARTIN. To be sure you have. You recollect admiring my manners at Benson's yesterday. You must remember Mr. Martin Stokes. You *can't* have forgotten him—not possible !

FLAM (*aside*). A friend of Benson !—a dangerous rencontre. Another moment, and our conversation might have taken an awkward turn. (*To him.*) So you are Stokes, eh ? Benson's friend Stokes ?

MARTIN. To be sure. Ha, ha ! I knew you couldn't have forgotten me. Pleasant Stokes they call me, clever Stokes sometimes ;—but that 's flattery.

FLAM. No, surely.

MARTIN. Yes, 'pon my life ! it is. Can't bear flattery,—don't like it at all.

FLAM. Well, Mr. Stokes——

MARTIN (*aside*). Now for the secret.

FLAM. I am very sorry you have had the trouble of coming up here, Mr. Stokes, because I have changed my plan, and shall not require your valuable services. (*Goes up to the table.*)

MARTIN (*aside*). Something wrong here : try him again. You 're sure you don't want me ?

FLAM. Quite.

MARTIN. That 's unlucky, because, as I have quarrelled with Benson——

FLAM. Quarrelled with Benson !

MARTIN. What ! didn't you know that ?

FLAM. Never heard of it. Now I think of it, Mr. Stokes, I *shall* want your assistance. Pray, sit down, Mr. Stokes.

322

MARTIN. With pleasure. (*They sit.*) I say, I *thought* you wanted me.

FLAM. Ah! you 're a sharp fellow.

MARTIN. You don't mean that ?

FLAM. I do, indeed.

MARTIN (*aside*). You would, if you knew all.

FLAM (*aside*). Conceited hound !

MARTIN (*aside*). Poor devil !

FLAM. Mr. Stokes, I needn't impress upon a gentleman of your intelligence, the necessity of secrecy in this matter.

MARTIN. Of course not : see all—say nothing.   Capital custom :— (*aside*) not mine though.   Go on.

FLAM. You wouldn't mind playing Benson a trick,—just a harmless trick ?

' MARTIN. Certainly not.   Go on.

' FLAM. I 'll trust you.

' MARTIN. So you may.   Go on.'

FLAM. A chaise and four will be waiting to-night, at ten o'clock precisely, at the little gate that opens from the garden into the lane.

' MARTIN. No : will it though ?   Go on.'

FLAM. ' Don't interrupt me, Stokes.'   Into that chaise you must assist me in forcing as quickly as possible and without noise——

' MARTIN. Yes.   Go on.

' FLAM. Whom do you think ?

' MARTIN. Don't know.'

FLAM. Can't you guess whom ?

MARTIN. No.

FLAM. Try.

MARTIN. Eh ! what ! —Miss——

FLAM. Hush, hush ! You understand me, I see. Not another word ; not another syllable.

MARTIN. But do you really mean to run away with——

FLAM (*stopping his mouth*). You understand me ;—that 's quite sufficient.

MARTIN (*aside*). He 's going to run away with Rose. Why, if I hadn't found this out, John Maddox,—one of my most particular friends, —would have gone stark, staring, raving mad with grief. (*To him.*) But what will become of Miss Lucy, when she has lost Rose ?

FLAM. No matter. We cannot take them both, without the certainty of an immediate discovery. 'Meet me at the corner of the 'avenue, before the ball commences, and I will communicate any 'further instructions I may have to give you. Meanwhile' take this (*gives him money*) as an earnest of what you shall receive when the girl is secured. Remember, silence and secrecy.

MARTIN. Silence and secrecy, (*exit* FLAM)—confidence and two guineas. I am perfectly bewildered with this tremendous secret. What shall I do? Where shall I go?—To my particular friend, old Benson, or young Benson, or George Edmunds? or—no; I'll go and paralyse my particular friend, John Maddox. Not a moment is to be lost. I am all in a flutter. Run away with Rose! I suppose he'll run away with Lucy next. *I* shouldn't wonder. Run away with Rose! I never did—— [*Exit hastily.*

SCENE II.—*An open spot in the Village.*

Enter SQUIRE NORTON.

SQUIRE. My mind is made up. This girl has opened her whole heart to me; and it would be worse than villainy to pursue her further. I will seek out Benson and Edmunds, and endeavour to repair the mischief my folly has occasioned. I have sought happiness in the dissipation of crowded cities, in vain. A country life offers health and cheerfulness; and a country life shall henceforth be mine, in all seasons.

Song.—SQUIRE NORTON.

There's a charm in Spring, when everything
　　Is bursting from the ground;
When pleasant showers bring forth the flowers,
　　And all is life around.

In summer day, the fragrant hay
　　Most sweetly scents the breeze;
And all is still, save murmuring rill,
　　Or sound of humming bees.

Old Autumn come, with trusty gun
　　In quest of birds we roam:
Unerring aim, we mark the game,
　　And proudly bear it home.

A winter's night has its delight,
    Well warm'd to bed we go ;
A winter's day, we 're blithe and gay,
    Snipe-shooting in the snow.

A country life without the strife
    And noisy din of town,
Is all I need, I take no heed
    Of splendour or renown.

And when I die, oh, let me lie
    Where trees above me wave ;
Let wild plants bloom, around my tomb,
    My quiet country grave !   [*Exit.*

SCENE III.—*The Rick-yard.   Same as* ACT I. SCENE I.

EDMUNDS *and* MADDOX *meeting.*

JOHN. Ah, George ! Why this is kind to come down to the old farm
    to-day, and take one peep at us, before we leave it for ever. I
    suppose it 's fancy, now, George, but to my thinking I never saw
    the hedges look so fresh, the fields so rich, or the old house so pretty
    and comfortable, as they do this morning. It 's fancy that, George,
    —an't it ?

EDMUNDS. It 's a place you may well be fond of, and attached to, for
    it 's the prettiest spot in all the country round.

JOHN. Ah ! you always enter into my feelings ; and speaking of that,
    I want to ask your advice about Rose. I meant to come up to you
    to-day, on purpose. Do you think she is fond of me, George ?

EDMUNDS (*smiling*). What do *you* think ? She has not shown any
    desperate warmth of affection, of late, has she ?

JOHN. No—no, she certainly has not, but she used to once, and the
    girl has got a good heart after all ; and she came crying to me,
    this morning, in the little paddock, and somehow or other, my heart
    melted towards her ; and—and—there 's something very pleasant
    about her manner,—isn't there, George ?

EDMUNDS. No doubt of it, as other people besides ourselves would
    appear to think.

JOHN. You mean Mr. Flam ? (EDMUNDS *nods assent.*) Ah ! it 's a

325

bad business, altogether; but still there are some excuses to be made for a young country girl, who has never seen a town gentleman before, and can't be expected to know as well as you and I, George, what the real worth of one is. However that may be, Rose came into the little paddock this morning, as I was standing there, looking at the young colts, and thinking of all our misfortunes; and first of all she walked by me, and then she stopped at a little distance, and then she walked back, and stopped again; and I heard her sobbing as if her heart would burst: and then she came a little nearer, and at last she laid her hand upon my arm, and looked up in my face: and the tears started into my eyes, George, and I couldn't bear it any longer, for I thought of the many pleasant days we had been happy together, and it hurt me to think that she should ever have done anything to make her afraid of me, or me unkind to her.

EDMUNDS. You're a good fellow, John, an excellent fellow. Take her; I believe her to have an excellent disposition, though it is a little disguised by girlish levity sometimes;—you may safely take her,—if she had far less good feeling than she actually possesses, she could never abuse your kind and affectionate nature.

JOHN. Is that your advice? Give me your hand, George (*they shake hands*), I will take her. You shall dance at our wedding, and I don't quite despair yet of dancing at yours, at the same time.

EDMUNDS. At mine! Where is the old man? I came here to offer him the little cottage in the village, which belongs to me. There is no tenant in it now: it has a pretty garden, of which I know he is fond, and it may serve his turn till he has had time to look about him.

JOHN. He is somewhere about the farm; walk with me across the yard, and perhaps we may meet him—this way. [*Exeunt.*

Enter YOUNG BENSON.

YOUNG BENSON. The worst portion of the poor old man's hard trial is past. I have lingered with him in every field on the land, and wandered through every room in the old house. I can neither blame his grief, nor console him in his affliction, for the farm has been the happy scene of my birth and boyhood; and I feel, in looking on it, for the last time, as if I were leaving the dearest friends of my youth, for ever.

326

Song.—YOUNG BENSON.

My fair home is no longer mine ;
  From its roof-tree I 'm driven away,
Alas ! who will tend the old vine,
  Which I planted in infancy's day !
The garden, the beautiful flowers,
  The oak with its branches on high,
Dear friends of my happiest hours,
  Among ye, I long hoped to die.
The briar, the moss, and the bramble,
  Along the green paths will run wild :
The paths where I once used to ramble,
  An innocent, light-hearted child.

At the conclusion of the song enter to the symphony OLD BENSON,
with LUCY *and* ROSE.

YOUNG BENSON (*advancing to meet him*). Come, father, come !

OLD BENSON. I am ready, boy. We have but to walk a few steps,
and the pang of leaving is over. Come, Rose, bring on that unhappy girl ; come !

As they are going, enter the SQUIRE, *who meets them.*

SQUIRE. I am in time.

BENSON (*to* YOUNG BENSON, *who is advancing*). Harry, stand back.
Mr. Norton, if by this visit you intend to mock the misery you
have inflicted here, it is a heartless insult that might have been
spared.

SQUIRE. You do me an injustice, Benson. I come here,—not to insult
your grief, but to entreat, implore you, to remain. The lease of
this farm shall be renewed ;—I beseech you to remain here.

BENSON. It is not the quitting even the home of my infancy, which
most men love, that bows my spirit down to-day. Here, in this
old house, for near two hundred years, my ancestors have lived
and died, and left their names behind them free from spot or
blemish. I am the first to cross its threshold with the brand of
infamy upon me. Would to God I had been borne from its porch
a senseless corpse many weary years ago, so that I had been spared
this hard calamity ! You have moved an old man's weakness, but
not with your revenge, sir. You implore me to remain here. I

327

spurn your offer. *Here!* A father yielding to the destroyer of his child's good name and honour! Say no more, sir. Let me pass.

Enter, behind, STOKES *and* EDMUNDS.

SQUIRE. Benson, you are guilty of the foulest injustice, not to me, but to your daughter. After her fearless confession to me this morning of her love for Edmunds, and her abhorrence of my professions, I honour her too much to injure her, or you.

LUCY. Dear father, it is true indeed. The noble behaviour of his honour to me, this morning, I can never forget, or be too grateful for.

BENSON. Thank God! thank God! I can look upon her once again. My child! my own child! (*he embraces her with great emotion.*) I have done your honour wrong, and I hope you'll forgive me. (*They shake hands.*)

MARTIN (*running forward*). So have I! so have I! I have done his honour wrong, and I hope he'll forgive me too. You don't leave the farm, then? Hurrah! (*A man carrying a pail, some harness, etc., crosses the stage.*) Hallo, young fellow! go back, go back! don't take another thing away, and bring back all you have carried off; they are going to stop in the farm. Hallo! you fellows! (*Calling off.*) Leave the barn alone, and put everything in its place. They are going to stop in the farm. [*Exit bawling.*

BENSON (*seeing* EDMUNDS). What! George here, and turning away from his old friend, too, without a look of congratulation or a shake of the hand, just at the time, when of all others, he had the best right to expect it! For shame, George, for shame!

EDMUNDS. My errand here is rendered useless. By accident, and not intentionally, I partly overheard just now the nature of the avowal made by your daughter to Mr. Norton this morning.

BENSON. You believe it, George. You cannot doubt its truth.

EDMUNDS. I *do* believe it. But I have been hurt, slighted, set aside for another. My honest love has been despised; my affection has been remembered, only to be tried almost beyond endurance. Lucy, all this from *you* I freely forgive. Be what you have been once, and what you may so well become again. Be the high-souled woman; not the light and thoughtless trifler that disgraces the name. Let me see you this, and you are mine again. Let me see you what you have been of late, and I never can be yours!

328

BENSON. Lead her in, Rose.   Come, dear, come!   (*The* BENSONS *and*
ROSE *lead her slowly away.*)

EDMUNDS. Mr. Norton, if this altered conduct be sincere, it deserves
a much better return than my poor thanks can ever be to you. If
it be feigned, to serve some purposes of your own, the consequences
will be upon your head.

SQUIRE. And I shall be prepared to meet them.

> *Duet.*—SQUIRE NORTON *and* EDMUNDS.

SQUIRE.   Listen, though I do not fear you,
                 Listen to me, ere we part.

EDMUNDS.   List to *you!*   Yes, I will hear you.

SQUIRE.   Yours alone is Lucy's heart,
                 I swear it, by that Heaven above me.

EDMUNDS.   What! can I believe my ears!
                 Could I hope that she still loves me!

SQUIRE.   Banish all these doubts and fears,
                 If a love were e'er worth gaining,
                 If love were ever fond and true,
                 No disguise or passion feigning,
                 Such is her young love for you.

                 Listen, though I do not fear you,
                 Listen to me ere we part.

EDMUNDS.   List to you! yes, I will hear you,
                 Mine alone is her young heart.   [*Exeunt severally.*

SCENE IV.—*The avenue leading to the Hall, by moonlight.*
The house in the distance, gaily illuminated.

Enter FLAM *and* MARTIN.

FLAM. You have got the letter I gave you for the Squire?

MARTIN. All right.   Here it is.

FLAM. The moment you see me leave the room, slip it into the
Squire's hand; you can easily do so, without being recognised, in
the confusion of the dance, and then follow me. You perfectly
understand your instructions?

MARTIN. Oh, yes,—I understand them well enough.

329

FLAM. There's nothing more, then, that you want to know?

MARTIN. No, nothing,—oh, yes there is. I want to know whether—whether——

FLAM. Well, go on.

MARTIN. Whether you could conveniently manage to let me have another couple of guineas, before you go away in the chaise. Payment beforehand,—capital custom. And if you don't, perhaps I may not get them at all, you know: (*aside*) seeing that I don't intend to go at all, I think it's very likely.

FLAM. You're a remarkably pleasant fellow, Stokes, in general conversation,—very,—but when you descend into particularities, you become excessively prosy. On some points,—money-matters for instance,—you have a very grasping imagination, and seem disposed to dilate upon them at too great a length. You must cure yourself of this habit,—you must indeed. Good-bye, Stokes; you shall have the two guineas doubled when the journey is completed. Remember,—ten o'clock. [*Exit* FLAM.

MARTIN. I shan't forget ten o'clock, depend upon it. Now to burst upon my particular friend, Mr. John Maddox, with the awful disclosure. He must pass this way on his road to the Hall. Here they come,—don't see him though. (*Groups of male and female Villagers in cloaks, etc., cross the stage on their way to the Hall.*)

MARTIN. How are you, Tom? How do, Will?

VILLAGERS. How do, Mas'r Stokes?

MARTIN (*shaking hands with them*). How do, Susan? Mind, Cary, you're my first partner. Always kiss your first partner,—capital custom. (*Kisses her.*) Good-bye! See you up at the Hall.

VILLAGERS. Ay, ay, Mas'r Stokes. [*Exeunt Villagers.*

MARTIN. Not among them. (*More Villagers cross.*) Nor them. Here he comes:—Rose with him too,—innocent little victim, little thinking of the atrocious designs that are going on against her!

Enter MADDOX *and* ROSE, *arm-in-arm.*

JOHN. Ha, ha, ha! that was a good 'un,—wasn't it? Ah! Martin, I wish I'd seen you a minute ago. I made such a joke! How you would ha' laughed!

MARTIN (*mysteriously beckoning* MADDOX *away from* ROSE, *and whispering*). I want to speak to you.

JOHN (*whispering*). What about?

330

ROSE. Lor'! don't stand whispering there, John. If you have any-thing to say, Mr. Stokes, say it before me.

JOHN (*taking her arm*). Ah! say it before her! Don't mind her, Martin; she's to be my wife, you know, and we're to be on the mutual-confidence principle; an't we,—Rose?

ROSE. To be sure. Why don't you speak, Mr. Stokes? I suppose it's the old story,—something wrong.

MARTIN. Something wrong! I rather think there is; and you little know what it is, or you wouldn't look so merry. What I have got to say—don't be frightened, Miss Rose,—relates to—don't alarm yourself, Master Maddox.

JOHN. I an't alarming myself; you're alarming me. Go on!

ROSE. Go on!—can't you?

MARTIN. Relates to Mr. Flam.

JOHN (*dropping* ROSE'S *arm*). Mr. Flam!

MARTIN. Hush!—and Miss Rose.

ROSE. Me! Me and Mr. Flam!

MARTIN. Mr. Flam intends at ten o'clock, this very night,—don't be frightened, Miss,—by force, in secret, and in a chaise and four, too,—to carry off, against her will, and elope with, Miss Rose.

ROSE. Me! Oh! (*Screams, and falls into the arms of* MADDOX.)

JOHN. Rub her hands, Martin, she's going off in a fit.

MARTIN. Never mind; she'd better go off in a fit than a chaise.

ROSE (*recovering*). Oh, John! don't let me go.

JOHN. Let you go!—not if I set the whole Hall on fire.

ROSE. Hold me fast, John.

JOHN. I'll hold you fast enough, depend upon it.

ROSE. Come on the other side of me, Mr. Stokes: take my arm; hold me tight, Mr. Stokes.

MARTIN. Don't be frightened, I'll take care of you. (*Takes her arm.*)

ROSE. Oh! Mr. Stokes.

MARTIN. Oh, indeed! Nothing wrong,—eh?

ROSE. Oh! Mr. Stokes,—pray forgive my having doubted that there was——Oh! what a dreadful thing! What is to be done with me?

MARTIN. Upon my word, I don't know. I think we had better shut her up in some place under ground,—hadn't we, John?—or, stay, —suppose we borrow the keys of the family vault, and lock her up there, for an hour or two.

331

JOHN. Capital!

ROSE. Lor'! surely you may find out some more agreeable place than that, John.

MARTIN. I have it.—I'm to carry her off.

BOTH. You!

MARTIN. Me,—don't be afraid of me :—all my management. You dance with her all the evening, and I'll keep close to you. If anybody tries to get her away, you knock him down,—and I'll help you.

JOHN. That's the plan;—come along.

ROSE. Oh, I am so frightened! Hold me fast, Mr. Stokes,—Don't let me go, John! [*Exeunt, talking.*

Enter LUCY.

LUCY. Light-hearted revellers! how I envy them! How painful is my situation,—obliged with a sad heart to attend a festivity, from which the only person I would care to meet will, I know, be absent. 'But I will not complain. He shall see that I can 'become worthy of him, once again. I have lingered here so long, 'watching the soft shades of evening as they closed around me, 'that I cannot bear the thought of exchanging this beautiful scene 'for the noise and glare of a crowded room.'

Song.—LUCY.

How beautiful at even-tide
To see the twilight shadows pale,
　　Steal o'er the landscape, far and wide,
O'er stream and meadow, mound and dale.
How soft is Nature's calm repose
When evening skies their cool dews weep:
　　The gentlest wind more gently blows,
As if to soothe her in her sleep!
　　　　The gay morn breaks,
　　　　　　Mists roll away,
　　　　All Nature awakes
　　　　　　To glorious day.
　　　　In my breast alone
　　　　　　Dark shadows remain ;
　　　　The peace it has known
　　　　　　It can never regain.

SCENE THE LAST.—*A spacious ball-room, brilliantly illuminated. A window at the end, through which is seen a moonlit landscape. A large concourse of country people, discovered.—The* SQUIRE,—FLAM,—*the* BENSONS,—LUCY,—ROSE,—MARTIN, *and* MADDOX.

SQUIRE. Welcome, friends, welcome all ! Come, choose your partners, and begin the dance.

FLAM (*to Lucy*). Your hand, for the dance ?

LUCY. Pray excuse me, sir ; I am not well. My head is oppressed and giddy. I would rather sit by the window which looks into the garden, and feel the cool evening air. (*She goes up. He follows her.*)

JOHN (*aside*). Stand by me, Martin. He's gone to order the chaise, perhaps.

ROSE. Oh! pray don't let me be taken away, Mr. Stokes.

MARTIN. Don't be frightened,—don't be frightened. Mr. Flam is gone. I'll give the Squire the note in a minute.

SQUIRE. Now,—begin the dance.

A Country Dance.

(MARTIN *and* MADDOX, *in their endeavours to keep close to* ROSE, *occasion great confusion. As the* SQUIRE *is looking at some particular couple in the dance,* MARTIN *steals behind him, thrusts the letter in his hands, and resumes his place. The* SQUIRE *looks round as if to discover the person who has delivered it ; but being unsuccessful, puts it up, and retires among the crowd of dancers. Suddenly a violent scream is heard, and the dance abruptly ceases. Great confusion.* MARTIN *and* MADDOX *hold* ROSE *firmly.*)

SQUIRE. What has happened ? Whence did that scream proceed ?

SEVERAL VOICES. From the garden !—from the garden !

EDMUNDS (*without*). Raise him, and bring him here. Lucy,—dear Lucy !

BENSON. Lucy ! My child ! (*Runs up the stage, and exit into garden.*)

MARTIN. *His* child ! Damme ! they can't get this one, so they're going to run away with the other. Here's some mistake here. Let me go, Rose. Come along, John. Make way there,—make way !

(*As they run towards the window,* EDMUNDS *appears at it, without a hat, and his dress disordered, with* LUCY *in his arms. He delivers her to her father and* ROSE.)

333

ROSE. Lucy,—dear Lucy,—look up !

BENSON. Is she hurt, George ?—is the poor child injured ?

EDMUNDS. No, it is nothing but terror; she will be better instantly. See! she is recovering now. (LUCY *gradually recovers, as* FLAM, *his clothes torn, and face disfigured, is led in by* MADDOX *and* MARTIN.)

BENSON. Mr. Norton, this is an act of perjury and baseness, of which another instant would have witnessed the completion.

SQUIRE (*to* FLAM). Rascal ! this is your deed.

FLAM (*aside to* NORTON). That's right, Norton, keep it up.

SQUIRE. Do not address me with your odious familiarity, scoundrel !

FLAM. You don't really mean to give me up ?

SQUIRE. I renounce you from this instant.

FLAM. You do ?—then take the consequences.

SQUIRE. Benson,—Edmunds,—friends, — I declare to you most solemnly that I had neither hand nor part in this disgraceful outrage. It has been perpetrated without my knowledge, wholly by that scoundrel.

FLAM. 'Tis false; it was done with his consent. He has in his pocket, at this moment, a letter from me, acquainting him with my intention.

ALL. A letter !

SQUIRE. A letter *was* put into my hands five minutes since; but it acquainted me, not with this fellow's intention, but with his real dishonourable and disgraceful character, to which I had hitherto been a stranger. (*To* FLAM.) Do you know that handwriting, sir ? (*Showing him the letter.*)

FLAM. Ellis's letter ! (*searching his pockets, and producing the other*). I must,—ass that I was !—I did—enclose the wrong one.

SQUIRE. You will quit my house this instant; its roof shall not shelter you another night. Take that with you, sir, and begone. (*Throws him a purse.*)

FLAM (*taking it up*). Ah ! I suppose you think this munificent, now —eh ? I could have made twice as much of you in London, Norton, I could indeed, to say nothing of my exhibiting myself for a whole week to these clods of earth, which would have been cheap, dirt-cheap, at double the money. Bye-bye, Norton ! Farewell, grubs ! [*Exit.*

SQUIRE. Edmunds, you have rescued your future wife from brutal violence; you will not leave her exposed to similar attempts in future?

EDMUNDS. Even if I would, I feel, now that I have preserved her, that I could not.

SQUIRE. Then take her, and with her the old farm, which from henceforth is your own.   *You* will not turn the old man out, I suppose?

EDMUNDS (*shaking* BENSON *by the hand*). I don't think we are very likely to quarrel on that score; and most gratefully do we acknowledge your honour's kindness.   Maddox!

JOHN. Hallo!

EDMUNDS. I shall not want that cottage and garden we were speaking of, this morning, now.   Let me imitate a good example, and bestow it on *your* wife, as *her* marriage portion.

ROSE. Oh, delightful!   Say certainly, John,—can't you?

JOHN. Thank 'ee, George, thank 'ee!   I say, Martin, I have arrived at the dignity of a cottage and a piece of ground, at last.

MARTIN. Yes, you may henceforth consider yourself on a level with me.

SQUIRE. Resume the dance.

MARTIN. I beg your pardon.   One word.   (*Whispers the* SQUIRE.)

SQUIRE. I hope not.   Recollect, you have been mistaken before, to-day.   You had better inquire.

MARTIN. I will.   (*To the audience.*)   My very particular friend, if he will allow me to call him so,——

SQUIRE. Oh, certainly.

MARTIN. My very particular friend, Mr. Norton, wishes me to ask my other particular friends here, whether there's — anything wrong?   We are delighted to hear your approving opinion in the old way.   You *can't* do better.   It's a capital custom.

Dance and Finale.—Chorus.

> Join the dance, with step as light
> As every heart should be to-night;
> Music, shake the lofty dome,
> In honour of our Harvest Home.

> Join the dance, and banish care,
> All are young, and gay, and fair;
> Even age has youthful grown,
> In honour of our Harvest Home.

335

Join the dance, bright faces beam,
Sweet lips smile, and dark eyes gleam ;
All these charms have hither come,
In honour of our Harvest Home.

Join the dance, with step as light,
As every heart should be to-night ;
Music, shake the lofty dome,
In honour of our Harvest Home.

Quintet.

Lucy—Rose—Edmunds—*The* Squire—Young Benson.

No light bound
Of stag or timid hare,
    O'er the ground
Where startled herds repair,
    Do we prize
So high, or hold so dear,
    As the eyes
That light our pleasures here.

No cool breeze
That gently plays by night,
    O'er calm seas,
Whose waters glisten bright ;
    No soft moan
That sighs across the lea,
    Harvest Home,
Is half so sweet as thee !

Chorus.

Hail to the merry autumn days, when yellow cornfields shine,
Far brighter than the costly cup that holds the monarch's wine !
Hail to the merry harvest time, the gayest of the year,
The time of rich and bounteous crops, rejoicing, and good cheer.
                              Hail ! Hail ! Hail !

IS SHE HIS WIFE?
OR, SOMETHING SINGULAR!
A COMIC BURLETTA
IN ONE ACT
[1837]

DRAMATIS PERSONÆ

At St. James's Theatre, March 6, 1837

Alfred Lovetown, Esq.	Mr. Forester.
Mr. Peter Limbury	Mr. Gardner.
Felix Tapkins, Esq. (*formerly of the India House, Leadenhall Street, and Prospect Place, Poplar; but now of the Rustic Lodge, near Reading*)	Mr. Harley.
John (*servant to Lovetown*).	
Mrs. Lovetown	Miss Allison.
Mrs. Peter Limbury	Madame Sala.

IS SHE HIS WIFE?

OR, SOMETHING SINGULAR!

Scene I.—*A Room opening into a Garden. A Table laid for Break-fast; Chairs, etc.* Mr. *and* Mrs. Lovetown, c., *discovered at Breakfast,* r. h. *The former in a dressing-gown and slippers, reading a newspaper. A Screen on one side.*

Lovetown (l. h. *of table, yawning*). Another cup of tea, my dear,— O Lord!

Mrs. Lovetown (r. h. *of table*). I wish, Alfred, you would endeavour to assume a more cheerful appearance in your wife's society. If you are perpetually yawning and complaining of *ennui* a few months after marriage, what am I to suppose you'll become in a few years? It really is very odd of you.

Lovetown. Not at all odd, my dear, not the least in the world; it would be a great deal more odd if I were not. The fact is, my love, I'm tired of the country; green fields, and blooming hedges, and feathered songsters, are fine things to talk about and read about and write about; but I candidly confess that I prefer paved streets, area railings and dustman's bells, after all.

Mrs. Lovetown. How often have you told me that, blessed with my love, you could live contented and happy in a desert?

Lovetown (*reading*). 'Artful impostor!'

Mrs. Lovetown. Have you not over and over again said that fortune and personal attractions were secondary considerations with you? That you loved me for those virtues which, while they gave addi-tional lustre to public life, would adorn and sweeten retirement?

Lovetown (*reading*). 'Soothing syrup!'

Mrs. Lovetown. You complain of the tedious sameness of a country life. Was it not you yourself who first proposed our residing permanently in the country? Did you not say that I should then have an ample sphere in which to exercise those charitable feelings

339

which I have so often evinced, by selling at those benevolent fancy fairs?

LOVETOWN (*reading*). 'Humane man-traps!'

MRS. LOVETOWN. He pays no attention to me,—Alfred dear,——

LOVETOWN (*stamping his foot*). Yes, my life.

MRS. LOVETOWN. Have you heard what I have just been saying, dear?

LOVETOWN. Yes, love.

MRS. LOVETOWN. And what can you say in reply?

LOVETOWN. Why, really, my dear, you've said it so often before in the course of the last six weeks, that I think it quite unnecessary to say anything more about it. (*Reads.*) 'The learned judge delivered a brief but impressive summary of the unhappy man's trial.'

MRS. LOVETOWN (*aside*). I could bear anything but this neglect. He evidently does not care for me.

LOVETOWN (*aside*). I could put up with anything rather than these constant altercations and little petty quarrels. I repeat, my dear, that I am very dull in this out-of-the-way villa—confoundedly dull, horridly dull.

MRS. LOVETOWN. And *I* repeat that if you took any pleasure in your wife's society, or felt for her as you once professed to feel, you would have no cause to make such a complaint.

LOVETOWN. If I did not know you to be one of the sweetest creatures in existence, my dear, I should be strongly disposed to say that you were a very close imitation of an aggravating female.

MRS. LOVETOWN. That's very curious, my dear, for I declare that if I hadn't known *you* to be such an exquisite, good-tempered, attentive husband, I should have mistaken you for a very great brute.

LOVETOWN. My dear, you're offensive.

MRS. LOVETOWN. My love, you're intolerable. (*They turn their chairs back to back.*)

MR. FELIX TAPKINS *sings without.*

'The wife around her husband throws
    Her arms to make him stay;
"My dear, it rains, it hails, it blows,
    And you cannot hunt to-day."
        But a hunting we will go,
    And a hunting we will go,—wo—wo—wo!
        And a hunting we will go.'

MRS. LOVETOWN. There's that dear, good-natured creature, Mr. Tapkins,—do you ever hear *him* complain of the tediousness of a country life? Light-hearted creature,—his lively disposition and rich flow of spirits are wonderful, even to me. (*Rising.*)

LOVETOWN. They need not be a matter of astonishment to anybody, my dear,—he's a bachelor.

MR. FELIX TAPKINS *appears at window,* L. H.

TAPKINS. Ha, ha! How are you both?—Here's a morning! Bless my heart alive, *what* a morning! I've been gardening ever since five o'clock, and the flowers have been actually growing before my very eyes. The London Pride is sweeping everything before it, and the stalks are half as high again as they were yesterday. They're all run up like so many tailors' bills, after that heavy dew of last night broke down half my rosebuds with the weight of its own moisture,—something like a dew that!—reg'lar *doo*, eh?—come, that's not so bad for a before-dinner one.

LOVETOWN. Ah, you happy dog, Felix!

TAPKINS. Happy! of course I am,—Felix by name, Felix by nature, —what the deuce should I be unhappy for, or anybody be unhappy for? What's the use of it, that's the point?

MRS. LOVETOWN. Have you finished your improvements yet, Mr. Tapkins?

TAPKINS. At Rustic Lodge? (*She nods assent.*) Bless your heart and soul! you never saw such a place,—cardboard chimneys, Grecian balconies,—Gothic parapets, thatched roof.

MRS. LOVETOWN. Indeed!

TAPKINS. Lord bless you, yes,—green verandah, with ivy twining round the pillars.

MRS. LOVETOWN. How very rural!

TAPKINS. Rural, my dear Mrs. Lovetown! delightful! The French windows, too! Such an improvement!

MRS. LOVETOWN. I should think they were!

TAPKINS. Yes, *I* should think they were. Why, on a fine summer's evening the frogs hop off the grass-plot into the very sitting-room.

MRS. LOVETOWN. Dear me!

TAPKINS. Bless you, yes! Something like the country,—quite a little Eden. Why, when I'm smoking under the verandah, after a shower of rain, the black beetles fall into my brandy-and-water.

341

MR. *and* MRS. LOVETOWN. No!—Ha! ha! ha!

TAPKINS. Yes. And I take 'em out again with the teaspoon, and lay bets with myself which of them will run away the quickest. Ha! ha! ha! (*They all laugh.*) Then the stable, too. Why, in Rustic Lodge the stables are close to the dining-room window.

LOVETOWN. No!

TAPKINS. Yes. The horse can't cough but I hear him. There's compactness. Nothing like the cottage style of architecture for comfort, my boy. By the bye, I have left the new horse at your garden-gate this moment.

MRS. LOVETOWN. The new horse!

TAPKINS. The new horse! Splendid fellow,—such action! Puts out its feet like a rocking-horse, and carries its tail like a hat-peg. Come and see him.

LOVETOWN (*laughing*). I can't deny you anything.

TAPKINS. No, that's what they all say, especially the—eh! (*Nodding and winking.*)

LOVETOWN. Ha! ha! ha!

MRS. LOVETOWN. Ha! ha! ha! I'm afraid you're a very bad man, Mr. Tapkins; I'm afraid you're a shocking man, Mr. Tapkins.

TAPKINS. Think so? No, I don't know,—not worse than other people similarly situated. Bachelors, my dear Mrs. Lovetown, bachelors—eh! old fellow? (*Winking to* LOVETOWN.)

LOVETOWN. Certainly, certainly.

TAPKINS. *We* know—eh? (*They all laugh.*) By the bye, talking of bachelors puts me in mind of Rustic Lodge, and talking of Rustic Lodge puts me in mind of what I came here for. You must come and see me this afternoon. Little Peter Limbury and his wife are coming.

MRS. LOVETOWN. I detest that man.

LOVETOWN. The wife is supportable, my dear.

TAPKINS. To be sure, so she is. You'll come, and that's enough. Now come and see the horse.

LOVETOWN. Give me three minutes to put on my coat and boots, and I'll join you. I won't be three minutes. [*Exit* LOVETOWN, R. H.

TAPKINS. Look sharp, look sharp!—Mrs. Lovetown, will you excuse me one moment? (*Crosses to* L.; *calling off.*) Jim,—these fellows never know how to manage horses,—walk him gently up and down, —throw the stirrups over the saddle to show the people that his master's coming, and if anybody asks what that fine animal's pedigree is, and who he belongs to, say he's the property of Mr. Felix Tapkins of Rustic Lodge, near Reading, and that he's the celebrated horse who ought to have won the Newmarket Cup last year, only he didn't.   [*Exit* TAPKINS.

MRS. LOVETOWN. My mind is made up,—I can bear Alfred's coldness and insensibility no longer, and come what may I will endeavour to remove it. From the knowledge I have of his disposition I am convinced that the only mode of doing so will be by rousing his jealousy and wounding his vanity. This thoughtless creature will be a very good instrument for my scheme. He plumes himself on his gallantry, has no very small share of vanity, and is easily led. I see him crossing the garden. (*She brings a chair hastily forward and sits* R. H.)

Enter FELIX TAPKINS, L. H. *window.*

TAPKINS (*singing*). 'My dear, it rains, it hails, it blows,——'

MRS. LOVETOWN (*tragically*). Would that I had never beheld him !

TAPKINS (*aside*). Hallo ! She's talking about her husband. I knew by their manner there had been a quarrel, when I came in this morning.

MRS. LOVETOWN. So fascinating, and yet so insensible to the tenderest of passions as not to see how devotedly I love him.

TAPKINS (*aside*). I thought so.

MRS. LOVETOWN. That he should still remain unmarried is to me extraordinary.

TAPKINS. Um !

MRS. LOVETOWN. He ought to have married long since.

TAPKINS (*aside*). Eh ! Why, they aren't married !—' ought to have married long since.'—I rather think he ought.

MRS. LOVETOWN. And, though I am the wife of another,——

TAPKINS (*aside*). Wife of another !

MRS. LOVETOWN. Still, I grieve to say that I cannot be blind to his extraordinary merits.

TAPKINS. Why, he's run away with somebody else's wife ! The villain !—I must let her know I'm in the room, or there's no telling what I may hear next. (*Coughs.*)

MRS. LOVETOWN (*starting up in affected confusion*). Mr. Tapkins ! (*They sit.*) Bring your chair nearer. I fear, Mr. Tapkins, that I

343

have been unconsciously giving utterance to what was passing in my mind. I trust you have not overheard my confession of the weakness of my heart.

TAPKINS. No—no—not more than a word or two.

MRS. LOVETOWN. That agitated manner convinces me that you have heard more than you are willing to confess. Then why—why should I seek to conceal from you—that though I esteem my husband, I—I—love—another?

TAPKINS. I heard you mention that little circumstance.

MRS. LOVETOWN. Oh! (*Sighs.*)

TAPKINS (*aside*). What the deuce is she Oh-ing at? She looks at me as if I were Lovetown himself.

MRS. LOVETOWN (*putting her hand on his shoulder with a languishing air*). Does my selection meet with your approbation?

TAPKINS (*slowly*). It doesn't.

MRS. LOVETOWN. No!

TAPKINS. Decidedly not. (*Aside.*) I'll cut that Lovetown out, and offer myself. Hem! Mrs. Lovetown.

MRS. LOVETOWN. Yes, Mr. Tapkins.

TAPKINS. I know an individual——

MRS. LOVETOWN. Ah! an individual!

TAPKINS. An individual,—I may, perhaps, venture to say an estimable individual,—who for the last three months has been constantly in your society, who never yet had courage to disclose his passion, but who burns to throw himself at your feet. Oh! (*Aside.*) I'll try an Oh or two now,—Oh! (*Sighs.*) That's a capital Oh!

MRS. LOVETOWN (*aside*). He must have misunderstood me before, for he is evidently speaking of himself. Is the gentleman you speak of handsome, Mr. Tapkins?

TAPKINS. He is generally considered remarkably so.

MRS. LOVETOWN. Is he tall?

TAPKINS. About the height of the Apollo Belvidere.

MRS. LOVETOWN. Is he stout?

TAPKINS. Of nearly the same dimensions as the gentleman I have just named.

MRS. LOVETOWN. His figure is——

TAPKINS. Quite a model.

MRS. LOVETOWN. And he is——

TAPKINS. Myself. (*Throws himself on his knees and seizes her hand.*)

Enter LOVETOWN, R. H.

TAPKINS *immediately pretends to be diligently looking for something on the floor.*

MRS. LOVETOWN. Pray don't trouble yourself. I'll find it. Dear me! how could I lose it?

LOVETOWN. What have you lost, love? I should almost imagine that you had lost yourself, and that our friend Mr. Tapkins here had just found you.

TAPKINS (*aside*). Ah! you always will have your joke,—funny dog! funny dog! Bless my heart and soul, there's that immortal horse standing outside all this time! He'll catch his death of cold! Come and see him at once,—come—come.

LOVETOWN. No. I can't see him to-day. I had forgotten. I've letters to write,—business to transact,—I'm engaged.

TAPKINS (*to* MRS. LOVETOWN). Oh! if he's engaged, you know, we'd better not interrupt him.

MRS. LOVETOWN. Oh! certainly! Not by any means.

TAPKINS (*taking her arm*). Good-bye, old fellow.

LOVETOWN (*seating himself at table*). Oh!—good-bye.

TAPKINS (*going*). Take care of yourself. I'll take care of Mrs. L.

[*Exeunt* TAPKINS *and* MRS. LOVETOWN, C.

LOVETOWN. What the deuce does that fellow mean by laying such emphasis on Mrs. L.? What's my wife to him, or he to my wife? Very extraordinary! I can hardly believe that even if he had the treachery to make any advances, she would encourage such a preposterous intrigue. (*Walks to and fro.*) She spoke in his praise at breakfast-time, though,—and they have gone away together to see that confounded horse. But stop, I must keep a sharp eye upon them this afternoon, without appearing to do so. I would not appear unnecessarily suspicious for the world. Dissembling in such a case, though, is difficult—very difficult.

Enter a Servant, L. H.

SERVANT. Mr. and Mrs. Peter Limbury.

LOVETOWN. Desire them to walk in.   [*Exit Servant,* L. H.
A lucky visit! it furnishes me with a hint. This Mrs. Limbury is a vain, conceited woman, ready to receive the attentions of anybody who feigns admiration for her, partly to gratify herself, and

partly to annoy the jealous little husband whom she keeps under
such strict control. If I pay particular attention to *her*, I shall
lull my wife and that scoundrel Tapkins into a false security, and
have better opportunities of observation. They are here.

Enter Mr. *and* Mrs. Limbury, l. h.

LOVETOWN. My dear Mrs. Limbury. (*Crosses to* c.)

LIMBURY. Eh?

LOVETOWN (*not regarding him*). How charming—how delightful—
how divine you look to-day.

LIMBURY (*aside*). Dear Mrs. Limbury, — charming, — divine and
beautiful look to-day! They are smiling at each other,—he
squeezes her hand. I see how it is. I always thought he paid her
too much attention.

LOVETOWN. Sit down,—sit down.

(LOVETOWN *places the chairs so as to sit between them, which*
LIMBURY *in vain endeavours to prevent.*)

MRS. LIMBURY. Peter and I called as we passed in our little pony-
chaise, to inquire whether we should have the pleasure of seeing
you at Tapkins's this afternoon.

LOVETOWN. Is it possible you can ask such a question? Do you
think I could stay away?

MRS. LIMBURY. Dear Mr. Lovetown! (*Aside.*) How polite,—
he's quite struck with me.

LIMBURY (*aside*). Wretched miscreant! a regular assignation before
my very face.

LOVETOWN (*to* MRS. LIMBURY). Do you know I entertained some
apprehensions — some dreadful fears — that you might not be
there.

LIMBURY. Fears that we mightn't be there? Of course we shall be
there.

MRS. LIMBURY. Now don't talk, Peter.

LOVETOWN. I thought it just possible, you know, that you might
not be agreeable——

MRS. LIMBURY. O, Peter is always agreeable to anything that is
agreeable to me. Aren't you, Peter?

LIMBURY. Yes, dearest. (*Aside.*) Agreeable to anything that's
agreeable to her! O Lor'!

MRS. LIMBURY.   By the bye, Mr. Lovetown, how do you like this bonnet?

LOVETOWN. O, beautiful!

LIMBURY (*aside*). I must change the subject. Do you know, Mr. Lovetown, I have often thought, and it has frequently occurred to me—when——

MRS. LIMBURY. Now don't talk, Peter. (*To* LOVETOWN.) The colour is so bright, is it not?

LOVETOWN. It might appear so elsewhere, but the brightness of those eyes casts it quite into shade.

MRS. LIMBURY. I know you are a connoisseur in ladies' dresses; how do you like those shoes?

LIMBURY (*aside*). Her shoes!   What will she ask his opinion of next?

LOVETOWN. O, like the bonnet, you deprive them of their fair chance of admiration.   That small and elegant foot engrosses all the attention which the shoes might otherwise attract.   That taper ankle, too——

LIMBURY (*aside*). Her taper ankle!   My bosom swells with the rage of an ogre.   Mr. Lovetown,—I——

MRS. LIMBURY. Now, pray do not talk so, Limbury. You've put Mr. Lovetown out as it is.

LIMBURY (*aside*). Put him out! I wish I could put him out, Mrs. Limbury. I must.

Enter Servant, hastily.

SERVANT. I beg your pardon, sir, but the bay pony has got his hind leg over the traces, and he's kicking the chaise to pieces!

LIMBURY. Kicking the *new* chaise to pieces!

LOVETOWN. Kicking the new chaise to pieces! The bay pony! Limbury, my dear fellow, fly to the spot! (*Pushing him out.*)

LIMBURY. But, Mr. Lovetown, I——

MRS. LIMBURY. Oh! he'll kick somebody's brains out, if Peter don't go to him.

LIMBURY. But perhaps he'll kick my brains out if I do go to him.

LOVETOWN. Never mind, don't lose an instant,—not a moment. (*Pushes him out, both talking together.*)   [*Exit* LIMBURY. (*Aside.*) Now for it,—here's my wife. Dearest Mrs. Limbury —(*Kneels by her chair, and seizes her hand.*)

347

Enter Mrs. Lovetown, c.

Mrs. Lovetown (*aside*). Can I believe my eyes? (*Retires behind the screen.*)

Mrs. Limbury. Mr. Lovetown!

Lovetown. Nay. Allow me in one hurried interview, which I have sought for in vain for weeks,—for months,—to say how devotedly, how ardently I love you. Suffer me to retain this hand in mine. Give me one ray of hope.

Mrs. Limbury. Rise, I entreat you,—we shall be discovered.

Lovetown. Nay, I will not rise till you promise me that you will take an opportunity of detaching yourself from the rest of the company and meeting me alone in Tapkins's grounds this evening. I shall have no eyes, no ears for any one but yourself.

Mrs. Limbury. Well,—well,—I will—I do——

Lovetown. Then I am blest indeed!

Mrs. Limbury. I am so agitated. If Peter or Mrs. Lovetown— were to find me thus—I should betray all. I'll teach my husband to be jealous! (*Crosses to* L. H.) Let us walk round the garden.

Lovetown. With pleasure,—take my arm. Divine creature! (*Aside.*) I'm sure she is behind the screen. I saw her peeping. Come.

[*Exit* Lovetown *and* Mrs. Limbury, L. H.

Mrs. Lovetown (*coming forward*). Faithless man! His coldness and neglect are now too well explained. O Alfred! Alfred! how little did I think when I married you, six short months since, that I should be exposed to so much wretchedness! I begin to tremble at my own imprudence, and the situation in which it may place me; but it is now too late to recede. I must be firm. This day will either bring my project to the explanation I so much desire, or convince me of what I too much fear,—my husband's aversion. Can this woman's husband suspect their intimacy? If so, he may be able to prevent this assignation taking place. I will seek him instantly. If I can but meet him at once, he may prevent her going at all. [*Exit* Mrs. Lovetown, R. H.

Enter Tapkins, L. H. *window.*

Tapkins. This, certainly, is a most extraordinary affair. Not her partiality for me,—that's natural enough,—but the confession I overheard about her marriage to another. I have been thinking

that, after such a discovery, it would be highly improper to allow
Limbury and his wife to meet her without warning him of the fact.
The best way will be to make him acquainted with the real state
of the case. Then he must see the propriety of not bringing his
wife to my house to-night. Ah! here he is. I'll make the awful
disclosure at once, and petrify him.

Enter LIMBURY, L. H. *window.*

LIMBURY. That damned little bay pony is as bad as my wife. There's
no curbing either of them ; and as soon as I have got the traces
of the one all right, I lose all traces of the other.

TAPKINS (R.). Peter!

LIMBURY (L.). Ah! Tapkins!

TAPKINS. Hush! Hush! (*Looking cautiously round.*) If you have
a moment to spare, I've got something of great importance to
communicate.

LIMBURY. Something of great importance, Mr. Tapkins! (*Aside.*)
What can he mean? Can it relate to Mrs. Limbury? The
thought is dreadful. You horrify me!

TAPKINS. You'll be more horrified presently. What I am about to
tell you concerns yourself and your honour very materially ; and I
beg you to understand that I communicate it—in the strictest
confidence.

LIMBURY. Myself and my honour! I shall dissolve into nothing
with horrible anticipations!

TAPKINS (*in a low tone*). Have you ever observed anything remarkable about Lovetown's manner?

LIMBURY. Anything remarkable?

TAPKINS. Ay,—anything very odd, and rather unpleasant?

LIMBURY. Decidedly! No longer than half an hour ago,—in this
very room, I observed something in his manner particularly odd
and exceedingly unpleasant.

TAPKINS. To your feelings as a husband?

LIMBURY. Yes, my friend, yes, yes ;—you know it all, I see!

TAPKINS. What! Do *you* know it?

LIMBURY. I'm afraid I do ; but go on—go on.

TAPKINS (*aside*). How the deuce can he know anything about it?
Well, this oddness arises from the peculiar nature of his connexion
with—— You look very pale.

349

LIMBURY. No, no,—go on,—' connexion with——'

TAPKINS. A certain lady,—you know whom I mean.

LIMBURY. I do, I do! (*Aside.*) Disgrace and confusion! I'll kill her with a look! I'll wither her with scornful indignation! Mrs. Limbury!—viper!

TAPKINS (*whispering with caution*). They—aren't—married.

LIMBURY. *They* aren't married! *Who* aren't?

TAPKINS. Those two, to be sure!

LIMBURY. *Those* two! *What* two?

TAPKINS. Why, them. And the worst of it is she's—she's married to somebody else.

LIMBURY. Well, of course I know that.

TAPKINS. You know it?

LIMBURY. Of course I do. Why, how you talk! Isn't she my wife?

TAPKINS. *Your* wife! Wretched bigamist! Mrs. Lovetown your wife?

LIMBURY. Mrs. Lovetown! What! Have you been talking of Mrs. Lovetown all this time? My dear friend! (*Embraces him.*) The revulsion of feeling is almost insupportable. I thought you were talking about Mrs. Limbury.

TAPKINS. No!

LIMBURY. Yes. Ha! ha! But I say, what a dreadful fellow this is —another man's wife! Gad, I think he wants to run away with every man's wife he sees. And Mrs. Lovetown, too—horrid!

TAPKINS. Shocking!

LIMBURY. I say, I oughtn't to allow Mrs. Limbury to associate with her, ought I?

TAPKINS. Precisely my idea. You had better induce your wife to stay away from my house to-night.

LIMBURY. I'm afraid I can't do that.

TAPKINS. What, has she any particular objection to staying away?

LIMBURY. She has a very strange inclination to go, and 'tis much the same ; however, I'll make the best arrangement I can!

TAPKINS. Well, so be it. Of course I shall see *you*?

LIMBURY. Of course.

TAPKINS. Mind the secret,—close—close—you know, as a Cabinet Minister answering a question.

LIMBURY. You may rely upon me.

[Exit LIMBURY, L. H., TAPKINS, R. H.

SCENE II.—*A Conservatory on one side.   A Summer-house on the other.*
Enter LOVETOWN *at* L. H.

LOVETOWN. So far so good.   My wife has not dropped the slightest
hint of having overheard the conversation between me and Mrs.
Limbury; but she cannot conceal the impression it has made upon
her mind, or the jealousy it has evidently excited in her breast.
This is just as I wished.   I made Mr. Peter Limbury's amiable
helpmate promise to meet me here.   I know that refuge for
destitute reptiles (*pointing to summer-house*) is Tapkins's favourite
haunt, and if he has any assignation with my wife, I have no
doubt he will lead her to this place.   A woman's coming down
the walk.   Mrs. Limbury, I suppose,—no, my wife, by all that's
actionable.   I must conceal myself here, even at the risk of a
shower of black beetles, or a marching regiment of frogs. (*Goes
into conservatory*, L. H.)

Enter MRS. LOVETOWN *from top*, L. H.

MRS. LOVETOWN. I cannot have been mistaken.   I am certain I saw
Alfred here; he must have secreted himself somewhere to avoid
me.   Can his assignation with Mrs. Limbury have been discovered?   Mr. Limbury's behaviour to me just now was strange
in the extreme; and after a variety of incoherent expressions he
begged me to meet him here, on a subject, as he said, of great
delicacy and importance to myself.   Alas! I fear that my
husband's neglect and unkindness are but too well known.   The
injured little man approaches.   I summon all my fortitude to bear
the disclosure.

Enter MR. LIMBURY *at top*, L. H.

LIMBURY (*aside*). Now as I could not prevail on Mrs. Limbury to
stay away, the only distressing alternative I have is to inform
Mrs. Lovetown that I know her history, and to put it to her good
feeling whether she hadn't better go.

LOVETOWN (*peeping*). Limbury! what the deuce can that little
wretch want here?

LIMBURY. I took the liberty, Mrs. Lovetown, of begging you to meet
me in this retired spot, because the esteem I still entertain for you,
and my regard for your feelings, induce me to prefer a private to
a public disclosure.

351

LOVETOWN (*peeping*). 'Public disclosure!' what on earth is he talking about? I wish he'd speak a little louder.

MRS. LOVETOWN. I am sensible of your kindness, Mr. Limbury, and believe me most grateful for it. I am fully prepared to hear what you have to say.

LIMBURY. It is hardly necessary for me, I presume, to say, Mrs. Lovetown, that I have accidentally discovered the whole secret.

MRS. LOVETOWN. The whole secret, sir?

LOVETOWN (*peeping*). Whole secret! What secret?

LIMBURY. The whole secret, ma'am, of this disgraceful—I must call it disgraceful—and most abominable intrigue.

MRS. LOVETOWN (*aside*). My worst fears are realised,—my husband's neglect is occasioned by his love for another.

LOVETOWN (*peeping*). Abominable intrigue! My first suspicions are too well founded. He reproaches my wife with her infidelity, and she cannot deny it,—that villain Tapkins!

MRS. LOVETOWN (*weeping*). Cruel—cruel—Alfred!

LIMBURY. You may well call him cruel, unfortunate woman. His usage of you is indefensible, unmanly, scandalous.

MRS. LOVETOWN. It is. It is, indeed.

LIMBURY. It's very painful for me to express myself in such plain terms, Mrs. Lovetown; but allow me to say, as delicately as possible, that you should not endeavour to appear in society under such unusual and distressing circumstances.

MRS. LOVETOWN. Not appear in society! Why should I quit it?

LOVETOWN (*peeping*). Shameful woman!

LIMBURY. Is it possible you can ask such a question?

MRS. LOVETOWN. What should I do? Where can I go?

LIMBURY. Gain permission to return once again to your husband's roof.

MRS. LOVETOWN. My husband's roof?

LIMBURY. Yes, the roof of your husband, your wretched, unfortunate husband!

MRS. LOVETOWN. Never!

LIMBURY (*aside*). She's thoroughly hardened, steeped in vice beyond redemption. Mrs. Lovetown, as you reject my well-intentioned advice in this extraordinary manner, I am reduced to the painful necessity of expressing my hope that you will,—now pray don't think me unkind,—that you will never attempt to meet Mrs. Limbury more.

MRS. LOVETOWN. What! Can you suppose I am so utterly dead to every sense of feeling and propriety as to meet that person,—the destroyer of my peace and happiness,—the wretch who has ruined my hopes and blighted my prospects for ever? Ask your own heart, sir, — appeal to your own feelings. *You* are naturally indignant at her conduct. *You* would hold no further communication with her. Can you suppose, then, *I* would deign to do so? The mere supposition is an insult!

[*Exit* MRS. LOVETOWN *hastily at top*, L. H.

LIMBURY. What can all this mean? I am lost in a maze of astonishment, petrified at the boldness with which she braves it out. Eh! it's breaking upon me by degrees. I see it. What did she say? 'Destroyer of peace and happiness,—person—ruined hopes and blighted prospects—*her*.' I see it all. That atrocious Lovetown, that Don Juan multiplied by twenty, that unprecedented libertine, has seduced Mrs. Limbury from her allegiance to her lawful lord and master. He first of all runs away with the wife of another man, and he is no sooner tired of her, than he runs away with another wife of another man. I thirst for his destruction. I— (LOVETOWN *rushes from the conservatory and embraces* LIMBURY, *who disengages himself.*) Murderer of domestic happiness! behold your victim!

LOVETOWN. Alas! you speak but too truly. (*Covering his face with his hands.*) I am the victim.

LIMBURY. I speak but too truly!—He avows his own criminality. I shall throttle him. I know I shall. I feel it.

Enter MRS. LIMBURY *at back*, L. H.

MRS. LIMBURY (*aside*). My husband here! (*Goes into conservatory.*)

Enter TAPKINS *at back*, L. H.

TAPKINS (*aside*). Not here, and her husband with Limbury. I'll reconnoitre. (*Goes into summer-house*, R. H.)

LIMBURY. Lovetown, have you the boldness to look an honest man in the face?

LOVETOWN. O, spare me! I feel the situation in which I am placed acutely, deeply. Feel for me when I say that from that conservatory I overheard the greater part of what passed between you and Mrs. Lovetown.

LIMBURY. You did?

353

LOVETOWN. Need I say how highly I approve both of the language you used, and the advice you gave her?

LIMBURY. What! you want to get rid of her, do you?

LOVETOWN. Can you doubt it?

TAPKINS (*peeping*). Hallo! he wants to get rid of her. Queer!

LOVETOWN. Situated as I am, you know, I have no other resource, after what has passed. I must part from her.

MRS. LIMBURY (*peeping*). What can he mean?

LIMBURY (*aside*). I should certainly throttle him, were it not that the coolness with which he refers to the dreadful event paralyses me. Mr. Lovetown, look at me! Sir, consider the feelings of an indignant husband, sir!

LOVETOWN. Oh, I thank you for those words. Those strong expressions prove the unaffected interest you take in the matter.

LIMBURY. Unaffected interest! I shall go raving mad with passion and fury! Villain! Monster! To embrace the opportunity afforded him of being on a footing of friendship.

LOVETOWN. To take a mean advantage of his being a single man.

LIMBURY. To tamper with the sacred engagements of a married woman.

LOVETOWN. To place a married man in a disgraceful and humiliating situation.

LIMBURY. Scoundrel! Do you mock me to my face?

LOVETOWN. Mock *you*! What d'ye mean? Who the devil are you talking about?

LIMBURY. Talking about—*you*!

LOVETOWN. Me!

LIMBURY. Designing miscreant! Of whom do *you* speak?

LOVETOWN. Of whom should I speak but that scoundrel Tapkins?

TAPKINS (*coming forward*, R.). Me! What the devil do you mean by that?

LOVETOWN. Ha! (*Rushing at him, is held back by* LIMBURY.)

LIMBURY (*to* TAPKINS). Avoid him. Get out of his sight. He's raving mad with conscious villainy.

TAPKINS. What are you all playing at *I spy I* over my two acres of infant hay for?

LOVETOWN (*to* TAPKINS). How dare you tamper with the affections of Mrs. Lovetown?

TAPKINS. O, is that all? Ha! ha! (*Crosses to* C.)

LOVETOWN. All!

TAPKINS. Come, come, none of your nonsense.

LOVETOWN. Nonsense! Designate the best feelings of our nature nonsense!

TAPKINS. Pooh! pooh! Here, I know all about it.

LOVETOWN (*angrily*). And so do I, sir! And so do I.

TAPKINS. Of course you do. And you've managed very well to keep it quiet so long. But you're a deep fellow, by Jove! you're a deep fellow!

LOVETOWN. Now, mind! I restrain myself sufficiently to ask you once again before I knock you down, by what right dare you tamper with the affections of Mrs. Lovetown?

TAPKINS. Right! O, if you come to strict right, you know, nobody has a right but her husband.

LOVETOWN. And who is her husband? Who is her husband?

TAPKINS. Ah! to be sure, that's the question. Nobody that I know. I hope—poor fellow——

LOVETOWN. I'll bear these insults no longer! (*Rushes towards* TAPKINS. LIMBURY *interposes.* LOVETOWN *crosses to* R. H. *A scream is heard from the conservatory—a pause.*)

TAPKINS. Something singular among the plants! (*He goes into the conservatory and returns with* MRS. LIMBURY.) A flower that wouldn't come out of its own accord. I was obliged to force it. Tolerably full blown now, at all events.

LIMBURY. My wife! Traitoress! (*Crosses to* L. H.) Fly from my presence! Quit my sight! Return to the conservatory with that demon in a frock-coat!

Enter MRS. LOVETOWN *at top,* L. H., *and comes down* C.

TAPKINS. Hallo! Somebody else!

LOVETOWN (*aside*). My wife here!

MRS. LOVETOWN (*to* LIMBURY). I owe you some return for the commiseration you expressed just now for my wretched situation. The best, the only one I can make you is, to entreat you to refrain from committing any rash act, however excited you may be, and to control the feelings of an injured husband.

TAPKINS. Injured husband! Decidedly singular!

LOVETOWN. The allusion of that lady I confess my utter inability to understand. Mr. Limbury, to you an explanation is due, and I make it more cheerfully, as my abstaining from doing so might

355

involve the character of your wife. Stung by the attentions which
I found Mrs. Lovetown had received from a scoundrel present,——
TAPKINS (*aside*). That's me.

LOVETOWN. I—partly to obtain opportunities of watching her closely,
under an assumed mask of levity and carelessness, and partly
in the hope of awaking once again any dormant feelings of
affection that might still slumber in her breast, affected a passion
for your wife which I never felt, and to which she never really
responded. The second part of my project, I regret to say, has
failed. The first has succeeded but too well.

LIMBURY. Can I believe my ears ? But how came Mrs. Peter
Limbury to receive those attentions ?

MRS. LIMBURY. Why, not because I liked them, of course, but to
assist Mr. Lovetown in his project, and to teach you the misery
of those jealous fears. Come here, you stupid little jealous,
insinuating darling. (*They retire up* L. H., *she coaxing him.*)

TAPKINS (*aside*). It strikes me very forcibly that I have made a slight
mistake here, which is something particularly singular. (*Turns
up* R. H.)

MRS. LOVETOWN. Alfred, hear me ! I am as innocent as yourself. Your
fancied neglect and coldness hurt my weak vanity, and roused
some foolish feelings of angry pride. In a moment of irritation
I resorted to some such retaliation as you have yourself described.
That I did so from motives as guiltless as your own I call Heaven
to witness. That I repent my fault I solemnly assure you.

LOVETOWN. Is this possible ?

TAPKINS. Very possible indeed ! Believe your wife's assurance and
my corroboration. Here, give and take is all fair, you know.
Give me your hand and take your wife's. Here, Mr. and Mrs. L.
(*To* LIMBURY.) Double L,—I call them. (*To* LOVETOWN.) Small
italic and Roman capital. (*To* MR. *and* MRS. LIMBURY, *who come
forward.*) Here, it's all arranged. The key to the whole matter
is, that I've been mistaken, which is something singular. If I
have made another mistake in calculating on *your* kind and lenient
reception of our last half-hour's misunderstanding (*to the audience*),
I shall have done something more singular still. Do you forbid
me committing any more mistakes, or may I announce my intention of doing something singular again ?

THE LAMPLIGHTER

A FARCE
IN ONE ACT
[1838]

DRAMATIS PERSONÆ

Mr. Stargazer.

Master Galileo Isaac Newton Flamstead Stargazer (*his son*).

Tom Grig (*the Lamplighter*).

Mr. Mooney (*an Astrologer*).

Servant.

Betsy Martin.

Emma Stargazer.

Fanny Brown.

THE LAMPLIGHTER[1]

SCENE I.—*The Street, outside of* MR. STARGAZER'S *house.* *Two
street Lamp-posts in front.*

TOM GRIG (*with ladder and lantern, singing as he enters*).

Day has gone down o'er the Baltic's proud bil-ler;
Evening has sigh'd, alas! to the lone wil-ler;
Night hurries on, night hurries on, earth and ocean to kiv-ver;
Rise, gentle moon, rise, gentle moon, and guide me to my——

That ain't a rhyme, that ain't—kiv-ver and lover! I ain't much
of a poet; but if I couldn't make better verse than that, I'd
undertake to be set fire to, and put up, instead of the lamp, before
Alderman Waithman's obstacle in Fleet Street. Bil-ler, wil-ler,
kiv-ver—shiver, obviously. That's what *I* call poetry. (*Sings.*)

Day has gone down o'er the Baltic's proud bil-ler—

(*During the previous speech he has been occupied in lighting
one of the lamps. As he is about to light the other,* MR.
STARGAZER *appears at window, with a telescope.*)

MR. STARGAZER (*after spying most intently at the clouds*). Holloa!
TOM (*on ladder*). Sir, to you! And holloa again, if you come to that.
MR. STARGAZER. Have you seen the comet?
TOM. What Comet—the Exeter Comet?
MR. STARGAZER. What comet? *The* comet—Halley's comet!
TOM. Nelson's, you mean. I saw it coming out of the yard, not five
minutes ago.
MR. STARGAZER. Could you distinguish anything of a tail?
TOM. Distinguish a tail? I believe you—four tails!
MR. STARGAZER. A comet with four tails; and all visible to the
naked eye! Nonsense! it couldn't be.
TOM. You wouldn't say that again if you was down here, old

[1] Printed from the manuscript in the Forster Collection at the South Kensington
Museum.

Bantam. (*Clock strikes five.*) You'll tell me next, I suppose, that that isn't five o'clock striking, eh?

MR. STARGAZER. Five o'clock—five o'clock! Five o'clock P.M. on the thirtieth day of November, one thousand eight hundred and thirty-eight! Stop till I come down—stop! Don't go away on any account—not a foot, not a step. (*Closes window.*)

TOM (*descending, and shouldering his ladder*). Stop! stop, to a lamp-lighter, with three hundred and seventy shops and a hundred and twenty private houses waiting to be set a light to! Stop, to a lamplighter!

As he is running off, enter MR. STARGAZER *from his house, hastily.*

MR. STARGAZER (*detaining him*). Not for your life!—not for your life! The thirtieth day of November, one thousand eight hundred and thirty-eight! Miraculous circumstance! extra-ordinary fulfilment of a prediction of the planets!

TOM. What are you talking about?

MR. STARGAZER (*looking about*). Is there nobody else in sight, up the street or down? No, not a soul! This, then, is the man whose coming was revealed to me by the stars, six months ago!

TOM. What do you mean?

MR. STARGAZER. Young man, that I have consulted the Book of Fate with rare and wonderful success,—that coming events have cast their shadows before.

TOM. Don't talk nonsense to me,—I ain't an event; I'm a lamp-lighter!

MR. STARGAZER (*aside*). True!—Strange destiny that one, announced by the planets as of noble birth, should be devoted to so humble an occupation. (*Aloud.*) But you were not *always* a lamplighter?

TOM. Why, no. I wasn't born with a ladder on my left shoulder, and a light in my other hand. But I took to it very early, though, —I had it from my uncle.

MR. STARGAZER (*aside*). He had it from his uncle! How plain, and yet how forcible, is his language! He speaks of lamplighting, as though it were the whooping-cough or measles! (*To him.*) Ay!

TOM. Yes, he was the original. You should have known him!— 'cod! he was a genius, if ever there was one. Gas was the death of him! When gas lamps was first talked of, my uncle draws himself up, and says, 'I'll not believe it, there's no sich a thing,' he says. 'You might as well talk of laying on an everlasting succession of glow-worms!' But when they made the experiment of lighting a piece of Pall Mall——

MR. STARGAZER. That was when it first came up?

TOM. No, no, that was when it was first laid down. Don't mind me; I can't help a joke, now and then. My uncle was sometimes took that way. When the experiment was made of lighting a piece of Pall Mall, and he had actually witnessed it, with his own eyes, you should have seen my uncle then!

MR. STARGAZER. So much overcome?

TOM. Overcome, sir! He fell off his ladder, from weakness, fourteen times that very night; and his last fall was into a wheelbarrow that was going his way, and humanely took him home. 'I foresee in this,' he says, 'the breaking up of our profession; no more polishing of the tin reflectors,' he says; 'no more fancy-work, in the way of clipping the cottons at two o'clock in the morning; no more going the rounds to trim by daylight, and dribbling down of the *ile* on the hats and bonnets of the ladies and gentlemen, when one feels in good spirits. Any low fellow can light a gas-lamp, and it's all up!' So he petitioned the Government for—what do you call that that they give to people when it's found out that they've never been of any use, and have been paid too much for doing nothing?

MR. STARGAZER. Compensation?

TOM. Yes, that's the thing,—compensation. They didn't give him any, though! And then he got very fond of his country all at once, and went about, saying how that the bringing in of gas was a death-blow to his native land, and how that its *ile* and cotton trade was gone for ever, and the whales would go and kill themselves, privately, in spite and vexation at not being caught! After this, he was right-down cracked, and called his 'bacco pipe a gas pipe, and thought his tears was lamp *ile*, and all manner of nonsense. At last, he went and hung himself on a lamp iron, in St. Martin's Lane, that he'd always been very fond of; and as he was a remarkably good husband, and had never had any secrets from his wife, he put a note in the twopenny post, as he went along, to tell the widder where the body was.

MR. STARGAZER (*laying his hand upon his arm, and speaking mysteriously*). Do you remember your parents?

361

TOM. My mother I do, very well!

MR. STARGAZER. Was she of noble birth?

TOM. Pretty well. She was in the mangling line. Her mother came of a highly respectable family,—such a business, in the sweetstuff and hardbake way!

MR. STARGAZER. Perhaps your father was——

TOM. Why, I hardly know about him. The fact is, there was some little doubt, at the time, who *was* my father. Two or three young gentlemen were paid the pleasing compliment; but their incomes being limited, they were compelled delicately to decline it.

MR. STARGAZER. Then the prediction is not fulfilled merely in part, but entirely and completely. Listen, young man,—I am acquainted with all the celestial bodies——

TOM. Are you, though?—I hope they are quite well,— every body.

MR. STARGAZER. Don't interrupt me. I am versed in the great sciences of astronomy and astrology; in my house there I have every description of apparatus for observing the course and motion of the planets. I'm writing a work about them, which will consist of eighty-four volumes, imperial quarto; and an appendix, nearly twice as long. I read what's going to happen in the stars.

TOM. Read what's going to happen in the stars! Will anything particular happen in the stars in the course of next week, now?

MR. STARGAZER. You don't understand me. I read in the stars what's going to happen here. Six months ago I derived from this source the knowledge that, precisely as the clock struck five, on the afternoon of this very day, a stranger would present himself before my enraptured sight,—that stranger would be a man of illustrious and high descent,—that stranger would be the destined husband of my young and lovely niece, who is now beneath that roof (*points to his house*);—that stranger is yourself: I receive you with open arms!

TOM. Me! I, the man of illustrious and high—I, the husband of a young and lovely—Oh! it can't be, you know! the stars have made a mistake—the comet has put 'em out!

MR. STARGAZER. Impossible! The characters were as plain as pike-staves. The clock struck five; you were here; there was not a soul in sight; a mystery envelops your birth; you are a man of noble aspect. Does not everything combine to prove the accuracy of my observations?

362

Tom. Upon my word, it looks like it! And now I come to think of it, I have very often felt as if I wasn't the small beer I was taken for. And yet I don't know,—you're quite sure about the noble aspect?

Mr. Stargazer. Positively certain.

Tom. Give me your hand.

Mr. Stargazer. And my heart, too! (*They shake hands heartily.*)

Tom. The young lady is tolerably good-looking, is she?

Mr. Stargazer. Beautiful! A graceful carriage, an exquisite shape, a sweet voice; a countenance beaming with animation and expression; the eye of a startled fawn.

Tom. I see; a sort of game eye. Does she happen to have any of the—this is quite between you and me, you know,—and I only ask from curiosity,—not because I care about it,—any of the ready?

Mr. Stargazer. Five thousand pounds! But what of that? what of that? A word in your ear. I'm in search of the philosopher's stone! I have very nearly found it—not quite. It turns everything to gold; that's its property.

Tom. What a lot of property it must have!

Mr. Stargazer. When I get it, we'll keep it in the family. Not a word to any one! What will money be to us? We shall never be able to spend it fast enough.

Tom. Well, you know, we can but try,—I'll do my best endeavours.

Mr. Stargazer. Thank you,—thank you! But I'll introduce you to your future bride at once :—this way, this way!

Tom. What, without going my rounds first?

Mr. Stargazer. Certainly. A man in whom the planets take especial interest, and who is about to have a share in the philosopher's stone, descend to lamplighting!

Tom. Perish the base idea! not by no means! I'll take in my tools though, to prevent any kind inquiries after me, at your door. (*As he shoulders the ladder the sound of violent rain is heard.*) Holloa!

Mr. Stargazer (*putting his hand on his head in amazement*). What's that?

Tom. It's coming down, rather.

Mr. Stargazer. Rain!

Tom. Ah! and a soaker, too!

Mr. Stargazer. It can't be!—it's impossible!—(*Taking a book from his pocket, and turning over the pages hurriedly.*) Look here,—here it is,—here's the weather almanack,—'Set fair,'—I knew it couldn't be! (*with great triumph*).

TOM (*turning up his collar as the rain increases*). Don't you think there's a dampness in the atmosphere?

MR. STARGAZER (*looking up*). It's singular,—it's *like* rain!

TOM. Uncommonly like.

MR. STARGAZER. It's a mistake in the elements, somehow. Here it is, 'set fair,'—and set fair it ought to be. 'Light clouds floating about.' Ah! you see, there are no light clouds;—the weather's all wrong.

TOM. Don't you think we had better get under cover?

MR. STARGAZER (*slowly retreating towards the house*). I don't acknowledge that it has any right to rain, mind! I protest against this. If Nature goes on in this way, I shall lose all respect for her,—it won't do, you know; it ought to have been two degrees colder, yesterday; and instead of that, it was warmer. This is not the way to treat scientific men. I protest against it!

[*Exeunt into house, both talking,* TOM *pushing* STARGAZER *on, and the latter continually turning back, to declaim against the weather.*

SCENE II.—*A Room in* STARGAZER'S *house.* BETSY MARTIN, EMMA STARGAZER, FANNY BROWN, *and* GALILEO, *all murmuring together as they enter.*

BETSY. I say again, young ladies, that it's shameful! unbearable!

ALL. Oh! shameful! shameful!

BETSY. Marry Miss Emma to a great, old, ugly, doting, dreaming As-tron-o-Magician, like Mr. Mooney, who's always winking and blinking through telescopes and that, and can't see a pretty face when it's under his very nose!

GALILEO (*with a melancholy air*). There never was a pretty face under *his* nose, Betsy, leastways, since I've known him. He's very plain.

BETSY. Ah! there's poor young master, too; he hasn't even spirits enough left to laugh at his own jokes. I'm sure I pity him, from the very bottom of my heart.

FANNY *and* EMMA. Poor fellow!

GALILEO. Ain't I a legitimate subject for pity? Ain't it a dreadful thing that I, that am twenty-one come next Lady-day, should be treated like a little boy?—and all because my father is so busy with the moon's age that he don't care about mine; and so much occupied in making observations on the sun round which the earth revolves, that he takes no notice of the son that revolves round him! I wasn't taken out of nankeen frocks and trousers till I became quite unpleasant in 'em.

ALL. What a shame!

GALILEO. I wasn't, indeed. And look at me now! Here's a state of things. Is this a suit of clothes for a major,—at least, for a gentleman who is a minor now, but will be a major on the very next Lady-day that comes? Is this a fit——

ALL (*interrupting him*). Certainly not!

GALILEO (*vehemently*). I won't stand it—I won't submit to it any longer. I *will* be married.

ALL. No, no, no! don't be rash.

GALILEO. I will, I tell you. I'll marry my cousin Fanny. Give me a kiss, Fanny; and Emma and Betsy will look the other way the while. (*Kisses her.*) There!

BETSY. Sir—sir! here's your father coming!

GALILEO. Well, then, I'll have another, as an antidote to my father. One more; Fanny. (*Kisses her.*)

MR. STARGAZER (*without*). This way! this way! You shall behold her immediately.

Enter MR. STARGAZER, TOM *following bashfully.*

MR. STARGAZER. Where is my——? Oh, here she is! Fanny, my dear, come here. Do you see that gentleman? (*Aside.*)

FANNY. What gentleman, uncle? Do you mean that elastic person yonder who is bowing with so much perseverance?

MR. STARGAZER. Hush! yes; that's the interesting stranger.

FANNY. Why, he is kissing his hand, uncle. What does the creature mean?

MR. STARGAZER. Ah, the rogue! Just like me, before I married your poor aunt,—all fire and impatience. He means love, my darling, love. I've such a delightful surprise for you. I didn't tell you before, for fear there should be any mistake; but it's all right, it's all right. The stars have settled it all among 'em. He's to be your husband!

FANNY. My husband, uncle? Goodness gracious, Emma! (*Converses apart with her.*)

Mr. Stargazer (*aside*). He has made a sensation already. His noble aspect and distinguished air have produced an instantaneous impression. Mr. Grig, will you permit me? (Tom *advances awkwardly*.)—This is my niece, Mr. Grig,—my niece, Miss Fanny Brown; my daughter, Emma,—Mr. Thomas Grig, the favourite of the planets.

Tom. I hope I see Miss Hemmer in a conwivial state? (*Aside to* Mr. Stargazer.) I say, I don't know which is which.

Mr. Stargazer (*aside*). The young lady nearest here is your affianced bride. Say something appropriate.

Tom. Certainly; yes, of course. Let me see. Miss (*crosses to her*)— I—thank 'ee! (*Kisses her, behind his hat. She screams.*)

Galileo (*bursting from* Betsy, *who has been retaining him*). Outrageous insolence! (Betsy *runs off*.)

Mr. Stargazer. Halloa, sir, halloa!

Tom. Who is this juvenile salamander, sir?

Mr. Stargazer. My little boy,—only my little boy; don't mind him. Shake hands with the gentleman, sir, instantly (*to* Galileo).

Tom. A very fine boy, indeed! and he does you great credit, sir. How d'ye do, my little man? (*They shake hands*, Galileo *looking very wrathful, as* Tom *pats him on the head*.) There, that's very right and proper. ''Tis dogs delight to bark and bite'; not young gentlemen, you know. There, there!

Mr. Stargazer. Now let me introduce you to that *sanctum sanctorum*, — that hallowed ground, — that philosophical retreat— where I, the *genius loci*,——

Tom. Eh?

Mr. Stargazer. The *genius loci*——

Tom (*aside*). Something to drink, perhaps. Oh, ah! yes, yes!

Mr. Stargazer. Have made all my greatest and most profound discoveries! where the telescope has almost grown to my eye with constant application; and the glass retort has been shivered to pieces from the ardour with which my experiments have been pursued. There the illustrious Mooney is, even now, pursuing those researches which will enrich us with precious metal, and make us masters of the world. Come, Mr. Grig.

Tom. By all means, sir; and luck to the illustrious Mooney, say I,— not so much on Mooney's account as for our noble selves.

Mr. Stargazer. Emma!

EMMA. Yes, papa.

MR. STARGAZER. The same day that makes your cousin Mrs. Grig, will make you and that immortal man, of whom we have just now spoken, one.

EMMA. Oh! consider, dear papa,——

MR. STARGAZER. You are unworthy of him, I know; but he,—kind, generous creature,—consents to overlook your defects, and to take you, for my sake,—devoted man!—Come, Mr. Grig!—Galileo Isaac Newton Flamstead!

GALILEO. Well? (*Advancing sulkily.*)

MR. STARGAZER. In name, alas! but not in nature; knowing, even by sight, no other planets than the sun and moon,—here is your weekly pocket-money,—sixpence! Take it all!

TOM. And don't spend it all at once, my man! Now, sir!

MR. STARGAZER. Now, Mr. Grig,—go first, sir, I beg!

[*Exeunt* TOM *and* MR. STARGAZER.

GALILEO. 'Come, Mr. Grig!'—'Go first, Mr. Grig!'—'Day that makes your cousin Mrs. Grig!'—I'll secretly stick a penknife into Mr. Grig, if I live to be three hours older!

FANNY (*on one side of him*). Oh! don't talk in that desperate way,—there's a dear, dear creature!

EMMA (*on the other side*). No! pray do not;—it makes my blood run cold to hear you.

GALILEO. Oh! if I was of age!—if I was only of age!—or we could go to Gretna Green, at threepence a head, including refreshments and all incidental expenses. But that could never be! Oh! if I was only of age!

FANNY. But what if you were? What could you do, then?

GALILEO. Marry you, cousin Fanny; I could marry you then lawfully, and without anybody's consent.

FANNY. You forget that, situated as we are, we could not be married, even if you *were* one-and-twenty;—we have no money!

EMMA. Not even enough for the fees!

GALILEO. Oh! I am sure every Christian clergyman, under such afflicting circumstances, would marry us on credit. The wedding-fees might stand over till the first christening, and then we could settle the little bill altogether. Oh! why ain't I of age!—why ain't I of age?

Enter BETSY, *in haste.*

BETSY. Well! I never could have believed it! There, Miss! I wouldn't have believed it, if I had dreamt it, even with a bit of bride-cake under my pillow! To dare to go and think of marrying a young lady, with five thousand pounds, to a common lamplighter!

ALL. A lamplighter?

BETSY. Yes, he's Tom Grig the lamplighter, and nothing more nor less, and old Mr. Stargazer goes and picks him out of the open street, and brings him in for Miss Fanny's husband, because he pretends to have read something about it in the stars. Stuff and nonsense! I don't believe he knows his letters in the stars, and that's the truth; or if he's got as far as words in one syllable, it's quite as much as he has.

FANNY. Was such an atrocity ever heard of? I, left with no power to marry without his consent, and he almost possessing the power to force my inclinations.

EMMA. It's actually worse than my being sacrificed to that odious and detestable Mr. Mooney.

BETSY. Come, Miss, it's not quite so bad as that neither; for Thomas Grig is a young man, and a proper young man enough too, but as to Mr. Mooney,—oh, dear! no husband is bad enough in my opinion, Miss; but he is worse than nothing,—a great deal worse.

FANNY. You seem to speak feelingly about this same Mr. Grig.

BETSY. Oh, dear no, Miss, not I. I don't mean to say but what Mr. Grig may be very well in his way, Miss; but Mr. Grig and I have never held any communication together, not even so much as how-d' ye-do. Oh, no indeed, I have been very careful, Miss, as I always am with strangers. I was acquainted with the last lamplighter, Miss, but he's going to be married, and has given up the calling, for the young woman's parents being very respectable, wished her to marry a literary man, and so he has set up as a bill-sticker. Mr. Grig only came upon this beat at five to-night, Miss.

FANNY. Which is a very sufficient reason why you don't know more of him.

BETSY. Well, Miss, perhaps it is; and I hope there's no crime in making friends in this world, if we can, Miss.

FANNY. Certainly not. So far from it, that I most heartily wish you could make something more than a friend of this Mr. Grig, and so lead him to falsify this prediction.

GALILEO. Oh! don't you think you could, Betsy?

EMMA. You could not manage at the same time to get any young friend of yours to make something more than a friend of Mr. Mooney, could you, Betsy?

GALILEO. But, seriously, don't you think you could manage to give us all a helping hand together, in some way, eh, Betsy?

FANNY. Yes, yes, that would be so delightful. I should be grateful to her for ever. Shouldn't you?

EMMA. Oh, to the very end of my life!

GALILEO. And so should I, you know, and lor'! we should make her so rich, when—when we got rich ourselves,—shouldn't we?

BOTH. Oh, that we should, of course.

BETSY. Let me see. I don't wish to have Mr. Grig to myself, you know. I don't want to be married.

ALL. No! no! no! Of course she don't.

BETSY. I haven't the least idea to put Mr. Grig off this match, you know, for anybody's sake, but you young people's. I am going quite *contrairy* to my own feelings, you know.

ALL. Oh, yes, yes! How kind she is!

BETSY. Well, I'll go over the matter with the young ladies in Miss Emma's room, and if we can think of anything that seems likely to help us, so much the better; and if we can't, we're none the worst. But Master Galileo mustn't come, for he is so horrid jealous of Miss Fanny that I dursn't hardly say anything before him. Why, I declare (*looking off*), there is my gentleman looking about him as if he had lost Mr. Stargazer, and now he turns this way. There—get out of sight. Make haste!

GALILEO. I may see 'em as far as the bottom stair, mayn't I, Betsy?

BETSY. Yes, but not a step farther on any consideration. There, get away softly, so that if he passes here, he may find me alone. (*They creep gently out,* GALILEO *returns and peeps in.*)

GALILEO. Hist, Betsy!

BETSY. Go away, sir. What have you come back for?

GALILEO (*holding out a large pin*). I wish you'd take an opportunity of sticking this a little way into him for patting me on the head just now.

369

BETSY. Nonsense, you can't afford to indulge in such expensive amusements as retaliation yet awhile. You must wait till you come into your property, sir. There.—Get you gone !

[*Exit* GALILEO.

Enter TOM GRIG.

TOM (*aside*). I never saw such a scientific file in my days. The enterprising gentleman that drowned himself *to see how it felt*, is nothing to him. There he is, just gone down to the bottom of a dry well in an uncommonly small bucket, to take an extra squint at the stars, they being seen best, I suppose, through the medium of a cold in the head. Halloa ! Here is a young female of attractive proportions. I wonder now whether a man of noble aspect would be justified in tickling her. (*He advances stealthily and tickles her under the arm.*)

BETSY (*starting*). Eh ! what ! Lor', sir !

TOM. Don't be alarmed. My intentions are strictly honourable. In other words, I have no intentions whatever.

BETSY. Then you ought to be more careful, Mr. Grig. That was a liberty, sir.

TOM. I know it was. The cause of liberty, all over the world,—that's my sentiment ! What is your name ?

BETSY (*curtseying*). Betsy Martin, sir.

TOM. A name famous both in song and story. Would you have the goodness, Miss Martin, to direct me to that particular apartment wherein the illustrious Mooney is now pursuing his researches ?

BETSY (*aside*). A little wholesome fear may not be amiss. (*To him, in assumed agitation.*) You are not going into *that* room, Mr. Grig ?

TOM. Indeed, I am, and I ought to be there now, having promised to join that light of science, your master (a short six, by the bye !), outside the door.

BETSY. That dreadful and mysterious chamber ! Another victim !

TOM. Victim, Miss Martin !

BETSY. Oh ! the awful oath of secrecy which binds me not to disclose the perils of that gloomy, hideous room.

TOM (*astonished*). Miss Martin !

BETSY. Such a fine young man,—so rosy and fresh-coloured, that he should fall into the clutches of that cruel and insatiable monster ! I cannot continue to witness such frightful scenes ; I must give warning.

370

TOM. If you have anything to unfold, young woman, have the goodness to give *me* warning at once.

BETSY (*affecting to recover herself*). No, no, Mr. Grig, it's nothing,—
it's ha! ha! ha!—don't mind me, don't mind me, but it certainly
is very shocking;—no,—no,—I don't mean that. I mean funny,—
yes. Ha! ha! ha!

TOM (*aside, regarding her attentively*). I suspect a trick here,—some
other lover in the case who wants to come over the stars;—but it
won't do. I'll tell you what, young woman (*to her*), if this is a
cloak, you had better try it on elsewhere;—in plain English, if
you have any object to gain and think to gain it by frightening
me, it's all my eye and, and—yourself, Miss Martin.

BETSY. Well, then, if you will rush upon your fate,—there (*pointing
off*)— that's the door at the end of that long passage and across
the gravelled yard. The room is built away from the house on
purpose.

TOM. I'll make for it at once, and the first object I inspect through
that same telescope, which now and then grows to your master's
eye, shall be the moon—the moon, which is the emblem of your
inconstant and deceitful sex, Miss Martin.

Duet.

AIR—'*The Young May-moon.*'

TOM.	There comes a new moon twelve times a year.
BETSY.	And when there is none, all is dark and drear.
TOM.	In which I espy—
BETSY.	And so, too, do I—
BOTH.	A resemblance to womankind very clear.
BOTH.	There comes a new moon twelve times in a year;
	And when there is none, all is dark and drear.
TOM.	In which I espy—
BETSY.	And so do I—
BOTH.	A resemblance to womankind very clear.

Second Verse.

TOM.	She changes, she's fickle, she drives men mad.
BETSY.	She comes to bring light, and leaves them sad.
TOM.	So restless wild—
BETSY.	But so sweetly wild—
BOTH.	That no better companion could be had.

371

BOTH.   There comes a new moon twelve times a year;
             And when there is none, all is dark and drear.

TOM.   In which I espy—

BETSY.   And so do I—

BOTH.   A resemblance to womankind very clear.   [*Exeunt.*

SCENE III.—*A large gloomy room; a window with a telescope directed
    towards the sky without, a table covered with books, instruments
    and apparatus, which are also scattered about in other parts of
    the chamber, a dim lamp, a pair of globes, etc., a skeleton in a
    case, and various uncouth objects displayed against the walls. Two
    doors in flat.* MR. MOONEY *discovered, with a very dirty face,
    busily engaged in blowing a fire, upon which is a crucible.*

    Enter MR. STARGAZER, *with a lamp, beckoning to* TOM GRIG, *who
        enters with some unwillingness.*

MR. STARGAZER. This, Mr. Grig, is the *sanctum sanctorum* of which
    I have already spoken; this is at once the laboratory and
    observatory.

TOM. It's not an over-lively place, is it?

MR. STARGAZER. It has an air of solemnity which well accords with
    the great and mysterious pursuits that are here in constant pro-
    secution, Mr. Grig.

TOM. Ah! I should think it would suit an undertaker to the life;
    or perhaps I should rather say to the death. What may that
    cheerful object be now? (*Pointing to a large phial.*)

MR. STARGAZER. That contains a male infant with three heads,—we
    use it in astrology;—it is supposed to be a *charm.*

TOM. I shouldn't have supposed it myself, from his appearance. The
    young gentleman isn't alive, is he?

MR. STARGAZER. No, he is preserved in spirits. (MR. MOONEY
    sneezes.)

TOM (*retreating into a corner*). Halloa! What the—— (MR.
    MOONEY *looks vacantly round.*) That gentleman, I suppose, is
    out of spirits?

MR. STARGAZER (*laying his hand upon* TOM's *arm and looking toward
    the philosopher*). Hush! that is the gifted Mooney. Mark well
    his noble countenance,—intense thought beams from every linea-
    ment. That is the great astrologer.

372

Tom. He looks as if he had been having a touch at the black art. I say, why don't he say something?

Mr. Stargazer. He is in a state of abstraction; see he directs his bellows this way, and blows upon the empty air.

Tom. Perhaps he sees a strange spark in this direction and wonders how he came here. I wish he 'd blow me out. (*Aside.*) I don't half like this.

Mr. Stargazer. You shall see me rouse him.

Tom. Don't put yourself out of the way on my account; I can make his acquaintance at any other time.

Mr. Stargazer. No time like the time present. Nothing awakens him from these fits of meditation but an electric shock. We always have a strongly charged battery on purpose. I 'll give him a shock directly. (Mr. Stargazer *goes up and cautiously places the end of a wire in* Mr. Mooney's *hand. He then stoops down beside the table as though bringing it in contact with the battery.* Mr. Mooney *immediately jumps up with a loud cry and throws away the bellows.*)

Tom (*squaring at the philosopher*). It wasn't me, you know,—none of your nonsense.

Mr. Stargazer (*comes hastily forward*). Mr. Grig,—Mr. Grig,— not that disrespectful attitude to one of the greatest men that ever lived. This, my dear friend (*to* Mooney),—is the noble stranger.

Mr. Mooney. A ha!

Mr. Stargazer. Who arrived, punctual to his time, this afternoon.

Mr. Mooney. O ho!

Mr. Stargazer. Welcome him, my friend,—give him your hand. (Mr. Mooney *appears confused and raises his leg.*) No—no, that 's your foot. So absent, Mr. Grig, in his gigantic meditations that very often he doesn't know one from the other. Yes, that 's your hand, very good, my dear friend, very good (*pats* Mooney *on the back, as he and* Tom *shake hands, the latter at arm's length*).

Mr. Stargazer. Have you made any more discoveries during my absence?

Mr. Mooney. Nothing particular.

Mr. Stargazer. Do you think—do you think, my dear friend, that we shall arrive at any great stage in our labours, anything at all approaching to their final consummation in the course of the night?

373

MR. MOONEY. I cannot take upon myself to say.

MR. STARGAZER. What are your opinions upon the subject?

MR. MOONEY. I haven't any opinions upon any subject whatsoever.

MR. STARGAZER. Wonderful man! Here's a mind, Mr. Grig.

TOM. Yes, his conversation's very improving indeed. But what's he staring so hard at me for?

MR. STARGAZER. Something occurs to him. Don't speak,—don't disturb the current of his reflections upon any account. (MR. MOONEY *walks solemnly up to* TOM, *who retreats before him; taking off his hat turns it over and over with a thoughtful countenance and finally puts it upon his own head.*)

MR. STARGAZER. Eccentric man!

TOM. I say, I hope he don't mean to keep that, because if he does, his eccentricity is unpleasant. Give him another shock and knock it off, will you?

MR. STARGAZER. Hush! hush! not a word. (MR. MOONEY, *keeping his eyes fixed on* TOM, *slowly returns to* MR. STARGAZER *and whispers in his ear.*)

MR. STARGAZER. Surely; by all means. I took the date of his birth, and all other information necessary for the purpose just now. (*To* TOM.) Mr. Mooney suggests that we should cast your nativity without delay, in order that we may communicate to you your future destiny.

MR. MOONEY. Let us retire for that purpose.

MR. STARGAZER. Certainly, wait here for a few moments, Mr. Grig: we are only going into the little laboratory and will return immediately. Now, my illustrious friend. (*He takes up a lamp and leads the way to one of the doors. As* MR. MOONEY *follows,* TOM *steals behind him and regains his hat.* MR. MOONEY *turns round, stares, and exit through door.*)

TOM. Well, that's the queerest genius I ever came across,—rather a singular person for a little smoking party. (*Looks into the crucible.*) This is the saucepan, I suppose, where they're boiling the philosopher's stone down to the proper consistency. I hope it's nearly done; when it's quite ready, I'll send out for sixpenn'orth of sprats, and turn 'em into gold fish for a first experiment. 'Cod! it'll be a comfortable thing though to have no end to one's riches. I'll have a country house and a park, and I'll plant a bit of it with a double row of gas-lamps a mile long, and go out with a

THE LAMPLIGHTER

French polished mahogany ladder, and two servants in livery behind me, to light 'em with my own hands every night. What's to be seen here? (*Looks through telescope.*) Nothing particular, the stopper being on at the other end. The little boy with three heads (*looking towards the case*). What a comfort he must have been to his parents!—Halloa! (*taking up a large knife*) this is a disagreeable-looking instrument,—something too large for bread and cheese, or oysters, and not of a bad shape for sticking live persons in the ribs. A very dismal place this,—I wish they'd come back. Ah!—(*coming upon the skeleton*) here's a ghastly object,—what does the writing say?—(*reads a label upon the case*) 'Skeleton of a gentleman prepared by Mr. Mooney.' I hope Mr. Mooney may not be in the habit of inviting gentlemen here, and making 'em into such preparations without their own consent. Here's a book, now. What's all this about, I wonder? The letters look as if a steam-engine had printed 'em by accident. (*Turns over the leaves, spelling to himself.*)

GALILEO *enters softly unseen by* TOM, *who has his back towards him.*

GALILEO (*aside*). Oh, you're there, are you? If I could but suffocate him, not for life, but only till I am one-and-twenty, and then revive him, what a comfort and convenience it would be! I overheard my cousin Fanny talking to Betsy about coming here. What can she want here? If she can be false,—false to *me*;—it seems impossible, but if she is?—well, well, we shall see. If I can reach that lumber-room unseen, Fanny Brown,—beware. (*He steals toward the door on the* L.—*opens it, and exit cautiously into the room. As he does so,* TOM *turns the other way.*)

TOM (*closing the book*). It's very pretty Greek, I think. What a time they are!

MR. STARGAZER *and* MOONEY *enter from room.*

MOONEY. Tell the noble gentleman of his irrevocable destiny.

MR. STARGAZER (*with emotion*). No,—no, prepare him first.

TOM (*aside*). Prepare him! 'prepared by Mr. Mooney.'—This is a case of kidnapping and slaughter. (*To them.*) Let him attempt to prepare me at his peril!

MR. STARGAZER. Mr. Grig, why this demonstration?

TOM. Oh, don't talk to me of demonstrations;—you ain't going to demonstrate me, and so I tell you.

MR. STARGAZER. Alas! (*Crossing to him.*) The truth we have to communicate requires but little demonstration from our feeble lips. We have calculated upon your nativity.

MOONEY. Yes, we have, we have.

MR. STARGAZER. Tender-hearted man! (MOONEY *weeps.*) See there, Mr. Grig, isn't that affecting?

TOM. What is he piping his boiled gooseberry eye for, sir? How should I know whether it's affecting or not?

MR. STARGAZER. For you, for you. We find that you will expire to-morrow two months, at thirty minutes—wasn't it thirty minutes, my friend?

MOONEY. Thirty-five minutes, twenty-seven seconds and five-sixths of a second. Oh! (*Groans.*)

MR. STARGAZER. Thirty-five minutes, twenty-seven seconds, and five-sixths of a second past nine o'clock.

MOONEY. A.M. (*They both wipe their eyes.*)

TOM (*alarmed*). Don't tell me, you've made a mistake somewhere;— I won't believe it.

MOONEY. No, it is all correct, we worked it all in the most satisfactory manner.—Oh! (*Groans again.*)

TOM. Satisfactory, sir! Your notions of the satisfactory are of an extraordinary nature.

MR. STARGAZER (*producing a pamphlet*). It is confirmed by the prophetic almanack. Here is the prediction for to-morrow two months,—'The decease of a great person may be looked for about this time.'

TOM (*dropping into his chair*). That's me! It's all up! inter me decently, my friends.

MR. STARGAZER (*shaking his hand*). Your wishes shall be attended to. We must have the marriage with my niece at once, in order that your distinguished race may be transmitted to posterity. Condole with him, my Mooney, while I compose my feelings, and settle the preliminaries of the marriage in solitude.

(*Takes up lamp and exit into room R. MOONEY draws up a chair in a line with TOM, a long way off. They both sigh heavily. GALILEO opens the lumber-room door. As he does so the room door opens and BETSY steals softly in, beckoning to EMMA and FANNY who follow. He retires again abruptly.*)

BETSY (*aside*). Now, young ladies, if you take heart only for one minute, you may frighten Mr. Mooney out of being married at once.

EMMA. But if he has serious thoughts?

BETSY. Nonsense, Miss, he hasn't any thoughts. Your papa says to him, 'Will you marry my daughter?' and he says, 'Yes, I will'; and he would and will if you ain't bold, but bless you, he never turned it over in his mind for a minute. If you, Miss (*to* EMMA), pretend to hate him and love a rival, and you, Miss (*to* FANNY), to love him to distraction, you'll frighten him so betwixt you that he'll declare off directly, I warrant. The love will frighten him quite as much as the hate. He never saw a woman in a passion, and as to one in love, I don't believe that anybody but his mother ever kissed that grumpy old face of his in all his born days. Now, do try him, ladies. Come, we're losing time.

> (*She conceals herself behind the skeleton case.* EMMA *rushes up to* TOM GRIG *and embraces him, while* FANNY *clasps* MOONEY *round the neck.* GALILEO *appears at his door in an attitude of amazement, and* MR. STARGAZER *at his, after running in again with the lamp, which before he sees what is going forward he had in his hand.* TOM *and* MOONEY *in great astonishment.*)

FANNY (*to* MOONEY). ⎱ Hush! hush!
EMMA (*to* GRIG). ⎰

> (TOM GRIG *and* MOONEY *get their heads sufficiently out of the embrace to exchange a look of wonder.*)

EMMA. Dear Mr. Grig, I know you must consider this strange, extraordinary, unaccountable conduct.

TOM. Why, ma'am, without explanation, it does appear singular.

EMMA. Yes, yes, I know it does, I know it will, but the urgency of the case must plead my excuse. Too fascinating Mr. Grig, I have seen you once and only once, but the impression of that maddening interview can never be effaced. I love you to distraction. (*Falls upon his shoulder.*)

TOM. You're extremely obliging, ma'am, it's a flattering sort of thing,—or it would be (*aside*) if I was going to live a little longer, —but you're not the one, ma'am;—it's the other lady that the stars have——

FANNY (*to* MOONEY). Nay, wonderful being, hear me—this is not a time for false conventional delicacy. Wrapt in your sublime visions, you have not [perceived]¹ the silent tokens of a woman's first and all-absorbing attachment, which have been, I fear, but too perceptible in the eyes of others; but now I must speak out. I hate this odious man. You are my first and only love. Oh! speak to me.

MOONEY. I haven't anything appropriate to say, young woman. I think I had better go. (*Attempting to get away.*)

FANNY. Oh! no, no, no (*detaining him*). Give me some encouragement. Not one kind word? not one look of love?

MOONEY. I don't know how to look a look of love.—I'm, I'm frightened.

TOM. So am I! I don't understand this. I tell you, Miss, that the other lady is my destined wife. Upon my word you mustn't hug me, you'll make her jealous.

FANNY. Jealous! of you! Hear me (*to* MOONEY). I renounce all claim or title to the hand of that or any other man and vow to be eternally and wholly yours.

MOONEY. No, don't, you can't be mine,—nobody can be mine.—I don't want anybody—I—I——

EMMA. If you will not hear her—hear *me*, detested monster.—Hear me declare that sooner than be your bride, with this deep passion for another rooted in my heart,—I——

MOONEY. You need not make any declaration on the subject, young woman.

MR. STARGAZER (*coming forward*). She shan't,—she shan't. That's right, don't hear her. She shall marry you whether she likes it or not,—she shall marry you to-morrow morning,—and you, Miss (*to* FANNY), shall marry Mr. Grig if I trundle you to church in a wheelbarrow.

GALILEO (*coming forward*). So she shall! so she may! Let her! let her! I give her leave.

MR. STARGAZER. You give her leave, you young dog! Who the devil cares whether *you* give her leave or not? and what are you spinning about in that way for?

GALILEO. I'm fierce, I'm furious,—don't talk to me,—I shall do somebody a mischief;—I'll never marry anybody after this, never,

---

¹ The word in brackets is wanting in the manuscript, and is here supplied conjecturally to complete the sense. See, however, *Reprinted Pieces*, ' The Lamplighter,' p. 295, line 27, of this Edition.—ED.

never, it isn't safe. I'll live and die a bachelor!—there—a bachelor! a bachelor! (*He goes up and encounters* BETSY. *She talks to him apart, and his wrath seems gradually to subside.*)

MOONEY. The little boy, albeit of tender years, has spoken wisdom. I have been led to the contemplation of womankind. I find their love is too violent for my staid habits. I would rather not venture upon the troubled waters of matrimony.

MR. STARGAZER. You don't mean to marry my daughter? Not if I say she *shall* have you? (MOONEY *shakes his head solemnly.*) Mr. Grig, you have not changed your mind because of a little girlish folly?

TOM. To-morrow two months! I may as well get through as much gold as I can in the meantime. Why, sir, if the pot nearly boils (*pointing to the crucible*),—if you're pretty near the philosopher's stone,——

MR. STARGAZER. Pretty near! We're sure of it—certain; it's as good as money in the Bank. (GALILEO *and* BETSY, *who have been listening attentively, bustle about, fanning the fire, and throwing in sundry powders from the bottles on the table, then cautiously retire to a distance.*)

TOM. If that's the case, sir, I am ready to keep faith with the planets. I'll take her, sir, I'll take her.

MR. STARGAZER. Then here's her hand, Mr. Grig,—no resistance, Miss (*drawing* FANNY *forward*). It's of no use, so you may as well do it with a good grace. Take her hand, Mr. Grig. (*The crucible blows up with a loud crash; they all start.*)

MR. STARGAZER. What!—the labour of fifteen years destroyed in an instant!

MOONEY (*stooping over the fragments*). That's the only disappointment I have experienced in this process since I was first engaged in it when I was a boy. It always blows up when it's on the point of succeeding.

TOM. Is the philosopher's stone gone?

MOONEY. No.

TOM. Not gone, sir?

MOONEY. No—it never came!

MR. STARGAZER. But we'll get it, Mr. Grig. Don't be cast down, we shall discover it in less than fifteen years this time, I dare say.

Tom (*relinquishing* Fanny's *hand*). Ah! Were the stars very positive about this union?

Mr. Stargazer. They had not a doubt about it. They said it *was* to be, and it must be. They were peremptory.

Tom. I am sorry for that, because they have been very civil to me in the way of showing a light now and then, and I really regret disappointing 'em. But under the peculiar circumstances of the case, it can't be.

Mr. Stargazer. Can't be, Mr. Grig! What can't be?

Tom. The marriage, sir. I forbid the banns. (*Retires and sits down.*)

Mr. Stargazer. Impossible! such a prediction unfulfilled! Why, the consequences would be as fatal as those of a concussion between the comet and this globe. Can't be! it must be, shall be.

Betsy (*coming forward, followed by* Galileo). If you please, sir, may I say a word?

Mr. Stargazer. What have you got to say?—speak, woman!

Betsy. Why, sir, I don't think Mr. Grig is the right man.

Mr. Stargazer. What!

Betsy. Don't you recollect, sir, that just as the house-clock struck the first stroke of five, you gave Mr. Galileo a thump on the head with the butt end of your telescope, and told him to get out of the way?

Mr. Stargazer. Well, if I did, what of that?

Betsy. Why, then, sir, I say, and I would say it if I was to be killed for it, that he's the young gentleman that ought to marry Miss Fanny, and that the stars never meant anything else.

Mr. Stargazer. He! Why, he's a little boy.

Galileo. I ain't. I'm one-and-twenty next Lady-day.

Mr. Stargazer. Eh! Eighteen hundred and—why, so he is, I declare. He's quite a stranger to me, certainly. I never thought about his age since he was fourteen, and I remember that birthday, because he'd a new suit of clothes then. But the noble family——

Betsy. Lor', sir! ain't it being of a noble family to be the son of such a clever man as you?

Mr. Stargazer. That's true. And my mother's father would have been Lord Mayor, only he died of turtle the year before.

Betsy. Oh, it's quite clear.

Mr. Stargazer. The only question is about the time, because the church struck afterwards. But I should think the stars, taking so much interest in my house, would most likely go by the house-clock,—eh! Mooney?

MOONEY. Decidedly,—yes.

MR. STARGAZER. Then you may have her, my son. Her father was a great astronomer; so I hope that, though you *are* a blockhead, your children may be scientific. There! (*Joins their hands.*)

EMMA. Am I free to marry who I like, papa?

MR. STARGAZER. Won't you, Mooney? Won't you?

MOONEY. If anybody asks me to again I'll run away, and never come back any more.

MR. STARGAZER. Then we must drop the subject. Yes, your choice is now unfettered.

EMMA. Thank you, dear papa. Then I'll look about for somebody who will suit me without the delay of an instant longer than is absolutely necessary.

MR. STARGAZER. How very dutiful!

FANNY. And, as my being here just now with Emma was a little trick of Betsy's, I hope you'll forgive her, uncle.

EMMA. }
GALILEO. } Oh, yes, do.

FANNY. And even reward her, uncle, for being instrumental in fulfilling the prediction.

EMMA. }
GALILEO. } Oh, yes; do reward her—do.

FANNY. Perhaps you could find a husband for her, uncle, you know. Don't you understand?

BETSY. Pray don't mention it, Miss. I told you at first, Miss, that I had not the least wish or inclination to have Mr. Grig to myself. I couldn't abear that Mr. Grig should think I wanted him to marry me; oh no, Miss, not on any account.

MR. STARGAZER. Oh, that's pretty intelligible. Here, Mr. Grig. (*They fall back from his chair.*) Have you any objection to take this young woman for better, for worse?

BETSY. Lor', sir! how ondelicate!

MR. STARGAZER. I'll add a portion of ten pounds for your loss of time here to-night. What do you say, Mr. Grig?

TOM. It don't much matter. I ain't long for this world. Eight weeks of marriage might reconcile me to my fate. I should go off, I think, more resigned and peaceful. Yes, I'll take her, as a reparation. Come to my arms! (*He embraces her with a dismal face.*)

MR. STARGAZER (*taking a paper from his pocket*). Egad! that reminds me of what I came back to say, which all this bustle drove out of my head. There's a figure wrong in the nativity (*handing the paper to* MOONEY). He'll live to a green old age.

TOM (*looking up*). Eh! What?

MOONEY. So he will. Eighty-two years and twelve days will be the lowest.

TOM (*disengaging himself*). Eh! here! (*calling off*). Hallo, you, sir! bring in that ladder and lantern.

A Servant enters in great haste, and hands them to TOM.

SERVANT. There's such a row in the street,—none of the gas-lamps lit, and all the people calling for the lamplighter. *Such* a row! (*Rubbing his hands with great glee.*)

TOM. Is there, my fine fellow? Then I'll go and light 'em. And as, under existing circumstances, and with the prospect of a green old age before me, I'd rather *not* be married, Miss Martin, I beg to assure the ratepayers present that in future I shall pay the strictest attention to my professional duties, and do my best for the contractor; and that I shall be found upon my beat as long as they condescend to patronise the Lamplighter. (*Runs off.* MISS MARTIN *faints in the arms of* MOONEY.)

CURTAIN

MR. NIGHTINGALE'S DIARY

A FARCE
IN ONE ACT
[1851]
BY CHARLES DICKENS AND MARK LEMON

DRAMATIS PERSONÆ

At Devonshire House, Tuesday, *May* 27, 1851

MR. NIGHTINGALE	. . . . . MR. DUDLEY COSTELLO.
MR. GABBLEWIG (*of the Middle Temple*). . . . MR. CHARLES DICKENS.
TIP (*his Tiger*) . . . . . . MR. AUGUSTUS EGG.
SLAP (*professionally Mr. Formiville*) . . . MR. MARK LEMON.
LITHERS (*landlord of the ' Water-Lily'*). . . MR. WILKIE COLLINS.
ROSINA . . . . MISS ELLEN CHAPLIN.
SUSAN . . . . MRS. COE.

MR. NIGHTINGALE'S DIARY

SCENE.—*The Common Room of the Water-Lily Hotel at Malvern. Door and Window in flat. A carriage stops. Door-bell rings violently.*

TIP (*without*). Now, then! Wai-ter! Landlord! Somebody! (*Enter TIP, through door, with a quantity of luggage.*)

Enter LITHERS, L., *running in.*

LITHERS. Here you are, my boy.

TIP (*much offended*). My boy! Who are you boying of! Don't do it. I won't have it. The worm will turn if it's trod upon.

LITHERS. I never trod upon you.

TIP. What do you mean by calling *me* a worm?

LITHERS. You called yourself one. You ought to know what you are better than I do.

GABBLEWIG (*without*). Has anybody seen that puppy of mine—answers to the name of 'Tip'—with a gold-lace collar? (*Enters.*) O, here you are! You scoundrel, where have you been?

LITHERS. Good gracious me! Why, if it ain't Mr. Gabblewig, Junior!

GABBLEWIG. What, Lithers! Do *you* turn up at Malvern Wells, of all the places upon earth?

LITHERS. Bless you, sir, I've been landlord of this little place these two years! Ever since you did me that great kindness—ever since you paid out that execution for me when I was in the greengrocery way, and used to wait at your parties in the Temple—which is five years ago come Christmas—I've been (through a little legacy my wife dropped into) in the public line. I'm overjoyed to see you, sir. How do you do, sir? Do you find yourself pretty well, sir?

GABBLEWIG (*moodily seating himself*). Why, no, I can't say I *am* pretty well.

TIP. No more ain't I.

MR. NIGHTINGALE'S DIARY

GABBLEWIG. Be so good as to take those boots of yours into the kitchen, sir.

TIP (*reluctantly*). Yes, sir.

GABBLEWIG. And the baggage into my bedroom.

TIP. Yes, sir. (*Aside.*) Here's a world!   [*Exit,* L.

LITHERS. The Queen's Counsellor, that is to be, looks very down—uncommonly down. Something's wrong. I wonder what it is. Can't be debt. Don't look like drinking. Hope it isn't dice! Ahem! Beg your pardon, Mr. Gabblewig, but you'd wish to dine, sir? He don't hear. (*Gets round, dusting the table as he goes, and at last stoops his head so as to come face to face with him.*) What would you choose for dinner, Mr. Gabblewig?

GABBLEWIG. O, ah, yes! Give me some cold veal.

LITHERS. Cold veal! He's out of his mind.

GABBLEWIG. I'm a miserable wretch. I *was* going to be married. I am *not* going to be married. The young lady's uncle refuses to consent. It's all off—all over—all up!

LITHERS. But there are other young ladies——

GABBLEWIG. Don't talk nonsense.

LITHERS (*aside*). All the rest are cold veal, I suppose. But,—you'll excuse my taking the liberty, being so much beholden to you,—but couldn't anything be done to get over the difficulty?

GABBLEWIG. Nothing at all. How's it possible? Do you know the nature of the uncle's objection? But of course you don't. I'll tell you. He says I speak too fast, and *am* too slow,—want reality of purpose, and all that. He says I'm all words. What the devil else does he suppose I *can* be, being a lawyer! He says I happen to be counsel for his daughter just now, but after marriage might be counsel for the opposite side. He says I am wanting in earnestness,—deficient in moral go-aheadism.

LITHERS. In which?

GABBLEWIG. Just so. In consequence of which you behold before you a crushed flower. I am shut up and done for,—the peace of the valley is fled;—I have come down here to see if the cold-water cure will have any effect on a broken heart. Having had a course of wet blanket, I am going to try the wet sheet;—dare say I shall finish before long with a daisy counterpane.

LITHERS (*aside*). Everybody's bit by the cold water. It will be the ruin of our business.

MR. NIGHTINGALE'S DIARY

GABBLEWIG. If the waters of Malvern were the waters of Lethe, I'd take a douche forty feet high, this afternoon, and drink five-and-twenty tumblers before breakfast to-morrow morning. Anything to wash out the tormenting remembrance of Rosina Nightingale.

LITHERS. Nightingale, Mr. Gabblewig?

GABBLEWIG. Nightingale. As the Shakespeare duet went, in the happy days of our amateur plays:

> The Nightingale alone,
> She, poor bird, as all forlorn,
> Lean'd her breast uptil a thorn.

I've no doubt she's doing it at the present moment—or leaning her head against the drawing-room window, looking across the Crescent. It's all the same.

LITHERS. The Crescent, Mr. Gabblewig?

GABBLEWIG. The Crescent.

LITHERS. Not at Bath?

GABBLEWIG. At Bath.

LITHERS (*feeling in his pockets*). Good gracious! (*Gives a letter.*) Look at that, sir.

GABBLEWIG. The cramped hand of the obstinate old bird, who might, could, and should have been—and wouldn't be my father-in-law! (*Reads.*) 'Christopher Nightingale's compliments to the landlord of the Water-Lily, at Malvern Wells.'

LITHERS. The present establishment.

GABBLEWIG (*reading*). 'And hearing it is a quiet, unpretending, well-conducted house, requests to have the following rooms prepared for him on Tuesday afternoon.'

LITHERS. The present afternoon.

GABBLEWIG (*reading*). 'Namely, a private sitting-room with a'—what! a weed? He don't smoke.

LITHERS (*looking over his shoulder*). A view, sir.

GABBLEWIG. Oh! 'with a view.' Ay, ay. 'A bedroom for Christopher N. with a'—what? with a wormy pew?

LITHERS (*looking over his shoulder*). A warming-pan.

GABBLEWIG. To be sure; but it's as like one as the other. 'With a warming-pan, and two suitable chambers for Miss Rosina Nightingale.'—Support me.

LITHERS. Hold up, Mr. Gabblewig.

MR. NIGHTINGALE'S DIARY

GABBLEWIG. You might knock me down with a feather.

LITHERS. But you needn't knock *me* down with a barrister. Hold up, sir.

GABBLEWIG (*reading*). 'And her maid. Christopher Nightingale intends to try the cold-water cure.'

LITHERS. I beg your pardon, sir. What's his complaint?

GABBLEWIG. Nothing.

LITHERS (*shaking his head*). He'll never get over it, sir. Of all the invalids that come down here, the invalids that have nothing the matter with them are the hopeless cases.

GABBLEWIG (*reading*). 'Cold-water cure, having drunk (see Diary) four hundred and sixty-seven gallons, three pints and a half of the various celebrated waters of England and Germany, and proved them all to be humbugs. He has likewise proved (see Diary) all pills to be humbugs. Miss Rosina Nightingale, being rather low, will also try the cold-water cure, which will probably rouse her.'— Never!

> Perhaps she, like me, may struggle with—

(And I have no doubt of it, Lithers, for she has the tenderest heart in the world)

> Some feeling of regret

(awakened by the present individual).

> But if she loved as I have loved,

(And I have no doubt she did—and does)

> She never can forget.

(And she won't, I feel convinced, if it's only in obstinacy.) (*Gives back letter.*)

LITHERS. Well, sir, what'll you do? I'm entirely devoted to you, and ready to serve you in any way. Will you have a ladder from the builder's, and run away with the young lady in the middle of the night; or would the key of the street-door be equally agreeable?

GABBLEWIG. Neither. Can't be done. If it could be done I should have done it at Bath. Grateful duty won't admit of union without consent of uncle,—uncle won't give consent;—stick won't beat dog,—dog won't bite pig,—pig won't get over the stile;—and so the lovers will never be married! (*Sitting down as before.*) Give me the cold veal, and the day before yesterday's paper.

> [*Exit* LITHERS, L., *and immediately returns with papers.*

388

MR. NIGHTINGALE'S DIARY

SLAP (*without*). Halloa, here! My name is Formiville. Is Mr. Formiville's luggage arrived? Several boxes were sent on before-hand for Mr. Formiville; are those boxes here? (*Entering at door, preceded by* LITHERS, *who bows him in.*) Do you hear me, my man? Has Mr. Formiville's luggage—I am Mr. Formiville—arrived?

LITHERS. Quite safely, sir, yesterday. Three boxes, sir, and a pair of foils.

SLAP. *And* a pair of foils. The same. Very good. Take this cap. (LITHERS *puts it down.*) Good. Put these gloves in the cap. (LITHERS *does so.*) Good. Give me the cap again, it's cold. (*He does so.*) Very good. Are you the landlord?

LITHERS. I am Thomas Lithers, the landlord, sir.

SLAP. Very good. You write in the title-pages of all your books, no doubt:—

> Thomas Lithers is my name,
> And landlord is my station;
> Malvern Wells my dwelling-place,
> And Chalk my occupation.

What have you got to eat, my man?

LITHERS. Well, sir, we could do you a nice steak; or we could toss you up a cutlet; or——

SLAP. What have you ready dressed, my man?

LITHERS. We have a very fine York ham, and a beautiful fowl, sir——

SLAP. Produce them! Let the banquet be served. Stay; have you——

LITHERS (*rubbing his hands*). Well, sir, we have, and I can strongly recommend it.

SLAP. To what may that remark refer, my friend?

LITHERS. I thought you mentioned Rhine-wine, sir.

SLAP. O truly. Yes, I think I did. Yes, I am sure I did. Is it very fine?

LITHERS. It is uncommon fine, sir. Liebfraumilch of the most delicious quality.

SLAP. You may produce a flask. The price is no consideration (*aside*)—as I shall never pay for it.

LITHERS. Directly, sir.

389

MR. NIGHTINGALE'S DIARY

SLAP. So. He bites. He will be done. If he *will* be done he *must* be done. I can't help it. Thus men rush upon their fate. A stranger? Hum! Your servant, sir. My name is Formiville——

GABBLEWIG (*who has previously observed him*). Of several provincial theatres, I believe, and formerly engaged to assist an amateur company at Bath, under the management of——

SLAP (*with a theatrical pretence of being affected*). Mr. Gabblewig! Heavens! This recognition is so sudden, so unlooked for,—it unmans me. (*Aside.*) Owe him fifteen pounds, four shirts, and a waistcoat. Hope he's forgotten the loan of those trifles.—O sir, if I drop a tear upon that hand——

GABBLEWIG. Consider it done. Suppose the tear, as we used to say at rehearsal. How are you going on? You have left the profession?

SLAP (*aside*). Or the profession left me. I either turned *it* off, or *it* turned *me* off; all one. (*Aloud.*) Yes, Mr. Gabblewig, I am now living on a little property—that is, I have expectations—(*aside*) of doing an old gentleman.

GABBLEWIG. I have my apprehensions, Mr. Formiville, otherwise I believe, Mr. Slap——

SLAP. Slap, sir, was my father's name. Do not reproach me with the misfortunes of my ancestors.

GABBLEWIG. I was about to say, Slap, otherwise Formiville, that I have a very strong belief that you have been for some time established in the begging-letter-writing business. And when a gentleman of that description drops a tear on my hand, my hand has a tendency to drop itself on his nose.

SLAP. I don't understand you, sir.

GABBLEWIG. I see you don't. Now the danger is, that I, Gabblewig, may take the profession of the law into my own hands, and eject Slap, otherwise Formiville, from the nearest casement or window, being at a height from the ground not exceeding five-and-twenty feet.

SLAP (*angrily*). Sir, I perceive how it is. A vindictive old person, of the name of Nightingale, who denounced me to the Mendicity Society, and who has pursued me in various ways, has prejudiced your mind somehow, publicly or privately, against an injured and calumniated victim. But let that Nightingale beware; for, if the Nightingale is not a bird, though an old one, that I will catch yet once again with chaff, and clip the wings of, too, I'm—(*Aside.*)

MR. NIGHTINGALE'S DIARY

Confound my temper, where's it running? (*Affects to weep in silence.*)

GABBLEWIG (*aside*). Oho! That's what brings him here, is it? A trap for the Nightingales! I may show the old fellow that I have some purpose in me, after all!—Those amateur dresses among my baggage!—Lithers's assistance—done! Mr. Formiville.

SLAP (*with injured dignity*). Sir!

GABBLEWIG (*taking up hat and stick*). As I am not ambitious of the honour of your company, I shall leave you in possession of this apartment. I believe you are rather absent, are you not?

SLAP. Sir, I *am*, rather so.

GABBLEWIG. Exactly. Then you will do me the favour to observe that the spoons and forks of this establishment are the private property of the landlord.   [*Exit*, L.

SLAP. And that man wallows in eight hundred a year, and half that sum would make my wife and children (if I had any) happy!

Enter LITHERS (L.), *with tray, on which are fowl, ham, bread, and glasses.*

But arise, black vengeance! Nightingale shall suffer doubly. Nightingale found me out. When a man finds me out in imposing on him, I never forgive him,—and when he don't find me out, I never leave off imposing on him. Those are my principles. What ho! Wine here!

LITHERS (*arranging table and chair*). Wine coming, sir, directly! My young man has gone below for it. (*Bell rings without.*) More company! Mr. Nightingale, beyond a doubt! (*Showing him in at door.*) This way, sir, if you please! Your letter received, sir, and your rooms prepared.

SLAP (*looking off melodramatically before seating himself at table*). Is that the malignant whom these eyes have never yet bel—asted with a look? Caitiff, tereremble!

Sits, as NIGHTINGALE *enters with* ROSINA *and* SUSAN. NIGHTINGALE *muffled in a shawl, and carrying a great-coat.*

NIGHTINGALE (*to* LITHERS). That'll do, that'll do. Don't bother, sir. I am nervous, and can't bear to be bothered. What I want is peace. Instead of peace, I've got (*looking at* ROSINA) what rhymes to it, and is not at all like it. (*Sits, covering his legs with his great-coat.*)

391

MR. NIGHTINGALE'S DIARY

ROSINA. O uncle! Is it not enough that I am never to redeem those pledges which——

NIGHTINGALE. Don't talk to me about redeeming pledges, as if I was a pawnbroker! Oh! (*Starts.*)

ROSINA. Are you ill, sir?

NIGHTINGALE. Am I ever anything else, ma'am! Here! Refer to Diary (*gives book*). Rosina, save me the trouble of my glasses. See last Tuesday.

ROSINA. I see it, sir (*turning over leaves*).

NIGHTINGALE. What's the afternoon entry?

ROSINA (*reading*). 'New symptom. Crick in back. Sensation as if self a stiff boot-jack suddenly tried to be doubled up by strong person.'

NIGHTINGALE (*starts again*). O!

ROSINA. Symptom repeated, sir?

NIGHTINGALE. Symptom repeated. I must put it down. (SUSAN *brings chair, and produces screw-inkstand and pen from her pocket.* NIGHTINGALE *takes the book on his knee, and writes.*) 'Symptom repeated.'—Oh! (*Starts again.*) 'Symptom re-repeated.' (*Writes again.*) Mr. Lithers, I believe?

LITHERS. At your service, sir.

NIGHTINGALE. Mr. Lithers, I am a nervous man, and require peace. We had better come to an understanding. I am a water patient, but I'll pay for wine. You'll be so good as to call the pump sherry at lunch, port at dinner, and brandy-and-water at night. Now, be so kind as to direct the chambermaid to show this discontented young lady her room.

LITHERS. Certainly, sir. This way, if you please, Miss. (*He whispers her. She screams.*)

NIGHTINGALE (*alarmed*). What's the matter?

ROSINA. O uncle! I felt as if—don't be frightened, uncle,—as if something had touched me here (*with her hand upon her heart*) so unexpectedly, that I—don't be frightened, uncle—that I almost dropped, uncle.

NIGHTINGALE. Lord bless me! Boot-jack and strong person contagious! Susan, a mouthful of ink. (*Dips his pen in her inkstand, and writes.*) 'Symptom shortly afterwards repeated in niece.' Susan, *you* don't feel anything particular, do you?

SUSAN. Nothing whatever, sir.

MR. NIGHTINGALE'S DIARY

NIGHTINGALE. You never do. You are the most aggravating young woman in the world.

SUSAN. Lor', sir, you wouldn't wish a party ill, I'm sure!

NIGHTINGALE. Ill! you *are* ill, if you only knew it. If you were as intimate with your own interior as I am with mine, your hair would stand on end.

SUSAN. Then I'm very glad of my ignorance, sir, for I wish it to keep in curl. Now, Miss Rosina! (*Exit* ROSINA, *making a sign of secrecy to* LITHERS, *who goes before.*) Oho! There's something in the wind that's not the boot-jack! [*Exit* SUSAN, L.

NIGHTINGALE (*seated*). There's a man, yonder, eating his dinner, as if he enjoyed it. I should say, from his figure, that he generally *did* enjoy his dinner. I wish I did. I wonder whether there is anything that would do me good. I have tried hot water, and hot mud, and hot vapour, and have imbibed all sorts of springs, from zero to boiling, and have gone completely through the pharmacopœia; yet I don't find myself a bit better. My Diary is my only comfort. (*Putting it into his great-coat pocket, unconsciously drops it.*) When I began to book my symptoms, and to refer back of an evening, then I began to find out my true condition. O! (*starts*) what's that? That's a new symptom. Lord bless me! Sensation as if small train of gunpowder sprinkled from left hip to ankle, and exploded by successful Guy Fawkes. I must book it at once, or I shall be taken with something else before it's entered. Susan, another mouthful of ink! Most extraordinary! [*Exit*, L.

(SLAP *cautiously approaches the Diary; as he does so,* GABBLEWIG *looks in and listens.*)

SLAP. What's this—hum! A Diary,—remarkable passion for pills, and quite a furor for doctors.—Very unconjugal allusions to Mrs. Nightingale.—Poor Maria, most valuable of sisters, to me an annuity,—to your husband a tormentor. Hum! shall I bleed him, metaphorically bleed him? Why not? He never regarded the claims of kindred; why should I? He returns. (*Puts down book.*)

Re-enter NIGHTINGALE, *looking about.*

NIGHTINGALE. Bless my heart, I've left my Diary somewhere. O! here is the precious volume—no doubt where I dropped it. (*Picks up book.*) If the stranger had opened it, what information he might have acquired! He'd have found out, by analogy, things concerning himself that he little dreams of. He has no idea how ill he is, or how thin he ought to be. [*Exit*, L.

SLAP. Now, then (*tucking up his wristbands*), for the fowl in earnest! Where is that wine! Hallo, where is that wine?

Enter (L.) GABBLEWIG, *disguised as Boots.*

GABBLEWIG. Here you are, sir! (*Starting.*) What do I behold! Mr. Formiville! the imminent tragedian?

SLAP. Who the devil are you? Keep off!

GABBLEWIG. What! Don't you remember me, sir?

SLAP. No, I don't indeed.

GABBLEWIG. Not wen I carried a banner, with a silver dragon on it; wen you played the Tartar Prince, at What's-his-name; and wen you used to bring the ouse down with that there pint about rewenge, you know?

SLAP. What! Do you mean when I struck the attitude, and said, ' Ar-recreant! The Per-rincess and r-r-revenge are both my own! She is my per-risoner—Tereremble!'

GABBLEWIG. Never! This to decide. (*They go through the motions of a broadsword combat.* SLAP, *having been run through the body, sits down and begins to eat voraciously.* GABBLEWIG, *who has kept the bottle all the while, sits opposite him at table.*) Ah! Lor' bless me, what a actor you was! (*Drinks.*) That's what I call the true tragic fire—wen you strike it out of the swords. Give me showers of sparks, and then I know what you're up to! Lor' bless me, the way I've seen you perspire! I shall never see such a actor agin.

SLAP (*complacently*). I *think* you remember me.

GABBLEWIG. Think? Why, don't you remember, wen you left Taunton, without paying that there washerwoman; and wen she——

SLAP. You needn't proceed, it's quite clear you remember me.

GABBLEWIG (*drinks again*). Lor' bless my heart, yes, what a actor you was! What a Romeo you was, you know. (*Drinks again.*)

SLAP. I believe there was something in me, as Romeo.

GABBLEWIG. Ah! and something *of* you, too, you know. The Montagues was a fine family, when you was the lightest weight among 'em. And Lor' bless my soul, what a Prince Henry you was! I see you a drinking the sack now, I do! (*Drinks again.*)

394

MR. NIGHTINGALE'S DIARY

SLAP. I beg your pardon, my friend, is that my wine?

GABBLEWIG (*affecting to meditate, and drinking again*). Lor' bless me, wot a actor! I seem to go into a trance like when I think of it. (*Is filling his glass again, when* SLAP *comes round and takes the bottle.*) I'll give you, Formiville and the Draymer! Hooray! (*Drinks, and then takes a leg of the fowl in his fingers.* SLAP *removes the dish.*)

SLAP (*aside*). At least he doesn't know that I was turned out of the company in disgrace. That's something. Are you the waiter here, my cool but discriminative acquaintance?

GABBLEWIG. Well, I'm a sort of a waiter and a sort of a half-boots: I was with a Travelling Circus, arter I left you. 'The riders— the riders! Be in time—be in time! Now, Mr. Merryman, all in to begin!' All that you know. But I shall never see acting no more. It went right out with you, bless you! (*All through this dialogue, whenever* SLAP, *in a moment of confidence, replaces the fowl or wine,* GABBLEWIG *helps himself.*)

SLAP (*aside*). I'll pump him—rule in life. Whenever no other work on hand, pump! (*To him.*) I forget your name.

GABBLEWIG. Bit—Charley Bit. That's my real name. When I first went on with the banners, I was Blitheringtonfordbury. But they said it came so expensive in the printing, that I left it off.

SLAP. Much business done in this house?

GABBLEWIG. Wery flat.

SLAP. Old gentleman in nankeen trowsers been here long?

GABBLEWIG. Just come. Wot do you think I've heerd? S'posed to be a bachelor, but got a wife.

SLAP. No!

GABBLEWIG. Yes.

SLAP. Got a wife, eh? Ha, ha, ha! You're as sharp as a lancet. Ha, ha, ha! Yes, yes, no doubt. Got a wife. Yes, yes.

GABBLEWIG (*aside*). Eh! A flash! The intense enjoyment of my friend suggests to me that old Nightingale hasn't got a wife,— that he's free, but don't know it. Fraud! Mum! (*To him*). I say, you're a—but Lor' bless my soul, wot a actor you wos!

SLAP. It's really touching, his relapsing into that! But I can't indulge him, poor fellow. My time is precious. You were going to say——

GABBLEWIG. I was going to say, you are up to a thing or two, and so—but, Lor' bless my heart alive, wot a Richard the Third you wos! Wen you used to come the sliding business, you know. (*Both starting up and doing it.*)

SLAP. This child of nature positively has judgment! It *was* one of my effects. Calm yourself, good fellow. 'And so'—you were observing——

GABBLEWIG (*close to him, in a sudden whisper*). And so I'll tell you. He hasn't really got a wife. She's dead. (SLAP *starts,*—GABBLE-WIG *aside.*) I am right. He knows it! Mrs. Nightingale's as dead as a door-nail. (*A pause; they stand close together, looking at each other.*)

SLAP. Indeed? (GABBLEWIG *nods.*) Some piece of cunning, I suppose. (GABBLEWIG *winks.*) Buried somewhere, of course? (GABBLEWIG *lays his fingers on his nose.*) Where? (GABBLEWIG *looks a little disconcerted.*) All's safe. No proof. (*Aloud.*) Take away.

GABBLEWIG (*as he goes up to table*). Too sudden on my part. Formiville wins first knock-down blow. Never mind. Gabblewig up again, and at him once more. (*Clears the table and takes the tray away.*)

SLAP. How does *he* know? He's in the market. Shall I buy him? Not yet. Necessity not yet proved. With Nightingale here, and my dramatic trunks upstairs, I'll strike at least another blow on the hot iron for myself, before I think of taking a partner into the forge. [*Exit*, L.

As GABBLEWIG *returns from clearing away, enter* SUSAN.

GABBLEWIG. Susan! Susan!

SUSAN. Susan, indeed! Well, diffidence ain't the prevailing complaint at Malvern.

GABBLEWIG. Don't you know me? Mr. Gabble——

SUSAN. —Wig! Why, la, sir, then *you*'re the boot-jack! Now I understand, of course.

GABBLEWIG. More than I do. I the boot-jack? Susan, listen! Did you know that Mr. Nightingale had been married?

SUSAN. Why, I never heard it exactly.

GABBLEWIG. But you've seen it, perhaps? Had a peep into that eternal Diary—eh?

SUSAN. Well, sir, to say the pious truth, I did read one day something or another about a—a wife. You see he married a wife when he was very young.

GABBLEWIG. Yes.

SUSAN. And she was the plague of his life ever afterwards.

GABBLEWIG. O, Rosina, can such things be! Yes. Susan, I think you are a native of Malvern?

SUSAN. Yes, sir, leastways I was so, before I went to live in London.

GABBLEWIG. *You* persuaded Mr. Nightingale to come down here, in order that he might try the cold-water cure?

SUSAN. La, sir!

GABBLEWIG. And in order that you might see your relations?

SUSAN. La, sir, how did you know?

GABBLEWIG. Knowledge of human nature, Susan. Now rub up your memory and tell me—did you ever know a Mrs. Nightingale who lived down here? Think,—your eyes brighten,—you smile;— you did know Mrs. Nightingale who lived down here.

SUSAN. To be sure I did, sir; but that could never have been——

GABBLEWIG. Your master's wife,—I suspect she was. She died?

SUSAN. Yes, sir.

GABBLEWIG. And was buried?

SUSAN. You know everything.

GABBLEWIG. In——

SUSAN. Why, in Pershore churchyard; my uncle was sexton there.

GABBLEWIG. Uncle living?

SUSAN. Ninety years of age. With a trumpet.

GABBLEWIG. That he plays on?

SUSAN. Plays on? No. Hears with.

GABBLEWIG. Good. Susan, make it your business to get me a certificate of the old lady's death, and that within an hour.

SUSAN. Why, sir?

GABBLEWIG. Susan, I suspect the old lady walks, and I intend to lay her ghost. You ask how?

SUSAN. No, sir, I didn't.

GABBLEWIG. You thought it. That you shall know by and by. Here comes the old bird. Fly! (*Exit* SUSAN.) Whilst I reconnoitre the enemy.   [*Exit, through door.*

Enter NIGHTINGALE *and* ROSINA.

ROSINA. My dear uncle, pray do nothing rash: you are in capital health at present, and who knows what the doctors may make you.

NIGHTINGALE. Capital health? I've not known a day's health for
these twenty years. (*Refers to Diary.*) 'January 6th, 1834.
Pain in right thumb: query, gout. Send for Blair's pills. Take
six. Can't sleep all night. Doze about seven.' (*Turns over leaf.*)
'March 12th, 1839: Violent cough: query, damp umbrella, left
by church-rates in hall? Try lozenges. Bed at six—gruel—
tallow nose — dream of general illumination. March 13th:
Miserable': cold always makes me miserable. 'Receive a letter
from Mrs. Nightin—' hem!

ROSINA. What did you say, sir?

NIGHTINGALE. Have the nightmare, my dear. (*Aside.*) Nearly
betrayed myself! (*Aloud.*) You hear this, and you talk about
capital health to a sufferer like me!

Enter SLAP, *at back, dressed as a smug physician.*
He appears to be looking about the room.

O! my spirits, my spirits! I wonder what water will do for them.

ROSINA. Why, reduce them, of course. Ah, my dear uncle, I often
think I am the cause of your disquietude. I often think that I
ought to marry.

NIGHTINGALE. Very kind of you, indeed, my dear.

Enter GABBLEWIG, *with a very large tumbler of water.*

O! all right, young man. I had better begin. So you think
that you really ought, my love,—purely on my account—to marry
a Magpie, don't you? (GABBLEWIG *starts and spills water over*
NIGHTINGALE.) What are you about?

GABBLEWIG. I beg pardon, sir. (*Aside to* ROSINA.) Bless you!

ROSINA. Ah! Gab!—O uncle—don't be frightened—but——

NIGHTINGALE (*about to drink, spills water*). Return of boot-jack and
strong person! I declare, I'm taking all this water externally,
when I ought to——

SLAP (*seizing his hand*). Rash man, forbear! Drain that chalice,
and your life's not worth a bodkin.

NIGHTINGALE. Dear me, sir! it's only water. I'm merely a pump
patient. (GABBLEWIG *and* ROSINA *speak aside, hurriedly.*)

SLAP. Persevere, and twelve men of Malvern will sit upon you in
less than a week, and, without retiring, bring in a verdict of
'Found drowned.'

MR. NIGHTINGALE'S DIARY

GABBLEWIG (*aside to* ROSINA). I have my cue, follow me directly. I'll bring you another glass, sir, in a quarter of an hour.

[*Exit at door.* ROSINA *steals after him.*

SLAP. A most debilitated pulse—(*taking away water*)—great want of coagulum—lymphitic to an alarming degree. Stamina (*strikes him gently*) weak—decidedly weak.

NIGHTINGALE. Right! Always was, sir. In '48,—I think it was '48—(*Refers.*)—Yes, here it is. (*Reads.*) 'Dyspeptic. Feel as if kitten at play within me. Try chalk and pea-flour.'

SLAP. And grow worse.

NIGHTINGALE. Astonishing! I did—yes. (*Reads.*)—'Fever—have head shaved.'

SLAP. And grow worse.

NIGHTINGALE. Amazing! Sir, you read me like a book. As there appears to be no dry remedy for my unfortunate case, I thought I'd try a wet one; and here I am, at the cold water.

SLAP. Water, unless in combination with alcohol, is poison to you. You want blood. In man there are two kinds of blood. One in a vessel called a vein, hence venous blood.—The other in the vessel called artery; hence arterial blood—the one dark, the other bright. Now, sir, the crassamentum of your blood is injured by too much water. How shall we thicken, sir? (*Produces bottle.*) By mustard and milk.

NIGHTINGALE. Mustard and milk!

SLAP. Mustard and milk, sir. Exhibited with a balsam known only to myself. (*Aside.*) Rum! (*Aloud.*) Single bottles, one guinea; case of twelve, ten pounds.

NIGHTINGALE. Mustard and milk! I don't think I ever tried—Eh? Yes. (*Opens Diary.*) 1836; I recollect I once took—I took—Oh, ah! 'Two quarts of mustard-seed, fasting.'

SLAP. Pish!

NIGHTINGALE. And you'd really advise me not to take water?

Enter at door GABBLEWIG *and* ROSINA, *both equipped in walking-dresses, thick shoes, etc. They keep walking about during the following.*

GABBLEWIG. Who says don't take water? Who says so?

NIGHTINGALE. Why, this gentleman, who is evidently a man of science.

MR. NIGHTINGALE'S DIARY

GABBLEWIG. Pshaw! Eh, dear. Not take water! Look at us—look at us—Mr. and Mrs. Poulter. Six months ago, I never took water, did I, dear?

ROSINA. Never!

GABBLEWIG. Hated it. Always washed in gin-and-water, and shaved with spirits of wine. Didn't I, dear?

ROSINA. Always!

GABBLEWIG. Then what was I? What were *we*, I may say, my precious?

ROSINA. You may.

GABBLEWIG. A flabby, dabby couple, like a pair of wet leather gloves; —no energy—no muscle—no go-ahead. Now you see what we are; eh, dear? Ten miles before breakfast—home—gallon of water —ten miles more—gallon of water and leg of mutton,—ten miles more,—gallon of water—in fact, we're never quiet, are we, dear?

ROSINA. Never.

GABBLEWIG. Walk in our sleep—sometimes—can't walk enough, that's a fact, eh, dear?

ROSINA. Yes, dear!

SLAP. Confound this fellow, he'll spoil all.

NIGHTINGALE. Well, sir, if you really could pull up for a few minutes, I should be extremely obliged to you.

GABBLEWIG. Here we are, then,—don't keep us long. (*Looks at watch*, ROSINA *does the same.*)—Say a minute, chronometer time.

NIGHTINGALE. You must know I'm an invalid.

GABBLEWIG. Five seconds.

NIGHTINGALE. Come down here to try the cold-water cure.

GABBLEWIG. Ten seconds.

NIGHTINGALE. Dear me, sir, I wish you wouldn't keep counting the time in that way; it increases my nervousness.

GABBLEWIG. Can't help it, sir,—twenty seconds;—go on, sir.

NIGHTINGALE. Well, sir, this gentleman tells me that my cran-erany——

SLAP. Crass. Crassa-mentum must not be made too sloppy.

NIGHTINGALE. And thereby he advises, sir,——

GABBLEWIG. Forty seconds,—eh, dear? (*Show watches to each other.*)

ROSINA. Yes, dear!

NIGHTINGALE. I wish you wouldn't—and that he advises me to try mustard and milk, sir.

400

MR. NIGHTINGALE'S DIARY

SLAP. In combination with a rare balsam known only to myself, one guinea a bottle,—case of twelve, ten pounds.

GABBLEWIG. Time's up. (*Walks again.*) My darling, mustard and milk? Eh, dear? Don't we know a case of mustard and milk,— Captain Blower, late sixteen stone, now ten and one half, all mustard and milk?

SLAP (*aside*). Can anybody have tried it?

GABBLEWIG (*to* NIGHTINGALE). Don't be done! If I see Blower, I'll send him to you;—can't stop longer, can we, dear?—ten miles and a gallon to do before dinner. Leg of mutton and a gallon at dinner. Five miles and a wet sheet after dinner. Come, dear! (*They walk out at door.*)

NIGHTINGALE. A very remarkable couple.—What do you think now, sir?

SLAP. Think, sir? I think, sir, that any man who professes to walk ten miles a day, is a humbug, sir; I couldn't do it.

NIGHTINGALE. But then the lady——

SLAP. I grieve to say that I think she's a humbugess. Those people, my dear sir, are sent about as cheerful examples of the effects of cold water. Regularly paid, sir, to waylay new comers.

NIGHTINGALE. La! do you think so? do you think there are people base enough to trade upon human infirmities?

SLAP. Think so?—I know it. There are men base enough to stand between you (*shows bottle*) and perfect health (*shakes bottle*) who would persuade you that perpetual juvenility was dear at one pound one a bottle, and that a green old age of a hundred and twenty was not worth ten pounds the case. That perambulating water-cart is such a man!

NIGHTINGALE. Wretch! What an escape I've had. My dear doctor. You are a doctor?

SLAP. D.D. and M.D., and corresponding member of the Mendicity Society.

NIGHTINGALE. Mendicity!

SLAP. Medical (what a slip).

NIGHTINGALE. Then I shall be happy to try a bottle to begin with. (*Gives money.*)

SLAP. Ah, one bottle. (*Gives bottle.*) I've confidence in your case, —you've none in mine. Ah! well!

NIGHTINGALE. A case be it then, and I'll pay the money at once.

Permit me to try a little of the mixture. (*Drinks.*) It's not very agreeable. I think I'll make a note in my Diary of my first sensations.

Enter at door GABBLEWIG *and* ROSINA, *the former as a great invalid, the latter as an old nurse.*

GABBLEWIG (*aside, calling*). Rosina, quick, your arm. (*Aloud.*) I tell you, Mrs. Trusty, I can't walk any further.

ROSINA. Now do try, sir; we are not a quarter of a mile from home.

GABBLEWIG. A quarter of a mile!—why, that's a day's journey to a man in my condition.

ROSINA. O dear! what shall I do?

NIGHTINGALE. You seem very ill, sir?

GABBLEWIG. Very, sir. I'm a snuff, sir,—a mere snuff, flickering before I go out.

ROSINA. Oh, sir! pray don't die here; try and get home, and go out comfortably.

GABBLEWIG. Did you ever hear of such inhumanity? and yet this woman has lived on board wages, at my expense, for thirty years.

NIGHTINGALE. My dear sir, here's a very clever friend of mine who may be of service.

GABBLEWIG. I fear not,—I fear not. I've tried everything.

SLAP. Perhaps not *everything*. Pulse very debilitated; great want of coagulum; lymphitic to an alarming degree; stamina weak—decidedly weak.

GABBLEWIG. I don't want you to tell me that, sir.

SLAP. Crassamentum queer—very queer. No hope, but in mustard and milk.

GABBLEWIG (*starting up*). Mustard and milk!

ROSINA. Mustard and milk!

SLAP (*aside*). Is this Captain Blower?

GABBLEWIG (*to* NIGHTINGALE). Are you, too, a victim? Have you swallowed any of that man-slaughtering compound?

NIGHTINGALE (*alarmed*). Only a little,—a very little.

GABBLEWIG. How do you feel? Dimness of sight,—feebleness of limbs?

NIGHTINGALE (*alarmed*). Not at present.

GABBLEWIG. But you will, sir,—you will. You'd never think I once rivalled that person, in rotundity.

MR. NIGHTINGALE'S DIARY

NIGHTINGALE. Never.

ROSINA. But he'll never do it again; he'll never do it again.

GABBLEWIG. You'd never think that Madame Tussaud wanted to model my leg, and announce it as an *Extraordinary addition.*

NIGHTINGALE. I certainly should *not* have thought it.

GABBLEWIG. She might now put it in the Chamber of Horrors. Look at it!

ROSINA. It's nothing at all out of the flannel, sir.

GABBLEWIG. All mustard and milk, sir. I'm nothing but mustard and milk!

NIGHTINGALE (*seizes* SLAP). You scoundrel! and to this state you would have reduced me.

SLAP. O, this is some trick, sir, some cheat of the water-doctors.

NIGHTINGALE. Why, you won't tell me that he's intended as a cheerful example of the effects of cold water?

SLAP. I never said he was,—he's one of the failures; but as two of a trade can never agree, I'll go somewhere else and spend your guinea. [*Exit.*

GABBLEWIG (*in his own voice*). What a brazen knave! Second knock-down blow to Gabblewig. Betting even. Anybody's battle. Gabblewig came up smiling and at him again.

NIGHTINGALE (*goes to* GABBLEWIG). My dear sir, what do I not owe you? (*Shakes his hand.*)

GABBLEWIG. O, don't do that, sir, I shall tumble to pieces like a fantoccini figure if you do. I am only hung together by threads.

NIGHTINGALE. But let me know the name of my preserver, that I may enter it in my Diary.

GABBLEWIG. Captain Blower, R.N. (NIGHTINGALE *writes.*) I'm happy to have rescued you from that quack. I declare the excitement has done me good. Rosi—Mrs. Trusty, I think I can walk now.

ROSINA. That's right, sir. Lean upon me.

GABBLEWIG. Oh! Oh!

NIGHTINGALE. What's the matter, Captain Blower?

GABBLEWIG. That's the milk, sir. Oh!

NIGHTINGALE. Dear me, Captain Blower!

GABBLEWIG. And that's the mustard, sir.

[*Exeunt at door* GABBLEWIG *and* ROSINA.

NIGHTINGALE. Really, this will be the most eventful day in my Diary, except one, — that day which consigned me to Mrs.

Nightingale and twenty years of misery. I've not seen her for nineteen; though I have periodical reminders that she is still in the land of the living, in the shape of quarterly payments of twenty-five pounds, clear of income-tax. Well! I'm used to it; and so that I never see her face again, I'm content. I'll go find Rosina, and tell her what has happened. Quite an escape, I declare. [*Exit*, L.

Enter at door Susan, *in bonnet, etc.*

Susan. What a wicked world this is, to be sure! Everybody seems trying to do the best they can for themselves, and what makes it worse, the complaint seems to be catching; for I'm sure I can't help telling Mr. Gabblewig what a traitor that Tip is. I hope Mr. G. won't come in my way, and tempt me. Ah! here he is, and I'm sure I shall fall.

Enter Gabblewig.

Gabblewig. Well, Susan, have you got the certificate?

Susan. No, sir, but uncle has, and he'll be here directly. Oh, sir, if you knew what I've heard!

Gabblewig. What?

Susan. I'm sure you'd give half-a-sovereign to hear; I'm sure you would.

Gabblewig. I'm sure I should, and there's the money.

Susan. Well, sir, your man Tip's a traitor, sir, a conspirator, sir. I overheard him and another planning some deception. I couldn't quite make out what, but I know it's something to deceive Mr. Nightingale.

Gabblewig. Find out with all speed what this scheme is about, and let me know. What's that mountain in petticoats? Slap, or I'm not Gabblewig!

Susan. And with him Tip, or I'm not Susan!

Gabblewig. Another flash! I guess it all! Susan, your mistress shall instruct you what to do. Vanish, sweet spirit!

[*Exeunt* Gabblewig, R., *and* Susan, L.

Enter at door, R., Slap *in female attire. Looks about cautiously.*

Slap. I hope he's not gone out. I've a presentiment that my good luck is deserting me; but before we *do* part company, I'll make a bold dash, and secure something to carry on with. Now, Calomel, —I mean Mercury,—befriend me. (*Rings.*)

MR. NIGHTINGALE'S DIARY

Enter LITHERS, L.

LITHERS. Did you ring, ma'am?

SLAP. Yes, young man; I wish to speak with a Mr. Nightingale, an elderly gent, who arrived this morning.

LITHERS. What name, ma'am?

SLAP. Name no consequence; say I come from M'ria.

LITHERS. M'ria?

SLAP. M'ria, a mutual friend of mine and Mr. Nightingale, and one he ought not to be ashamed of.

LITHERS. Yes, ma'am. (*Aside.*) Mr. Gabblewig's right. [*Exit.*

SLAP. M'ria has been dead these twelve years, during which time my victim has paid her allowance with commendable regularity to me, her only surviving brother. Ah, I thought that name was irresistible, and here he is.

Enter NIGHTINGALE, L., *closing door at back.*

His trepidation is cheering. He'll bleed freely; what a lamb it is! (*Curtseys as* NIGHTINGALE *comes down.*) Your servant, sir.

NIGHTINGALE. Now don't lose a moment; you say you come from Maria: what Maria?

SLAP. Your Maria.

NIGHTINGALE. I am sorry to acknowledge the responsibility.

SLAP. Ah, sir; that poor creature's much changed, sir.

NIGHTINGALE. For the worse, of course?

SLAP. I'm afraid so. No gin now, sir.

NIGHTINGALE. Then it's brandy.

SLAP. Lives on it, sir, and breaks more windows than ever. She's heard that you've come down here.

NIGHTINGALE. So I suppose, by this visit.

SLAP. She lives about a mile from Malvern.

NIGHTINGALE (*starts*). What! I thought she was down in Yorkshire.

SLAP. Was and is is two different things. She wanted for to come and see you.

NIGHTINGALE. If she does, I'll stop her allowance.

SLAP. And have her call every day? M'ria's my friend,—but I know that wouldn't be pleasant. She'd a proposal to make, so, M'ria, says I,—I'll see your lawful husband,—as you is, sir, and propose for you.

NIGHTINGALE. I'll listen to nothing.

MR. NIGHTINGALE'S DIARY

SLAP. Not if it puts the sad sea-waves between you and M'ria for ever?

NIGHTINGALE (*interested*). Eh!

SLAP. You know she'd a brother, an excellent young man, who went to America ten years ago.

NIGHTINGALE (*takes out Diary*). I know. (*Reads aside.*) '16th of May 1841, sent fifty pounds to Mrs. N.'s vagabond brother, going to America—qy. to the devil?'

SLAP. He has written to M'ria to say that if you'll give her two hundred pounds, and she'll come out, he'll take care of her for ever.

NIGHTINGALE. Done!—it's a bargain.

SLAP. *He bites!*—and her son for a hundred more.

NIGHTINGALE. What son?

SLAP. Ah, sir! you don't know your blessings. Shortly after you and M'ria separated, a son was born; but M'ria, to revenge herself —which was wrong; oh, it was wrong in her, that was,—never let you know it; but sent him to the Workus, as a fondling she had received in a basket.

NIGHTINGALE. I don't believe a word of it.

SLAP. She said you wouldn't. But seeing is believing, and so I've brought the innocent along with me. I've got the Pretty, here.

NIGHTINGALE. Here! in your pocket?

SLAP. No—at the door. (*They rise.*)

NIGHTINGALE. At the door!

SLAP. Come in, Christopher! Named after you, sir! for in spite of M'ria's feelings, you divided her heart with Old Tom.

Enter at door TIP *as a Charity Boy.*

NIGHTINGALE. O nonsense!

SLAP. Christopher, behold your Par. (*Boxes him.*) What do you stand there for like a eight-day clock or a idol, as if Pars were found every day?

TIP (*aside*). Don't; you make me nervous. (*Aloud.*) And is that my Par!

SLAP. Yes, child. Me, who took you from the month, can vouch for it.

TIP. O Par!

NIGHTINGALE. Keep off, you young yellow-hammer; or I'll knock

406

MR. NIGHTINGALE'S DIARY

you down. Hark 'ee, ma'am. If you can assure me of the departure of your friend and this cub, I will give you the money! For twenty years I have been haunted by——

Enter GABBLEWIG *at door, disguised as Old Woman.*

GABBLEWIG. Which the blessed innocent has been invaygled of, and man-trapped,—leastways boy-trapped ;—and never no more will I leave this 'ouse until I find a parent's 'ope—a mother's pride—and nobody's (as I'm aweer on) joy.

NIGHTINGALE *and* SUSAN *place Chair.*

SLAP (*aside*). What on earth is this! Who is a mother's pride and nobody's joy? (*To* TIP.) You don't mean to say you are?

TIP (*solemnly*). I'm a horphan. (*Goes up to* GABBLEWIG.) What are you talking about, you old Bedlam?

GABBLEWIG. Oh! (*screaming and throwing her arms about his neck*) —my 'ope—my pride—my son!

TIP (*struggling*). Your son!

GABBLEWIG (*aside to him*). If you don't own me for your mother, you villain, on the spot, I'll break every bone in your skin, and have your skin prepared afterwards by the Bermondsey tanners.

TIP (*aside*). My master!—My mother! (*They embrace.*)

SLAP. Are you mad? Am I mad? Are we all mad? (*To* TIP.) Didn't you tell me that whatever I said——

TIP. *You* said? What is your voice to the voice of Natur? (*Embraces his master again.*)

SLAP. Natur! Natur! ah-h-h! (*Screams. Chair brought.*) O you unnat'ral monster! Who see your first tooth dawn on a deceitful world? Who watched you running alone in a go-cart, and tipping over on your precious head upon the paving-stones in the confidence of childhood? Who give you medicine that reduced you when you was sick, and made you so when you wasn't?

GABBLEWIG (*rising*). Who? Me!

SLAP. You, ma'am?

GABBLEWIG. Me, ma'am, as is well beknown to all the country round, which the name of this sweetest of babbies as was giv to his own joyful self when blest in best Whitechapel mixed upon a pincusheon, and mother saved likewise was Absolom. Arter his own parential father, as never (otherwise than through being bad

407

in liquor) lost a day's work in the wheel-wright business, which it was but limited, Mr. Nightingale, being wheels of donkey shays and goats, and one was even drawed by geese for a wager, and went right into the centre aisle of the parish church on a Sunday morning on account of the obstinacy of the animals, as can be certified by Mr. Wigs the beadle afore he died of drawing on his Wellington boots, to which he was not accustomed, arter a hearty meal of beef and walnuts, to which he was too parshal, and in the marble fountain of that church this preciousest of infants was made Absolom, which never can be unmade no more, I am proud to say, to please or give offence to no one nowheres and nohows.

SLAP. Would you forswear your blessed mother, M'ria Nightingale, lawful wedded wife of this excellent old gent? Why don't the voice o' Natur claim its par?

NIGHTINGALE. O, don't make *me* a consideration on any account!

GABBLEWIG. M'ria Nightingale, which affliction sore long time she bore——

NIGHTINGALE. And so did I.

GABBLEWIG. Physicians was in vain,—which she never had none partickler as I knows of, exceptin one which she tore his hair by handfuls out in consequence of differences of opinion relative to her complaint, but it was wrote upon her tombstone ten year and more ago, and dead she is as the hosts of the Egyptian Fairies.

NIGHTINGALE. Dead! Prove it, and I'll give you fifty pounds.

SLAP. Prove it! I defies her. (*Aside.*) I'm done.

GABBLEWIG. Prove it!—which I can and will, directly minit, by my brother the sexton, as I will here produce in the twinkling of a star or human eye. (*Aside.*) From this period of the contest Gabblewig had it all his own way, and went in and won. No money was laid out, at any price, on Formiville. Fifty to one on Gabblewig freely offered, and no takers. [*Exit at door.*

SLAP (*aside*). I don't like this,—so exit Slap!

NIGHTINGALE (*seizing him*). No, ma'am, you don't leave this place till the mystery is cleared up.

SLAP. Unhand me, monster! I claims my habeas corpus. (*Breaks from him.* NIGHTINGALE *goes to the door and prepares to defend the pass with a chair.*) (*To* TIP.) As for you, traitor, though I'm not pugnacious, I'll give you a lesson in the art of self-defence you shall remember as long as you live.

MR. NIGHTINGALE'S DIARY

Tip. You! the bottle imp as has been my ruin! Reduce yourself to my weight, and I'll fight you for a pound. (*Squares.*)

Gabblewig (*without*). I'll soon satisfy the gentleman.

Slap. Then I'm done! very much done! I see nothing before me but premature incarceration, and an old age of gruel.

Enter Gabblewig *at door as Sexton.*

Nightingale. He's very old! My invaluable centenarian, will you allow me to inquire——

Sexton. I don't hear you.

Nightingale. He's very deaf. (*Aloud.*) Will you allow me to inquire——

Sexton. It's no use whispering to me, sir, I'm hard o' hearing.

Nightingale. He's very provoking. (*Louder.*) Whether you ever buried——

Sexton. Brewed? Yes, yes, I brewed—that is, me and my wife, as has been dead and gone now this forty year, next hop-picking—(my wife was a Kentish woman)—we brewed, especially one year, the strongest beer ever you drunk. It was called in our country Samson with his hair on—alluding to its great strength, you understand,—and my wife, she said——

Nightingale (*very loud*). Buried—not brewed!

Sexton. Buried? O, ah! Yes, yes. Buried a many. They was strong, too,—once.

Nightingale. Did you ever bury a Mrs. Nightingale?

Sexton. Ever bury a Nightingale? No, no, only Christians.

Nightingale (*in his ear*). Missis—Mis-sis Nightingale?

Sexton. O yes, yes. Buried *her*—rather a fine woman,—married (as the folks told me) an uncommon ugly man. Yes, yes. Used to live here. Here (*taking out pocket-book*) is the certificate of her burial. (*Gives it.*) I got it for my sister. O yes! Buried *her*. I thought you meant a Nightingale. Ha, ha, ha!

Nightingale. My dear friend, there's a guinea, and it's cheap for the money. (*Gives it.*)

Sexton. I thank 'ee, sir, I thank 'ee. (*Aside.*) Formiville heavily grassed, and a thousand to one on Gabblewig! [*Exit at door.*

Nightingale (*after reading certificate*). You — you — inexpressible swindler. If you were not a woman, I'd have you ducked in the horse-pond.

409

MR. NIGHTINGALE'S DIARY

TIP (*on his knees*). O, sir, do it. He deserves it.

NIGHTINGALE. He?

TIP. Yes, sir, she's a he. He deluded me with a glass of rum-and-water; and the promise of a five-pound note.

NIGHTINGALE. You scoundrel!

SLAP. Sir, you are welcome to your own opinion. I am not the first man who has failed in a great endeavour. Napoleon had his Waterloo,—Slap has his Malvern. Henceforth, I am nobody. The eagle retires to his rock.

Enter GABBLEWIG *in his own dress.*

GABBLEWIG. You had better stop here. Be content with plain Slap, —discard counterfeit Formiville,—and we'll do something for you.

SLAP. Mr. Gabblewig! [*Exit at door.*

GABBLEWIG. Charley Bit, Mr. Poulter, Captain Blower, respectable female, and deaf sexton, all equally at anybody's service.

NIGHTINGALE. What do I hear?

GABBLEWIG. Me.

NIGHTINGALE. And what do I see?

ROSINA (*entering at door*). Me! Dear uncle, you would have been imposed upon and plundered, and made even worse than you ever made yourself, but for——

GABBLEWIG. Me. My dear Mr. Nightingale, you did think I could do nothing but talk. If you now think I can act—a little—let me come out in a new character. (*Embracing* ROSINA.) Will you?

NIGHTINGALE. Will I? Take her, Mr. Gabblewig. Stop, though. Ought I to give away what has made me so unhappy. Memorandum —Mrs. Nightingale—see Diary. (*Takes out book.*)

GABBLEWIG. Stop, sir! Don't look! Burn that book, and be happy! —(*Brings on* SLAP *at door.*)—Ask your doctor. What do *you* say, Mustard and Milk?

SLAP. I say, sir, try me; and when you find I am not worth a trial, don't try me any more. As to that gentleman's destroying his Diary, sir, my opinion is that he might perhaps refer to it once again.

GABBLEWIG (*to audience*). Shall he refer to it once more? (*To* NIGHTINGALE.) Well, I think you may.

THE END

NO THOROUGHFARE

A DRAMA
IN FIVE ACTS AND
A PROLOGUE

[1867]

BY CHARLES DICKENS AND
WILKIE COLLINS

NO THOROUGHFARE

CAST OF CHARACTERS

At New Royal Adelphi Theatre, December 26, 1867

VEILED LADY	MRS. BILLINGTON.
SARAH (*otherwise* SALLY) GOLDSTRAW	MRS. ALFRED MELLON.
LITTLE WALTER WILDING	MASTER SIDNEY.
FIRST HUSBAND	MR. R. ROMER.
SECOND HUSBAND	MR. PRITCHARD.
FIRST WIFE	MRS. STOKER.
SECOND WIFE	MRS. D'ESTE.
MR. WALTER WILDING	MR. BILLINGTON.
MR. BINTRY (*a man of law*)	MR. G. BELMORE.
JOEY LADLE (*head cellarman*)	MR. BENJAMIN WEBSTER.
GEORGE VENDALE	MR. H. G. NEVILLE.
JULES OBENREIZER	MR. FECHTER.
MARGUERITE	MISS CARLOTTA LECLERCQ.
MADAME DOR	MRS. A. LEWIS.
JEAN MARIE (*a guide*)	MR. C. F. SMITH.
JEAN PAUL (*ditto*)	MR. BRANSCOMBE.
FATHER FRANCIS	MR. R. PHILLIPS.
MONKS	{ MR. ALDRIDGE. { MR. TOMLINSON. }

Time of playing.—Three hours and forty minutes.

MUSIC.—A 'mysterious' theme always to OBENREIZER's entrances. Melodrama music to Scene 1st, Act 4th, on and after OBENREIZER's entrance with knife.

REMARKS.—Except VENDALE and JOEY, all pronounce 'Obenreizer' in the English manner, that is 'Oben-righ-sir.' JOEY calls him 'Open-razor,' and VENDALE gives it the Swiss or German pronunciation, 'Oben-right-zer.'

STAGE DIRECTIONS.—R. means Right of Stage, facing the Audience; L. Left; C. Centre; R. C. Right of centre; L. C. Left of centre. D. F. Door in the Flat, or Scene running across the back of the Stage; C. D. F. Centre Door in the Flat; R. D. F. Right Door in the Flat; L. D. F. Left Door in the Flat; R. D. Right Door; L. D. Left Door; 1 E. First Entrance; 2 E. Second Entrance; U. E. Upper Entrance; 1, 2, or 3 G. First, Second or Third Groove.

COSTUMES (MODERN).

OBENREIZER.—Act 1st: *Black hat, black neck-tie, long-skirted black frock-coat, light pants, dark vest, hair rather long behind, cane.* Act 2nd, Scene 1st: *Black suit, coat is short-skirted;* Scene 3rd: *Same, with hat and gloves.* Act 3rd, Scene 1st: *Same, with hat and gloves;* Scene 3rd: *Travelling dress; round, black Astracan cap, russet waistcoat with some of the breast buttons*

NO THOROUGHFARE

left unbuttoned, showing white vest under, wallet with strap, watch. Act 4th, Scene 1st: *Same as last, with pants tucked into top of boots;* 2nd entrance, *in waistcoat, with sleeves drawn tight, collar open;* Scene 2nd and 3rd: *Same as* 1st entrance; Scene 1st: *Well buttoned up, thick gloves.* Act 5th: *Russet waistcoat, black pants in high boots, black coat, snuff-box.*

GEORGE VENDALE.—Act 1st: *Suit of grey mixture, cut-away coat, black low-crowned hard felt hat, watch and chain.* Act 2nd, Scene 1st and 2nd: *Grey pants, black high hat, black coat, white vest, jewels in case, to bring on with him.* Act 3rd, Scene 1st: *Black suit;* Scene 3rd: *Dark grey pants, black coat and vest, hat.* Act 4th, Scene 1st: *Same;* Scenes 2nd and 3rd: *Pants in high russet boots, tall black felt hat, black overcoat buttoned up to neck, thick gloves.* Act 5th: *Same as last, but without hat, gloves and overcoat.*

MR. BINTRY.—*Black suit, with brown overcoat in Act 5th. Grizzled wig and iron-grey side whiskers, white stand-up collar and cravat, black gloves.*

WALTER WILDING.—*Black suit, except grey pants; light hair and fair complexion; an habitual action of putting his hand to his head when pausing for a word.*

JOEY LADLE.—Act 1st and 2nd: *Black hair, bald on top of head and forehead, small black side whiskers; dark suit of velveteen; leather apron, much wrinkled and stained, from his neck to mid-leg, with collar-strap and waist-string; small skull-cap of oil-skin; slow in speech and thick in comprehension. Made up stout.* Act 3rd, Scene 1st: *Same;* Scene 3rd: *Same without apron; coat on.* Act 4th, Scene 3rd: *Muffler round neck, black overcoat and cap; black gloves, legs bandaged in the Italian brigand style.* Act 5th: *Same as last.*

LANDLORD.—*As a Swiss peasant; grey stockings, blue breeches, banded vest, in red and blue, embroidered; black felt hat.*

GUIDES.—*Felt hats, pinned up with crosses; long cloaks, sheep-skin jackets, high boots, alpenstocks (pine poles six feet long, with iron at end).*

FIRST AND SECOND HUSBAND *in* Scene 2nd, Prologue: *Ordinary walking dresses. The* FIRST *is a man of fifty;* the SECOND *a young man of twenty-five. Hats and gloves.*

FATHER FRANCIS, A MONK.—*Russet gown, sandals; tonsure on black wig; black beard.*

A MONK.—*Like* FATHER FRANCIS.

LITTLE WALTER WILDING.—*In dark blue jacket and pants; fair-haired and fair complexion.*

FOUNDLING BOYS.—*A number, about twelve years old, in blue suits.*

TWO MEN.—*To bring in flowers,* Act 2nd, Scene 1st: *Ordinary dress, coats and caps.*

MARGUERITE.—Act 1st: *Straw hat, with red and blue ribbons; blue dress, with bodice cut square and low, in Swiss fashion; gilt buckle to waist-belt, buckles to shoes; light hair, braided; ear-rings, and cross at neck.* Acts 2nd and 3rd: *House dress, dark colour, Swiss waist.* Act 4th: *Plain dress, with mantle of same, with hood; hair braided.* Act 5th: *Blue dress, with four inches deep black border at bottom hem; black jacket, with gilt buttons.*

VEILED LADY.—*Black dress, black bonnet, with long black veil; face pale.*

SALLY GOLDSTRAW.—Prologue, Scene 1st: *Black dress, shawl and bonnet;* Scene

NO THOROUGHFARE

2nd: *Same dress, white cuffs and collar; apron.* Act 1st: *White bonnet, with fancy ribbons; shawl, plain dress.* Act 2nd: *Dark dress, black apron.* Act 4th: *In black.*

FIRST WIFE.—*A woman of forty; grey hair, slightly empurpled face; shawl and bonnet trimmed gaily; coloured dress.*

SECOND WIFE.—*Walking dress, bonnet and mantle.*

MADAME DOR.—Act 1st: *Bonnet, dark dress, with black 'lace square'; she is made up stout, with her hair frizzled out on each side of face, to make it seem broader.* Act 2nd: *House dress, hair as before; she walks sidewise, keeping her face from the other performers when crossing stage or making an exit.*

TWO GIRLS (for the Hospital).—Prologue, Scene 1st: *Dark dresses, bonnets and mantles;* Scene 2nd: *Neat brown dresses, white cuffs, collars, aprons and caps.*

PROPERTIES

Prologue, Scene 1st: Small wad of paper, as of two coins in it, for VEILED LADY; *Scene 2nd:* Two large platters, with roast meat on them, for tables—L. 1 and 2 E.; carving-knives and forks to them, and spoons; knives, forks and plates for the boys; cloth, castors, cruets, etc., to set table; on L. 1 and 2 E., C. on F. and R. 1 E. set, framed placards, headed 'Patrons, 1760,' etc. *Act 1st, Scene 1st:* Wine-baskets, boxes and casks to make picture of stage; a hackney-coach, to hold two persons, to cross L. U. E. to D. C. in wall set on four grooves; eye-glasses for BINTRY; candle to burn, held in the end of a cleft stick, two feet long; a large cask and two small ones, to serve as table and chairs; bottle and two glasses; umbrella for BINTRY; an odd glove for MADAME DOR to be rubbing with cloth. *Act 2nd, Scene 1st:* Two books on table, R. C. front; stockings and ball of worsted for MADAME DOR; jewels in case for VENDALE, needlework for MARGUERITE; two large handsome gilt flower-stands with flowers, to be brought on D. in F.; jewels in case for OBENREIZER; *Scene 3rd:* A long rod; three candles to burn at end of cleft sticks; a starting-mallet, tasting-rod and tin measures laid on barrels; a small cask placed R. C.; cobweb to fall. *Act 3rd, Scene 1st:* Writing materials on desk up L.; three letters, strong box in flat, R. to E.; framed calendar over mantelpiece; straw L. side, about the painted set of open wine-box, two bottles for same; quill to be worn by VENDALE behind his ear; *Scene 2nd:* Small basket for SALLY; *Scene 3rd:* Long pipe for OBENREIZER; small travelling-trunk, pen and ink on R. table; flat writing-case. *Act 4th, Scene 1st:* Pipe as before for OBENREIZER; box of matches, candle to burn; red fire in fireplace, bottle and two glasses; writing-case of *Scene 3rd, Act 3rd*; knife for OBENREIZER; *Scene 2nd:* Two alpenstocks (pine poles six feet long, tipped with iron hook); leather case, with strap, to go over shoulders, for OBENREIZER; *Scene 3rd:* The two alpenstocks. *Act 5th, Scene 1st:* A large brass-clasped Bible and bag of money for FATHER FRANCIS; snuff-box for OBENREIZER; in clock-safe, two packets of papers on upper shelf, three on lower; bell to strike eight; legal paper for BINTRY; small vial for OBENREIZER; pen and ink, lighted candle on table R.

NO THOROUGHFARE

PROLOGUE

SCENE I.—*Gas down*—VEILED LADY *enters* L. *to* C., *pauses, then to* R., *by gate in* F.—*Two Girls enter by gate in* F., *draw their shawls closer around them, cross and exeunt* L.—VEILED LADY *follows them to* C., *looking at their faces, shakes her head, stops, returns to gate.*—SALLY GOLDSTRAW *enters by gate, crosses to exit* L., *but* VEILED LADY *overtakes her and stops her,* C.

SALLY. What do you want of me?

VEILED LADY. I wish to speak with you. I must speak with you.

SALLY. What is it you want?

VEILED LADY. You are called Sally Goldstraw, you are one of the nurses at the hospital, and I must speak with you.

SALLY. You seem to know all about me, ma'am. May I make so bold as to ask who you are?

VEILED LADY. Come, look at me under this lamp (*to gate, removing veil*).

SALLY (*shakes head*). No, ma'am (*replaces the* LADY'S *veil*), I don't know you; I never saw you before this night.

VEILED LADY. Do I look like a happy woman?

SALLY. No! you look as if you had something on your mind.

VEILED LADY. I *have* something on my mind, Sally! I am one of those miserable mothers who have never known what happy motherhood is! My child is one of those poor children in this foundling hospital, put there when a boy, and I have never seen him!

SALLY. O dear, dear, dear! what can I say, what can I do?

VEILED LADY. Carry your memory back twelve years. The day when you entered the foundling must have been a memorable one!

SALLY. It was. But twelve years is a long time!

VEILED LADY. If it is long to you, think how long it must be to me! I have paid the penalty of my disgrace! My family forced

415

me to live in a foreign land ever since. But now I find myself released,—free to come back. Sally Goldstraw, I have come back. It lies in your power to make me a happy woman!

SALLY. Me! and how can I do that?

VEILED LADY. Here are two guineas in this paper. (*Offers roll of paper.*) Take my poor little present, and I will tell you.

SALLY (*repulses paper*). You may know my face, but not my nature, ma'am. There is not a child in all the house that I belong to, who has not a good word for Sally. Could I be so well thought of if I was to be bought?

VEILED LADY. I did not mean to buy you; I meant only to reward you very slightly.

SALLY. I want no reward. If there is anything I can do for you, ma'am, that I will do for its own sake. You are much mistaken in me if you think that I will do it for money. What is it you want?

VEILED LADY. The day when you entered the foundling hospital must be a marked day in your life?

SALLY. It is a marked day!

VEILED LADY. You must remember what passed on that day?

SALLY. Everything!

VEILED LADY. Then you remember a child that was received in your care?

SALLY. I do remember the child.

VEILED LADY (*eagerly*). That child is still living?

SALLY. Living and hearty!

VEILED LADY (*clasps hands*). Thank heaven! You still take care of him?

SALLY. Oh, let me go. I am doing wrong to listen to you! (*Crosses to* L. C., *detained by* VEILED LADY.)

VEILED LADY. What of the child?

SALLY He—he is still here. He was still here when I came back from our country establishment to learn the ways of the place.

VEILED LADY. I, too, have learnt the ways of the place. They have given my child a name—a Christian name and a surname? Tell me, what have they called him?

SALLY. Oh, you mustn't ask me! indeed, you must not! (*to* L.).

VEILED LADY. His Christian name! You must tell me! I am his mother! Come back, come back! (C.) You may some day be a mother! As you hope to be a happy wife, as you are a living, loving woman! tell me the name of my child (*detaining* Sally *by shawl*).

Sally. Don't! please don't! you are trying to make me do wrong!

Veiled Lady. The surname and the Christian name, Sally! (*clinging to* Sally).

Sally. Oh, don't, don't kneel to me!

Veiled Lady. His name, Sally, his name!

Sally. You promise——

Veiled Lady. Anything!

Sally. Put your two hands in mine (Lady *does so*) and promise that you will not ask me to tell you anything but the surname and the Christian name!

Veiled Lady. I promise!

Sally (*putting her lips close to her face*). Walter Wilding!

Veiled Lady. Walter Wilding! (*sob*) kiss him for me! (*Exit* Sally, *hiding her face,* l.) Oh! (*sobbing, goes along flat to* r.) Oh!

[*Exit, sobbing,* r.

Scene II.—*Gas up*—First *and* Second Husbands *and* Wives *discovered* l. c., *the two Girls,* l., *at table carving—Boys enter,* r. u. e., *and sing* 'God Save the Queen.'[1] *They take seats.* Veiled Lady *enters,* r. u. e. *to* l. c., *down stage, earnestly regarding the Boys.*

First Wife. Mr. Jones, whatever made you bring me here?

First Husband. Why, my dear, you wanted to come!

First Wife. How dare you tell me that I wanted to come?

First Husband. You did! to see the pretty children——

First Wife. I—I—I! The man who would bring his wife to see these examples of vice is lost to the commonest sense of decency! I blush for human nature!

First Husband. Human nature is very much obliged to you, my dear.

First Wife. Ugh! give me your arm, Mr. Jones! you are a fool.

First Husband. When I married you, that left no doubt of it! (*to* r., *proscenium* e., *with* First Wife) but you had better keep that opinion to yourself.   [*Exit* r., *pros.* e.

Second Wife. Oh, I should like to kiss these dear boys.

Second Husband. Kiss them! Think of your own boys at home.

Second Wife. It is sad to think that none of them have ever known a mother's love, or sat on a father's knee! It is a noble charity.

---

[1] Or any school devotional hymn.

SECOND HUSBAND. A noble charity indeed! I have counted more than forty boys in this room, and every one of them is as well-kept and fat as our Tom! [*Leads* WIFE *off* R., *proscenium* E.

SALLY (*to* VEILED LADY). Didn't you faithfully promise you would not ask me to say anything more? (L. C. *front*.)

VEILED LADY. I told you I would not ask you to say more, but point me him out, dear Sally, good Sally!

SALLY (*aside*). Oh! I am going to do wrong again!

VEILED LADY. My heart is breaking! to know that my boy is here, but I can't tell which he is!

SALLY. You must not speak so loud here! Be patient a moment. I am going to walk round the table. Follow me with your eyes. The boy that I stop at and speak to will *not* be the one. *But* the boy that I touch will be Walter Wilding. (VEILED LADY *nods.* SALLY *goes up to* R. U. E. *corner, around table, comes down* R. *side of table, and bends over the* SECOND BOY *to speak to him, resting her right hand on the left shoulder of* WILDING, *the* FIRST BOY *at front end. After seeming to speak, pats* WILDING's *shoulder, looks over at* VEILED LADY, *turns and goes off* R., *proscenium* E.)

VEILED LADY. Ah! (*slowly to head of table, to* WILDING.) How old are you, my boy?

WILDING. I am twelve.

VEILED LADY. Ah! Are you well and happy?

WILDING. Yes, ma'am.

VEILED LADY. Would you like to be provided for and be your own master when you grow up?

WILDING. Yes, ma'am!

VEILED LADY (*with growing emotion*). Would you like to have a home of your own and a mother who loves you? (*Sob.*)

WILDING. Oh, yes, ma'am!

(VEILED LADY *embraces him sobbing.—All the Boys rise and sing* 'God save the Queen.')

WILDING—VEILED LADY.
C., *at head of table.*

Boys at table.   *The two Girls.*
R. *to* C.   L.

CURTAIN

ACT I

SCENE.—*Court-yard in Wine Merchant's discovering* WALTER WILD-ING *and* MR. BINTRY *seated at cash table*, R. C., *front—two men carry cases from* L. U. E. *off* R. 2 E.

WILDING. I don't know how it may appear to you, Mr. Bintry, but what with the emotion, and what with the heat of the weather, I feel that old singing in the head, and buzzing in my ears.

BINTRY. A little repose will refresh you, Mr. Wilding.

WILDING. How do you like the forty-five years' old port?

BINTRY. How do I like it? I a lawyer! Did you ever hear of a lawyer who did not like port? Capital wine! much too good to be given away—even to lawyers!

WILDING. And now to my affairs. I think we have got everything straight, Mr. Bintry? (BINTRY *nods.*) A partner secured?

BINTRY (*nods*). Partner secured. (*Drinks.*)

WILDING. A housekeeper advertised for?

BINTRY (*nods*). A housekeeper advertised for, to 'apply personally at Cripple Corner, Great Tower Street, from ten to twelve.'

WILDING. My late dear mother's affairs wound up—and all charges paid?

BINTRY (*chuckling and slapping his vest pockets lightly*). All charges paid, without an item being taxed! the most unprofessional thing I ever heard of in all my career. (*Looks* R. 1 E.) Dear me! you have her portrait there?

WILDING. My mother's. One I have in my own room—the other there in my counting-house in full view. Ah! it seems but yesterday when she came to the Foundling to give me a home, and ask me if I could love her. Oh, you (her lawyer) know how I loved her! And now that I can love her no more, I honour and revere her memory. The utmost love was cherished between us, and we never were separated till death took her from me six months ago. Everything I have I owe to her. I hope my love for her repaid her. She had been deeply deceived, Mr. Bintry, and had cruelly suffered. But she never spoke of that—she never betrayed her betrayer!

BINTRY (*drinking*). She had made up her mind, and she *could* hold her peace. (*Aside.*) A devilish deal more than *you* ever can!

419

WILDING. I am not ashamed of her! I mean, not ashamed of being a foundling. I never knew a father, but I can be a father to all in my employment. I hope my new partner will second my desire, and that the housekeeper will help me, my people living in the same house, and eating at the same table with me.

JOEY *enters from cellar door,* L. 2 E., *with candle in stick which he puts* L. *on barrel, comes down* C.

JOEY. Respecting this same boarding and lodging, (*cap in hand*) young Master Wilding?

BINTRY. Ah, ha! This is one of your new family! That boy in a leather pinafore won't cost much in washing.

WILDING. Yes, Joey? (*interrogatively*).

JOEY. If you wish to board and lodge me, take me. I can peck as well as most men. Where I pecks ain't so high a h'objeck as what I peck, nor even so high a h'objeck as how much I peck.

BINTRY. Master Joey, you ought to have been a lawyer. Where *we* peck is not so high an object as what we peck and how much we peck! Human nature is much the same in all professions. Mr. Wilding, I'll try another glass of the forty-five.

JOEY. Is it all to live in the house, young Master Wilding? The two other cellarmen, the three porters, the two 'prentices, and the odd men?

WILDING. Yes, Joey, I hope we shall be a united family.

JOEY. Ah, I hope they may be.

WILDING. They? Rather say we, Joey!

JOEY. Don't look to me to make jolly on it, young Master Wilding. It's all werry well for you gentlemen that is accustomed to take your wine into your systems by your conwivial throttles to put a lively face upon it; but I have been accustomed to take my wine in at the pores. And took that way, it acts depressing! It's one thing, gentlemen, to charge your glasses in a dining-room with a Hip Hurrah and a Jolly Companions Every One! and another thing to charge yourself by the pores in a low cellar. I've been a cellarman all my life, and what's the consequence? I'm as muddled a man as lives—you won't find a muddleder than me, or my ekal in moloncolly!

BINTRY. I don't want to stop the flow of Master Joey's philosophy, but it is past ten o'clock, and the new housekeeper is coming.

WILDING. Let her come! my friend George Vendale is to see them and recommend the one that seems best.

BINTRY (*rises*). I'll look in again presently. (JOEY *goes up* c. *with him to open* D. *in* F.) Thank you, Joey.   [*Exit* D. *in* F.

JOEY (*comes down* c.). So you have taken a new partner, young Master Vendale, sir?

WILDING. Yes, Joey.

JOEY. But don't change the name of the firm again, young Master Wilding! It was bad luck enough to make it Yourself and Co. Better by far have left it Pebbleson Nephew, that good luck always stuck to! Never change luck when it is good, sir! never change luck. (*Up* L.)

Enter from set house on stoop, L., GEORGE VENDALE.

VENDALE. Well, I have seen the new housekeeper. Her name is Sarah Goldstraw!

WILDING (*startled,* R. C.). Goldstraw! Surely I have heard that name before.

VENDALE. If she is an old acquaintance, all the better. Here she is. I'll go and inspect the rest of the establishment.

          [*Exit down back of stairs,* L. U. E.

Enter from house and down front steps, SALLY.

WILDING. I *have* seen her before!

SALLY (*aside*). Wilding! Wilding! It is a common name enough! (*Recognises* WILDING.) Ah!

JOEY (*to* WILDING). Take her, young Master Wilding. You won't find a match for Sarah Goldstraw in a hurry! (*Aside*.) I feel as if I had taken something new into my system at the pores! Has that pleasant woman brought the pleasant sunshine into this moloncolly place, I wonder? I will think over it in the cellar.

          [*Exit* L. 2 E. *cellar door.*

WILDING. Will you please step this way into the counting-room?

SALLY (*aside*). I must be mistaken. (*Crosses to* R. 1 E., *opens door, starts.*) Oh, my!

WILDING (R. C.). What's the matter?

SALLY. Nothing.

WILDING. Nothing?

SALLY. No! excepting—what—what is that—that portrait hanging up in the counting-house?

WILDING. The portrait of my late dear mother!

SALLY. Of your mother? (*Aside.*) It is like the lady who spoke to me twelve years ago. (*Aloud.*) I hope you will pardon my taking up your time, sir. (*Crossing to* L.) I don't think this place will suit me! (R.)

WILDING. Stop, stop! There is something wrong here! something I do not understand!—Your face puzzles me! Ah! (*Hand to forehead, bewildered.*) I have it! You were at the Foundling twelve years ago!

SALLY. What shall I say?

WILDING. You were the nurse who was kind to my mother, and pointed me out to her!

SALLY. Great heaven forgive me! I was.

WILDING. Great heaven forgive you? What do you mean? Speak out.

SALLY. Dreadful consequences have followed, I am afraid, because I forgot my duty, for that lady——

WILDING. That lady! She calls my mother the lady. When you speak of my mother why don't you say—my mother?

SALLY. Oh! sir, I was deceived and so was the lady.

WILDING. Why can't you speak plainer? You mean my mother?

SALLY. I will speak the truth, but I wish I hadn't to do it, sir! When I was away to our country institution, there came to our house a lady, a Mrs. Miller, who adopted out one of the children. Six months afterwards I came back, and knew nothing about that. That's how the child was taken away——

WILDING. You—you mean me?

SALLY. No, sir. I mean the child of that lady. (*Points off* R. 1 E.) You were not her child. You cannot regret it more than I do. A few days after I had gone away the child was adopted and taken away. But another boy had just been received, and so they gave him his place and called *him* Walter Wilding! Of course, I knew nothing of this! I thought you were still the same infant that I had cared for at the first. Indeed, I was not to blame! It was not my fault.

WILDING. Is it dark, or am I dreaming? Give me your hand! (SALLY *comes to him,* C.)

SALLY. What is the matter?

WILDING. I can't see you! The noise is in my head.

SALLY. Shall I get some water? Shall I call for help?

WILDING. No! give me your hand! How do I know your story is true?

SALLY. Would I have told you if I were mistaken.

WILDING. Oh! I loved her so dearly. I felt so fondly that I was her son!

SALLY. Let your head rest on my shoulder, — not the first time, my boy. I have rocked you to sleep in my arms when a child, many and many's the time. (*Embraces* WILDING, *who is seated on barrel,* L. *of table-barrel.*)

WILDING. Oh, Sally, why did you not speak before?

SALLY. I couldn't, sir! I did not know it till two years ago, when I went to the institution to see one of the girls, and she told me all. If I had only not come here for the housekeeper's place you would never have known to your dying day what you know now! Oh, don't blame me! You forced me to speak! don't blame me!

WILDING. You would have concealed this from me, if you could? (C.) Don't talk that way! She left me all that I possess in the persuasion that I was her son. I am not her son. Would you have me enjoy the fortune of another man? He must be found! What was the name of the lady who adopted the child?

SALLY. Mrs. Miller, sir.

WILDING. Where does she live?

SALLY. No one knows, sir. She took the child to Switzerland.

WILDING. Switzerland? What part of Switzerland?

SALLY. No one knows, sir.

BINTRY enters R. 1 E.

BINTRY. How are you getting on with the new housekeeper? Bless me, what is the matter?

JOEY, with candle, enters L. 2 E., cellar-door, slowly, stays up L.

WILDING. Sally, tell him in your own words,—I cannot speak. (*To* L., *leaning against banisters.*)

BINTRY (*to* SALLY). Step into the counting-house for a little time. I will be with you.

[Exit SALLY, R. 1 E. D., crosses to WILDING.

JOEY (*comes down*). I hope, young Master Wilding, that Sarah Goldstraw is not going to be sent away?

WILDING. Sarah Goldstraw is a good, kind-hearted woman, and shall stay here. Mr. Bintry, the lost Walter Wilding must be found.

423

BINTRY. Not easy after a lapse of twenty years. At this time of day, you will find it no thoroughfare, sir, no thoroughfare.

WILDING. It must be done. I will make my will, and leave all I have to him before I sleep this night.

Enter VENDALE, R. 1 E.

My friend, you don't know what a blow has befallen me.

VENDALE (*shaking* WILDING's *hand*). Sarah has just told me.

WILDING. You will take my side, George! You will help me to find the lost man! If neither of you will help me, I will go to Switzerland myself.

VENDALE. Don't talk like that. I am your partner in all ways.

BINTRY. How will you find the lost man? If we advertise, we lay ourselves open to every rogue in the kingdom. (R. C.)

WILDING. You don't understand me! It is because I loved her that I feel it my duty to do justice to her son! If he is a living man, I will find him, for her sake, his and my own! (C.) I am only a miserable impostor!

VENDALE. Don't talk like that! As to your being an impostor, that is simply absurd, for no man can be that without being a consenting party to the imposition. You need not distress yourself. We will help you. Come, compose yourself. (L. C.)

JOEY, *who has been up at gate in* F., *comes down with letter and card.*

WILDING. What is it, Joey?

JOEY. A foreign gentleman give me this card and letter.

WILDING (*reads card*). Jules Obenreizer!

VENDALE (*takes letter*). Obenreizer! from Switzerland.

WILDING. Switzerland!

VENDALE. I have seen him before.

WILDING. Something tells me I am near the man!

VENDALE. Mr. Obenreizer is an old travelling companion, whose acquaintance I made in Switzerland. (*Reads letter.*) 'Mr. Obenreizer is fully accredited as our agent, and we do not doubt you will esteem his merits.' Signed 'Defresnier & Co., Neuchâtel.' (C.)

WILDING. So you met him on the mountains? (R. C.)

BINTRY (L. *aside*). Mr. Vendale seems confused. That is a bad sign to begin with.

VENDALE. Yes, he was with a young lady——

WILDING. His daughter?

424

VENDALE. No! he is no older than you are. His niece.

BINTRY. And you fell in love with her? Excuse my legal habit of helping out an unwilling witness!

VENDALE (*laughs*). I am not an unwilling witness, Mr. Bintry! I do love her—I loved her then, and I shall love her to the end of the calendar! Is that an unwilling answer?

BINTRY. I can't say. I am not professionally acquainted with the subject.

WILDING. George, you seem confused?

VENDALE. The fact is, I rather talked of my family, to make an impression on the young lady.

WILDING. Come, if you object you need not meet him.

VENDALE. Pshaw! Mr. Obenreizer is recommended to our house, and we would be sure to meet in the way of business, so that the sooner it is over the better for me.

> JOEY *opens gate and lets in* OBENREIZER, *who comes down* C.
> *to shake* WILDING's *hand.*

WILDING. I am glad to see you, sir. This is my friend and legal adviser, Mr. Bintry.

OBENREIZER (*shakes* BINTRY's *hand*). Charmed!   charmed to make Mr. Bintry's acquaintance. (L.)

BINTRY (*aside*). He is too civil by half. I don't like him.

WILDING. Mr. Vendale you know!

VENDALE (*shakes* OBENREIZER's *hand*). You are doubtless surprised to meet me here as partner with Mr. Wilding?

OBENREIZER. On the contrary, no. As I said when we were on the mountains. We call them vast, but the world is so little, one cannot keep away from some persons. (*Quickly.*) Not that any one would wish to get rid of you, Mr. Vendale! Oh, dear no! So glad to have met you! So glad! (*Half embracing* VENDALE.)

BINTRY (*aside*). Rather a tigerish way of being glad.

OBENREIZER. Though you are descended from so fine a family, you have condescended to come into trade? Stop though. Wines? Is it trade in England or profession? Not fine arts? (*Smiling.*)

VENDALE. Mr. Obenreizer, I was but a silly young fellow in the first flush of coming into the fortune my parents left me. I hope what I said when we travelled together was more youthful openness of speech than vanity!

425

OBENREIZER. You tax yourself too heavily! You tax yourself, my faith! as if you were your government taxing you! I liked your conversation! I like your conversion. It is the misfortune of trade that any lower people may take to it and climb by it. I for example—I a man of low origin—for what I know of it—no origin at all!

WILDING (*aside to* BINTRY, L.). Do you hear that?

BINTRY. No! I am deaf on principle to all humbugs!

VENDALE (R. C., *to* OBENREIZER). And Madame Dor?

OBENREIZER. Oh, she is well. She is with Marguerite——

BINTRY. You seem rather young to be a young lady's guardian, Mr. Obenreizer?

OBENREIZER. Young in years, Mr. Bintry, but old in discretion and in experience. Her father was my half-brother—if he was my brother?—a poor peasant, and when he was dying, leaving her a little fortune, he called me to him, and told me, 'All for Marguerite.' Ah, Mr. Wilding! I may be this, or I may be that, but one thing I know! I shall live and I shall die true to my trust! (*Pause.*) Well, we are house-hunting now, and she shall have a home replete with gratified wishes! (*Aside.*) Though where the money is to come from is another matter. (*Turns up* c. *a little.*)

WILDING (*to* BINTRY). He is not sure of his origin! he is doubtful of his parentage! Do you hear that?

BINTRY. No! Mr. Wilding, I do *not* hear that!

VENDALE (R. C., *to* OBENREIZER). And Madame Dor?

OBENREIZER. Oh, she is well. She is with Marguerite——

VENDALE. Abroad?

OBENREIZER. Here! here waiting for me without.

WILDING. What! ladies kept waiting at my door? I will go bring them in——

OBENREIZER. Not for worlds! (*Prevents* VENDALE *and* WILDING *going up* c., *goes up* c. *to gate, which* JOEY *opens slowly.*)

WILDING (*to* BINTRY). I must do something in this!

BINTRY. There is one thing you can do—hold your tongue!

OBENREIZER (*leads in* MARGUERITE *and* MADAME DOR *down* c.). My niece! (MARGUERITE *comes down* L. C., *to* VENDALE.) Madame Dor! (MADAME DOR *crosses sidewise to* R., *side of barrel-table, back to characters on stage, rubbing glove.*) The guardian angel of my wardrobe! you will excuse her—she is now at my gloves! to-morrow, it may be, darning my stockings or making pudding. Ah! you English, who delight in domestic matters. You like it in your pictures, you like it in your books! Ah, Madame Dor makes me my good, solid, heavy, indigestible English pudding! Only look at her back—(*points to* MADAME DOR, R. *by table*) it is as broad as her heart! (C.)

VENDALE (*to* MARGUERITE). Mr. Obenreizer was saying that the world is so small a place that people cannot escape one another. If it had been less, I might have found you sooner! It is still a curious coincidence that you come to London the day I become partner in a house to which Mr. Obenreizer's firm in Switzerland introduce him.

OBENREIZER (*coming between*). Ah! London is the place—city of luxury, if you are rich, like Mr. Vendale here! Some are lucky! While they were saying to him, 'Come here, my darling, kiss me!' I was called 'Little wretch, come taste the stick!' (*gesture with cane*) I dwelt among a sorry set in Switzerland! Would I could forget it! (WILDING *touches* BINTRY *to notice*.)

MARGUERITE. For my part, I love Switzerland.

OBENREIZER (*quickly, tenderly*). Marguerite, so do I. But speak in proud England!

MARGUERITE. I speak in proud earnest! And I am not noble, but a peasant's daughter.

VENDALE. And I honour and fully appreciate your sentiment!

OBENREIZER. Ah! (*interposing*) Marguerite, we will set about our house-hunting.

WILDING. Mr. Obenreizer! (C.)

BINTRY. Mr. Wilding, will you hold your tongue?

OBENREIZER. My dear Mr. Vendale, you must come see us often when we are settled. Mr. Wilding, the same. Mr. Bintry! (*bows*). We will transact business together, and be firm friends. Adieu! (*Bows, escorts* MARGUERITE *and* MADAME DOR *in* C.—VENDALE L. *side, with* BINTRY *and* WILDING R. C.)

VENDALE (*aside*). How he guards his niece!

WILDING. This may be the lost man!

CURTAIN

427

ACT II

Scene I.—*Room in* Obenreizer's *house, discovering* Marguerite *standing at window,* l. *in* f., *and* Madame Dor *seated at table by same*—Obenreizer, r.

Marguerite (*aside*). Not come—not come yet! (*Turns sadly from looking out of window.*)

Obenreizer (*counting money,* r. 1 e., *at press in set*). One hundred —two—four hundred—fifty—four hundred and fifty. Fifty pounds still wanted to make up the missing sum. That sum I must replace, or I am a lost man! (*To table* r. *front.*) Ah! this miserable luxury—this hollow show! Has Marguerite any idea of what this splendour costs me? Has she even noticed it? Yes, within the last few weeks she has been more animated and kinder. Something like affection is in her ways. She does not even think of that man Vendale.

Marguerite (*aside*). Still no signs of him!

Obenreizer (*aside*). What! he has sent nothing as a birthday present. He has forgotten her, then! Oh, if he had sent her a present it would have been something so rich that her proud spirit would have revolted. I will put up the money. Yet (*hesitating*) I might replace it by a month. Nonsense! it is not to be thought of. Disgrace myself? Ah! it would ruin me for life! What would Marguerite say when she looked on me as a felon! I will put the money up ; he will not come.

Marguerite (*suddenly*). Oh! he is crossing the square. Here he comes. (*Turns to* d. *in* f.)

Orenreizer. He! Who?

Marguerite. Mr. Vendale.

Obenreizer (*aside*). Then he has not forgotten her! (r. *front.*)

Enter Vendale, d. *in* f.

Vendale (*to* Marguerite). Permit me to wish you many happy returns of the day. Will you accept a little memento? (*Gives jewel case.*)

Marguerite. Jewels! They are too rich for me!

Vendale. You have not opened it yet.

MARGUERITE. So simple a present (*turning to* OBENREIZER) I may keep?

OBENREIZER (*sneering*). The modesty of wealth!

MARGUERITE (*to* VENDALE). I own that you have pleased and flattered me. (*Puts on brooch.*)

OBENREIZER (*aside*). He forces me to it. (*Gets money from press,* R. 1 E.; *aloud.*) Mr. Vendale has reminded me that I have not yet made my offering; you will excuse me? (VENDALE *bows—up to* D. *in* F.; *aside.*) Ah, Mr. Vendale, come what may, you will not get the upper hand of me now!   [*Exit,* D. *in* F.

VENDALE (*aside*). I will wait here with the greatest pleasure till he comes back! My opportunity has come at last. No! Madame Dor! Is there no means of getting this piece of human furniture out of the room? (MADAME DOR *leans forward, sleeping.*) She lets her work fall unheeded to the floor. Oh! best of women, yield to the voice of Nature, and fall asleep. (MADAME DOR *does so—*VENDALE *comes down* C. *to* MARGUERITE.) I have something to say to you—a secret to impart. (*Seated beside her.*)

MARGUERITE. What claim have I to any secret of yours, Mr. Vendale?

VENDALE. You have not forgotten the happy time when we first met and were travelling together. Out of all the impressions I brought back from Switzerland, there was one impression chief. Can you guess what it is?

MARGUERITE. I cannot guess. An impression of the mountains?

VENDALE. No, more precious.

MARGUERITE. Of the lakes?

VENDALE. No! the lakes have not grown dearer to me every day! Marguerite, all that makes life worth having, hangs, for me, on a word from your lips. Marguerite, I love you!

MARGUERITE. Oh, Mr. Vendale! Have you forgotten the distance between us?

VENDALE (*prevents her rising*). There can be but one distance between us, Marguerite—that of your own making. There is no higher rank in goodness and in beauty than yours!

MARGUERITE. Ah! Think of your family, and think of mine! (*Rises.*)

VENDALE. If you dwell on such an obstacle, I shall think only that I have offended you! (*Rises.*)

MARGUERITE (*forgetting herself*). Oh, no, George!

VENDALE. Say you love me!

MARGUERITE. I love you! (*Embrace, starts, goes up to* L. U. *corner.*)

OBENREIZER *enters,* D. *in* F.—MADAME DOR *is awakened by* MARGUERITE.

OBENREIZER (*as men bring in flowers in stand and place them up* C. *against* F.). Now you will see that your birthday is not forgotten. (R. *front.*)

MARGUERITE (C. *up*). I thank you.

OBENREIZER. Oh, not for them! My present is not made yet! Flowers will fade. Wear these! (*presents jewel-case*) and give them a beauty which is not their own.

MARGUERITE (*takes case*). Oh, how could you buy these for me! how can you expect me to wear these? I would have been contented with the flowers. (*Goes up to* L. U. *corner.*) Madame Dor, we will be late. We must dress for dinner. [*Exit* L. D. *with* MADAME DOR.

OBENREIZER (*aside*). She wears *his* offering round her neck! My crime is useless! I have put my whole life in peril, and *this* is my reward! Oh, curses on her glitter and her beauty!

VENDALE. What is the matter, friend? (L. C.)

OBENREIZER (*sarcastically*). Friend! Nothing!

VENDALE. Stay! I have something to say to you. (C. *front.*)

OBENREIZER (R. C. *front*). Excuse me. I am not quite myself. You want to speak to me—oh! on business, I suppose.

VENDALE. On something much more important than mere business.

OBENREIZER. I am at your service. Go on. (*Seated* R. *side of table,* VENDALE *seated* L. *side.*)

VENDALE. Perhaps you may have noticed latterly that my admiration for your charming niece——

OBENREIZER. Noticed? Not I!

VENDALE. Has grown into a deeper feeling——

OBENREIZER (*uneasily*). Shall we say friendship, Mr. Vendale?

VENDALE (*rises*). I ask you to give me her hand in marriage!

OBENREIZER (*starts up*). You ask *me*! (*Restrains his anger.*)

VENDALE. Stay, I beg you to tell me plainly what objection you see to my suit?

OBENREIZER. The immense one that my niece is the daughter of a poor peasant and you the son of an English gentleman.

VENDALE. I ought to know my own countrymen better than you do, Mr. Obenreizer. In the estimation of everybody whose opinion is worth having, my wife would be the one sufficient justification of my marriage. We are both men of business, and you naturally expect me to satisfy you that I have the means of supporting a wife. I am in a trade which I see my way to gradually improving. As it stands at present I can state my annual income at fifteen hundred pounds. Do you object to me on pecuniary grounds?

OBENREIZER (*abruptly*). Yes!

VENDALE. Yes! It is not enough?

OBENREIZER. It is not half enough for a foreign wife who has half your social prejudices to conquer. Tell me, Mr. Vendale, on your £1500 a year, can your wife live in a fashionable quarter, have a butler to wait at her table, and a carriage and horses to drive about in? Yes or no?

VENDALE. Come to the point! You view this question as a question of terms?

OBENREIZER. Terms, as you say! terms beyond your reach!

VENDALE. Sir!

OBENREIZER. Make your income three thousand pounds and come to me then!

VENDALE. Then I will speak with her.

OBENREIZER. You surely would not speak to my niece on this subject?

VENDALE. I have opened my whole heart to her, and have reason to hope——

OBENREIZER (*passionately*). What! Mr. Vendale, as a man of honour, speaking to a man of honour, how can you justify such conduct as this?

VENDALE. The best excuse is the assurance that I have had from her own lips that she loves me——(R. *front.*)

OBENREIZER (*passionately*). She lo—Oh! (*violently*) we'll soon see about that! (*Goes over to* L. D.) Marguerite! Marguerite! (*Aside.*) How lovely she looks!

Enter, L. D., MARGUERITE.

MARGUERITE. You wish to speak to me?

OBENREIZER. Yes, my child, I wish to speak to you—to ask a question. Mr. Vendale says——(*hand to forehead, as in pain*).

MARGUERITE. How altered you are in your manner. Are you not well? What have I done? (*up* L.).

431

OBENREIZER (*forgetting himself*). Done! you have turned the knife in the wound! No! I don't mean that! I mean——But we are forgetting Mr. Vendale. He has *said* (*sneering*) that you said you loved him? It is not true, my child?

MARGUERITE (*comes down* L. C.). It is true!

OBENREIZER. Oh! Great God! (*in a suppressed voice,* C.).

MARGUERITE. You frighten me!

VENDALE (*triumphantly*). Are you satisfied now?

OBENREIZER. Wait! wait a little! I have my authority yet, as she is my ward. Marguerite, you know that your father entrusted you to me, you cannot marry without my consent. Whatever Mr. Vendale says—if I say wait, you will wait!

MARGUERITE. Oh! (VENDALE *glances at her imploringly.*)

VENDALE. Oh, Marguerite!

OBENREIZER (*violently*). You *will* wait, my child?

MARGUERITE. Yes! (*submissively clasps her hands and hangs her head*).

OBENREIZER. Are you answered?

VENDALE (*firmly*). I am. You have heard from her own lips that she loves me. I will make the fifteen hundred three thousand pounds.

OBENREIZER. Make it three thousand!

VENDALE. Adieu, Marguerite!

MARGUERITE. Oh! George! (VENDALE *turns.*)

OBENREIZER. Ah, Mr. Vendale! You are not her husband yet! (*going up* L. *with one hand of* MARGUERITE'S *in his,* VENDALE *at* D. *in* F.).

(*Scene closes in.*)

SCENE II.—*Room in* WILDING'S *house.*—MR. BINTRY *enters* R., *hands under his coat-tails, in thought, crosses to* L., *turns and to* D. R. *in* F.

Enter SALLY, R. D.

SALLY. Oh, Mr. Bintry, so you have come to see master!

BINTRY. Yes, I have come to see how he is getting on.

SALLY. I am afraid he is worse. The new doctor has ordered that he must not be disturbed. (C.)

BINTRY (R. C.). Another doctor called in! When I was here last, Mr. Wilding could walk and talk.

SALLY. He can walk and talk yet, but I must agree with the doctors.

He is dying—growing back more and more like him I used to call my little child at the Foundling.

BINTRY. Well, Miss Goldstraw, you may be old enough to be his mother, but you certainly don't look it.

SALLY. Thank you, sir, for the compliment!

BINTRY. You are heartily welcome.

SALLY. Don't you think, sir, you could make him better by doing more as he wishes, sir?

BINTRY. Miss Goldstraw, you have your duty to perform, and I have mine. My duty as a professional man is to keep my old friend from all rogues—Mr. Obenreizer, for example. (*Crosses to* L.)

SALLY. But you go contrary to his will, sir.

BINTRY. Contrary to his will—I wish we could go contrary to his will. I drew it up and had it executed! the most absurd document ever put on paper! Vendale and I were bound by it as executors to find a lost man, no matter what he is! and give up to him a fortune. By drawing up that document I have committed professional suicide, and yet the worthy woman says I have not humoured my client!

SALLY. Excuse me, sir. I see closer than you. It is wearing his life out.

BINTRY. Come, speak out if you think I can be of any service to my old friend! What can I do?

SALLY. Find the lost man!

BINTRY. If I do, I'll be——(*stops short on* SALLY *lifting her hands*).

SALLY. Oh, sir! if you'd only promise to let him have his own way, and try to find the lost man?

BINTRY. Was there ever such perversity! Here's a man dying to find a man who will rob him of every penny he possesses and leave him a pauper. Humph! Well, I'll put an advertisement in the papers, telling the client to apply to my office, to me, mind you—it will be a devilish lucky man who will get a fortune out of me, I can tell you! (*Crosses to* L. *and returns to* C.)

SALLY (R. C.). Thank you, sir, for my master. Ah, you may have a rough outside, but I see that you are a warm-hearted man!

BINTRY (*going* R., *turns and comes close to* SALLY, *after pause*). Miss Goldstraw, don't you take away my character! Well, I will set about it, and come to-morrow.   [*Exit* R.

SALLY (*to* D. *in* F., *which opens*). Oh, my dear master!

Enter WILDING, D. *in* F.

WILDING. I thought I heard Mr. Bintry? (*to* C. *assisted by* SALLY).

SALLY (R. C.). He was here only a minute. He is coming again to-morrow, sir.

WILDING. Always to-morrow! When it is now that we ought to find the man. (*Querulously.*) Nobody helps me.

SALLY. Mr. Bintry says he will try, sir.

WILDING. Mr. Bintry is too suspicious, and drives people away. (*Aside.*) The more I think of it the more I see that everything points one way. Obenreizer is the man! I think of him by day, and I dream of him by night. (*Aloud.*) Sally, I may call you Sally?

SALLY. Dear, yes, sir.

WILDING. For the sake of the old times let it be Sally.

SALLY. Of course, sir. Do you try to be the good boy that you always were at the Foundling, the good patient little boy. Try to be patient now.

WILDING. Something tells me I must lose no time. I must see Mr. Obenreizer at once.

SALLY. Yes, sir, I will send for him.

WILDING. I must and will see him.

SALLY. Yes, yes, sir.

WILDING. Where is Mr. Vendale?

SALLY. Gone to Mr. Obenreizer's.

WILDING. Ah! gone to propose to his pretty niece. Vendale's a dear good friend, and I wish him all success. He is not so suspicious as Mr. Bintry, and I think he will aid me.

SALLY. I am sure of it, sir.

WILDING. Then you will send for Mr. Obenreizer?

SALLY. I promise to send there, sir.

WILDING. You will relieve my mind.

SALLY. I will do it, sir, but be a good child, and go to bed.

WILDING. Sally, Sally! how little changed things are since we met for the first time. Mr. Obenreizer says, 'The world is so small that it is not strange how often the same people come together at various stages of life.' After all, I have come round to my foundling nurse to die!

SALLY. No! no! dear Master Wilding, not going to die! (*Leads him out* D. *in* F.) No! [*Exit* D. *in* F.

434

SCENE III.—*Cellar in* WILDING'S *stores*—JOEY *discovered up* R. *measuring casks and bins, etc.* VENDALE *comes down* L. *platform to front.*

VENDALE. Poor Wilding! I would tell him what took place at Obenreizer's, but he has troubles of his own to engross him. My spirits are depressed, spite of myself, as if something evil was overhanging me. Can I do what I have engaged myself to do? Can I double this business in a year's time? I have been wandering about these old cellars like a perturbed spirit. Oh, you are here, are you, Joey? (*Takes candle and comes down* L. *side listlessly, comes down around and up* C.)

JOEY. Oughtn't it rather to go, Oh, *you're* here, are you, Master George? For it's my business here, and not yours!

VENDALE. Don't grumble, Joey.

JOEY. I don't grumble! It's what I took in at the pores. Have a care that something in *you* don't begin a - grumbling, Master George! Stop here long enough, and the wapors will be at work —trust 'em for it! So you've regularly come into the business, Master George?

VENDALE. Yes, Joey. I hope you don't object?

JOEY. Oh! I don't, bless you! But wapors object that you're too young. You and Master Wilding are too young. Master has not changed the luck of the firm.

VENDALE. Pooh!

JOEY. Pooh! is an easy word to speak, Master George, but I have not been a cellarman down here all my life for nothing. I know by what I notices down here when it's a-going to rain, when it's a-going to hold up, when it's a-going to blow, and when it's a-going to be calm. I know when the luck's changed quite as well.

VENDALE (*taking rod up*). Has this growth on the roof anything to do with your divination, Joey? We are famous for this growth in our vaults, aren't we?

JOEY. We are, Master George, and if you'll take advice by me, you'll let it alone.

VENDALE. Why, Joey?

JOEY. For three good reasons!

VENDALE. Let's hear the good reasons for letting the fungus alone. (*Playing with webs.*)

435

JOEY. Why, because it rises from the casks of wine and may leave you to judge what sort of wapors a cellarman takes into his system when he walks in the same, and because at one stage of its growth it's maggots!

VENDALE. Maggots! What other reason?

JOEY. I wouldn't keep touching of it, Master George, if I was you! Take a look at its colour!

VENDALE. I am looking. Well, Joey, the colour?

JOEY. Is it like (*mysteriously*) clotted blood, Master George?

VENDALE. It is rather like.

JOEY. Is it more than like! (*Shakes his head.*)

VENDALE. Say it is exactly like! What then? (*Playing with the cobweb as before.*)

JOEY. Well, Master George, they do say——

VENDALE (*carelessly*). Who?

JOEY. How should I know who? Them as says pretty well everything! How can I tell who they are?

VENDALE. True. Go on, Joey!

JOEY. They do say, that the man who gets by any accident a piece of that right upon his breast——

VENDALE (*playing with stick and web, mechanically*). On his breast?

JOEY. For sure and certain——

VENDALE. For sure and certain?

JOEY. Will die by murder!

VENDALE. Murder! (*Web drops on his left breast and vest, lets rod fall.*)

OBENREIZER *appears on platform*, L. *front.*

VENDALE. What do you want here?

OBENREIZER (*comes down* L. *platform to stage to* C.). Mr. Vendale, I come on a sad errand. You need a friend—a true friend. I will try to be it again. I hope you will forget how we parted, when I say that I regret my manner of receiving you. (*To* C.) Mr. Vendale, I ask your pardon.

VENDALE. I accept the apology.

OBENREIZER (*softly*). Won't you shake hands with me? (*They shake hands.*) Mr. Vendale, prepare yourself for a shock.

VENDALE. What is it?

OBENREIZER. I come to bring you sad tidings——

VENDALE. Is it of Wilding? Is my poor friend worse?

OBENREIZER. Worse!

VENDALE. Not——

OBENREIZER. He is——

VENDALE. Dead?

OBENREIZER. Dead!

JOEY (*up* C.). Dead!

VENDALE. Dead! My poor friend! Ah, Joey, your superstition spoke truth. This was a warning of death.

JOEY (*comes down* R. C.). I did not say death, Master George, I said murder!

| JOEY. | OBENREIZER. | VENDALE. |
| R. | C. | L. |

CURTAIN

ACT III

SCENE I.—*Counting-room in* WILDING'S *house, discovering* VENDALE *at table* R. C. *front, and* SALLY *beside him.*

SALLY. Have you any more questions to ask me, sir?

VENDALE. Yes — tell me again all that passed just before poor Wilding died.

SALLY. He had been asking for Mr. Obenreizer, who had been sent for—and when he came he sat up to try to speak to him, but before he could say a word, he fell back again. The doctor ordered Mr. Obenreizer to leave the room. Mr. Wilding died soon after—only spoke a word, but I am sure he breathed your name.

VENDALE. I am sure of that! (*with emotion*). So no one knows what he wanted so eagerly to say to Mr. Obenreizer. The mystery is wrapped in denser obscurity than ever. My poor dear friend! I know what his trust was, and if the missing man is to be found, I will find him. (*Knock* R. 1 E. D.) Who's there? Come in.

Enter JOEY, R. 1 E. D., *with letter.*

JOEY. A letter, sir, from foreign parts.

VENDALE (*takes letter*). From Defresnier and Co., of Neuchâtel. The answer to mine.

437

JOEY (*to* SALLY, L. U. E. *corner*). Do you find yourself, miss, getting over the shock of young Master Wilding's death?

SALLY. Mr. Joey, we all have to submit to losses in this world. I am learning, I hope, to submit to mine. [*Exit* L. U. E.

JOEY (*aside*). Beautiful language! beautiful! The parson himself couldn't have said it better than she. I'll try to remember it before I forget it, like the catechism. 'We must all submit to learning, which is one of the losses in this world!'

VENDALE (*aside*, R. C. *front*). Just when it is most important for me to increase the value of the business, it is threatened with a loss of five hundred pounds. Ah, Marguerite!

JOEY (*comes down* R. *side*). Ah! Master George, I know what's on your mind. It's those six cases of red wine sent from the place called Noocattle, instead of the white.

VENDALE. The devil take the six cases!

JOEY. The devil sent them, sir. It's foreign to my nature to crow over the house I serve, but hasn't it come true what I said to young Master Wilding, respecting the changing the name of the firm, when I said that you might find one of these days that he'd changed the luck of the firm? Did I set myself up as a prophet? No! Has what I said to him come true? Yes! What's the consequence? You write to them at Noocattle, and they write back. You, not satisfied, write to them again; and they, not satisfied, write back again; and that's the letter you have in your hand, as chock full of bad news as a egg is full of meat. In the time of Pebbleson Nephew, young Master George, no such thing was ever known as a mistake made in a consignment to our house. I don't want to intrude my moloncolly on you, sir, so let me recommend the beautiful language of Miss Goldstraw, fitted to the case: 'We must all learn to submit to our losses, which is one of the learnings in this world!' Reflect over them, Mr. Vendale. I'm going to the wapors awaiting in the cellar for me! [*Exit* R. 1 E.

VENDALE. This is most unfortunate! (*To desk up* L.) Let me put the correspondence in order. (*Takes up letters.*) First I write to Defresnier and Co., saying the number of cases per last consignment was quite correct, but on six of them being opened they were found to contain a red wine instead of champagne, a mistake probably caused by a similarity of the brand. The matter can be easily set right by your sending us six cases of champagne, or by crediting us with the value of six cases red on the five hundred pounds last remitted you, to which they reply : 'The statement of the error has led to a very unexpected discovery—a serious affair for you and us. Having no more champagne of the vintage last sent to you, we made arrangements to credit your firm with the value of the six cases, when a reference to our books resulted in the moral certainty that no such remittance as you mention ever reached our house, and a literal certainty that no such remittance has been paid to our account at the bank. We have not even a suspicion who the thief is, but we believe you will assist us towards discovery by seeing whether the receipt (forged of course) purporting to come from our house is entirely in MSS. or a numbered and printed form. Anxiously waiting your reply, we remain,' etc. etc. Ah ! Next I write to the Swiss firm, and receive the answer I hold in my hand. (*Reads.*) 'Dear Sir : Your discovery that the forged receipt is executed on one of our regular forms has caused inexpressible surprise and distress to us. At the time when your remittance was stolen but three keys were in existence opening the strong box in which our receipt-forms are invariably kept. My partner had one key, I another. The third was in possession of a gentleman who, at that period, occupied a position of trust in our house. I cannot prevail on myself to inform you who the person is. Forgive my silence, the motive of it is good.' Who can this be ? However, it is useless for me to inquire in my position. 'The handwriting on your receipt must be compared with certain specimens in our possession. I cannot send you them, for business reasons, and must beg you to send the receipt to Neuchâtel, and, in making this request, I must accompany it by a word of warning. If the person, at whom suspicion now points, really proves to be the person who has committed this forgery and theft, the only evidence against him is the evidence in your hands, and he is a man who will stick at nothing to obtain and destroy it. I strongly urge you not to trust the receipt to the post. Send it, without loss of time, by a private messenger accustomed to travelling, capable of speaking French ; a man of courage, a man of honesty, and, above all, a man who can be trusted to let no stranger scrape acquaintance with him on the route. Tell no one — absolutely no one — but your messenger of the turn this matter has now taken. The safe transit of the receipt may depend on your interpreting *literally* the advice which I give you at the end of this letter.' Now I know the man who writes these words. He would not have written them without good reasons. Who can I send? There is no man I know of. None of the clerks speak French.

Music to OBENREIZER'S *entrance.*

OBENREIZER (*in* R. 1 E.). May I come in?

VENDALE. Certainly.

OBENREIZER, R. 1 E., *puts hat and cane on table up* R. C., *against flat, and comes down.*

JOEY (R. 1 E., *aside*). He stole in here just as he stole into the cellars to tell of Master Wilding's death. He was by when the web fell on Master George, he is by when that letter of bad news comes. I will watch. I don't like this Mr. Openrazor!

[*Exit* R. 1 E.

OBENREIZER. Ah, Mr. Vendale, you look as if there was something the matter!

VENDALE. Yes, you come at a bad time. I am threatened with the loss of five hundred pounds. (R. 2 E.)

OBENREIZER. *Five* hundred pounds! (*Aside.*) Ah!

VENDALE (*at safe in wall* R. 2 E.). Your own house is one of the parties in the affair.

OBENREIZER. Indeed! (*Aside.*) The forged receipt. (*Aloud.*) Tell me how it has happened. (*Aside.*) I wonder where he has got the receipt? If he only takes it out of his safe——

VENDALE. Ah! (*Takes paper out of safe*, R. 2 E.) Here is the forged receipt.

OBENREIZER (*up* L., *aside*). He is alone. I am stronger than him. (*About to cross to* R.)

Enter JOEY, R. 1 E.

JOEY. Did you call, Master George?

VENDALE. No! Joey, don't disturb me!

JOEY. I'll keep the door open this time.   [*Exit* R 1 E.

OBENREIZER (*aside*). Force is hopeless! I must try fraud! Well?

VENDALE. Well, the latest letter wishes me to send your house the

forged receipt to compare it with writing in their hands. It is
wished that I must keep the whole proceedings a profound secret
from everybody.

OBENREIZER. Not even excepting me ! Well ?

VENDALE. Not excepting. (*Surprised*.) Oh ! not excepting you.
They must have forgotten you.

OBENREIZER. They must have forgotten me. Then under the circumstances I can hardly advise. Yet why not take it yourself. Nothing
could happen better. I am going to Switzerland to-night.

VENDALE. And Marguerite ?

OBENREIZER (*gaily*). Oh ! come to the house and dine with us at
seven. We can go off at once by the mail-train to-night. Is it
agreed ?

VENDALE. By the mail-train to-night ?

OBENREIZER. Ah ! well (*looking at watch*) at seven ! (*up* R. *at* D. *in* F.)

VENDALE. At seven to-night.

JOEY (*enters* R. 1 E.). I will take your luggage for you to Mr. Openrazor's house.

VENDALE. You have been listening, Joey ?

JOEY. Not listening, Master George, but I heard every word for
all that.

JOEY.	OBENREIZER, D. *in* F.	VENDALE.
R.	R. C.	C.

SCENE II.—*Room in* WILDING's *house—enter*, L., SALLY *and* JOEY.

SALLY (C.). Mr. Joey, why do you follow me about into my part of
the house ?

JOEY. Miss Goldstraw, if you was to go down into the cellars I 'd
follow you there with the greatest pleasure.

SALLY. But why do you follow me at all ?

JOEY. For the same reason that the first man followed the first woman.

SALLY. Ay, but she led him all wrong afterwards, and I don't want
to lead you wrong, Mr. Joey.

JOEY. Then there 's another reason : I want to see you change your
name, which if Goldstraw is good, to Ladle, which is better ! That
was well said, I think !

441

SALLY. Well, I never! Is it you of all men that would want me to change the name of the firm? What next, I wonder?

JOEY. Woman is not the *firm*. (*Putting arm round* SALLY's *waist*.)

SALLY. Do you speak with your arm, Mr. Joey, and do you think I listen with my waist? (*Puts his arm away.*)

JOEY. Then there's another thing, Miss Goldstraw. I want you to bring back the luck of the firm!

SALLY. Me! you want me? Why, bless your innocent soul, I was the cause of all the trouble that has come into the house. If it had not been for me, none of this would have happened. If you, Joey, knew all, you would hate me.

JOEY (*shakes head*). If you brought the cross of luck, why, that's the very reason you should bring the good luck home again. (*Aside.*) That was well said, I think!

SALLY. Why, what can I do, Mr. Joey? (*Puts arm around her.*) Mr. Joey, may I ask, did you ever make love before?

JOEY. Yes; but I never got as far as this.

SALLY (*laughs*). The idea of any man making love in an apron like that!

JOEY (*aside*). She remarks my apron. Now, what follows from her being in love with my apron? Why, that she should be in love with me! (*Aloud.*) You are at liberty, Miss Goldstraw, to like any part of me, so long as you like me. Now just let my arm speak to your waist a little, while I tell you that I have something else besides wapors in my head, I have. I would go on further with the love-making but for that and my having to go to take Mr. George's luggage to Mr. Openrazor's; and in the state of mind I am in, and with the spirit of prophecy strong upon me, I don't know where I shall spend the night.

SALLY. Dear me! (*Puts aside arm.*) You'll excuse me, Master Joey, but the institution of marriage is a serious thing, and the more a man and a woman look at it in that light before marriage, the better for the parties afterwards! [*Exit* D. *in* F.

JOEY. Beautiful language! Let me turn that over in my mind before I forget it! The 'institution of a man and a woman is a serious matter, and the sooner they look at it in that light the better for all parties afterwards!' [*Exit* L. 1 E. *as he speaks*.

442

SCENE III.—*Same as* SCENE I., ACT II., *discovering* OBENREIZER *at table, up* L., *packing travelling-bag and putting its strap round his neck, having pipe in his hand, etc.,* MARGUERITE *and* VENDALE R. C. *front.*

VENDALE. I am all ready now, and going away.

MARGUERITE (*aside to him*). Must you go, George? Oh, do not go!

VENDALE. It is business that compels me to go. I know the parting must be hard, but I shall be back in a month.

MARGUERITE. It is not the parting, but you are going with him. Have you done anything to offend Mr. Obenreizer?

VENDALE. I?

MARGUERITE. Hush! You know the little photograph of you I have. This afternoon it happened to be on the mantelpiece, when he took it up, and I saw his face in the glass. I know you have offended him! He is merciless, he is revengeful.

VENDALE. You are letting your fancy frighten you. Obenreizer and I were never better friends than at this moment.

MARGUERITE. Don't go, George, or go alone. It is near seven. It will be too late in a few minutes. Change your mind, George, change your mind!

JOEY *enters,* D. *in* F., *and comes down* R. *to* VENDALE, *to give him letter.*

JOEY. A letter with a foreign postmark, Master George. (*Goes up to take trunk to* L. *by window, then by* D. *in* F., *waiting.*)

VENDALE. From Neuchâtel.

MARGUERITE. The journey is put off? (*Hands clasped with joy.*)

OBENREIZER (*aside, coming down* C.). The journey put off!

VENDALE (*after reading*). On the contrary. (*Reads.*) 'Dear Sir: I am called away by urgent business to Milan, where I should prevail on you to meet me.' My journey is not deferred, you see, but lengthened. (*To* OBENREIZER.) In this wintry weather I cannot expect you to accompany me on the additional route.

OBENREIZER. Why not?—Fellow-travellers, be it more or less long. To Switzerland I would have gone with you; to Milan you say now. Well, I will go with you to your journey's end!

VENDALE. Thanks, my companion.

MARGUERITE (*aside to* VENDALE). Oh, George! look at his smile now.

OBENREIZER (*looks at his watch*). Are you ready? Can I take anything for you? You have no travelling-bag. Here's mine, with the compartment for papers, open at your service. (*To* L. *after this.*)

VENDALE. Thank you. I have only one paper of importance with me, and that paper I am bound to take charge of myself. (*Touching breast-pocket of coat.*) Here it must remain till we get to Milan. (*Goes up* C.) Joey, change the address on my trunk. JOEY *goes* L., *frustrating* OBENREIZER, *who wanted to take up trunk, brings trunk to table, up* C.) Milan, Joey. M-i-l-a-n, if you don't know how to spell it.

JOEY (*aside*). I know how to spell more than that. Miss Marguerite don't seem to like the idea of Master George going on this journey with Mr. Openrazor no more than I do. I'd give something to know her mind on the subject. (*Writes on label on trunk.*)

OBENREIZER. Marguerite, adieu. My friend, *en route*, or we'll be too late for the mail train.

MARGUERITE (C.). George! (*Embraces George.*)

OBENREIZER. George, how precious you are to her! Don't be alarmed (*half embraces* VENDALE *by the shoulders*); I will take care of him. Come on (*out* D. *in* F.).

MARGUERITE. George, George, George, don't go!

VENDALE. I must.

(*Voice of* OBENREIZER *off* R. U. E.). Vendale!

VENDALE. I am coming.

(*Voice of* OBENREIZER). Vendale!

JOEY. He may come back.

VENDALE. Farewell, Marguerite.   [*Exit hastily* D. *in* F.

MARGUERITE. Don't go. Ah! gone in spite of all that I could do! Oh, what is to be done?

JOEY (*comes down* R. C.). Miss Marguerite, the warning of danger's on you as it is on me?

MARGUERITE. Yes.

JOEY. Will you try to fend it off?

MARGUERITE. Yes. Joey, I am no fine lady; I am one of the people like you. I will go save him.

JOEY. And I will go with you! I will go with you!

CURTAIN

ACT IV

SCENE I.—*Interior of Swiss Inn, discovering* VENDALE R. *by fire,*
OBENREIZER *over* L. *by table, pipe in hand.*

VENDALE. How still it is in the night! Is not that the rustling of the waterfall that we hear?

OBENREIZER. Yes! the waterfall on the slope of the mountain. It sounds like the old waterfall at home that my mother showed to travellers—if she was my mother!

VENDALE. If? Why do you say, if?

OBENREIZER. How do I know? I was very young and all the rest of the family were men and women, and my so-called parents were old enough to be—to be my ancestors! Anything is possible in a case like mine.

VENDALE. Did you ever doubt——

OBENREIZER. Doubt? Everything!

VENDALE. At least you are Swiss?

OBENREIZER. How do I know? I say to you, at least you are English. How do you know?

VENDALE. By what I have been told from infancy.

OBENREIZER (*sneering*). Ah! you know by what you have been told from infancy! I know of myself *that* way—it must satisfy me! While you sat on your mother's lap in your father's carriage, rolling through the rich English streets all luxury surrounding you, I was a famished, naked child among men and women with hard hand to beat me! Bah! so ends my biography. But it is getting cold here! You have let your fire go out! (*To* D. *in* F.) Halloa there! some wood! (*To* R. *by table.*)

Enter LANDLORD, *with wood.*

A drop of brandy will do neither of us any harm—we have let our flasks get empty. (*To* LANDLORD.) A bottle of brandy!

LANDLORD. Yes, gentlemen!　　　　　　　　　　[*Exit* D. *in* F.

VENDALE. I am afraid you will find it but bad brandy in such a place. (*To* L. *front, walking up and down.*)

OBENREIZER. Bad brandy is better than none.

Enter LANDLORD, *puts bottles on table.*

LANDLORD. There, gentlemen.

OBENREIZER. *Très bien*—well! You know you are to have the guide ready.

LANDLORD. Yes, sir!

VENDALE. And you 're to wake us at four. (L. *front.*)

LANDLORD. Yes, sir!

OBENREIZER (*doses glass and brings to* VENDALE). Now for the laudanum!

LANDLORD. Any more orders, gentlemen?

OBENREIZER. No! you can go to bed. [*Exit* LANDLORD D. *in* F. How is it? you are a better judge than I am; bad, eh?

VENDALE. I don't like the flavour.

OBENREIZER (*carelessly*). You don't like the flavour? (*Tastes brandy.*) Pah! how is it? bad! Do you lock your door at night when you are travelling? (*Up* R. *by table.*)

VENDALE. Not I. I sleep too soundly. (*Beginning to be heavy of head.*)

OBENREIZER. You are so sound a sleeper! What a blessing!

VENDALE. Anything but a blessing to the east end of the house if I had to be knocked up from the outside of my door.

OBENREIZER. Ha! ha! I, too, leave open my door. By the bye, let me advise you, as a Swiss, you know, always when you travel in my country, put your papers—and, of course, your money—under your pillow. (*By bed, with illustrative gesture.*) Always the safest place.

VENDALE. You are not complimentary to your countrymen.

OBENREIZER (*shrugging shoulders*). Ah! my countrymen are like most men: they will take what they can get.

VENDALE. I have only one paper of importance, and I have no fear of that.

OBENREIZER. But we have to be up early in the morning. Your candle is burning low. I wish you good-night. (*Exit* D. *in* F.) Under the pillow, you know.

VENDALE. Good-night. (*Candle put out—crosses to* L. *window.*) It's a strange fellow-traveller I have. Pshaw! he is my companion of his own proposal, and can have no motive in sharing this undesirable journey. How cold it is! (*Turns from window, beginning*

446

to be unsteady of foot.) I wonder what Wilding could have had to say to him? Can Obenreizer be the—missing man! He speaks English as if it had been the first language of his infancy. How would I like this man to be rich? to be Marguerite's guardian, and yet standing in no relationship to her? (*Abruptly.*) But what are these considerations to come between me and fidelity to the dead? (*Crosses to* R., *reeling.*) No! I am bent on the discharge of my solemn duty, and that duty must and shall be performed. (*Leans on table.*) I will speak to Obenreizer in the morning. (*Seated in chair, back to audience,* R. *side of table.*) In the morning. (*Goes to sleep.*)

Music to OBENREIZER'S *entrance.*

OBENREIZER *opens* D. *in* F., *slowly, a little way, his hand appears, then his face—pause—he enters—pause—he closes door quickly, but so as not to make noise—pause—he listens, goes cautiously to bed, knife in hand, puts hand under pillow—pause—shakes his head, goes to table,* L., *opens writing-case by springing the lock with his knife. While opening case, puts knife in mouth to overhaul papers, then lays knife on table; starts at movement of* VENDALE, *snatches up knife, lays it down. Finishes search, crosses to bed.*

VENDALE. Who is it? (*Springs up.*)

OBENREIZER. Eh! (*Intense surprise.*) Oh! (*Forced voice of anxiety*) you are not in bed—are you ill? (*Up* R. C.)

VENDALE. What do you mean? (*Hand to forehead.*)

OBENREIZER. There *is* something wrong! You are not ill?

VENDALE. Ill? No!

OBENREIZER. I have had a bad dream about you. I tried to rest after it, but it was impossible. Ha! ha! I know you will laugh at me. I was a long while waiting outside your door before I came in. Ha! ha! ha! It is so easy to laugh at a dream that you have not dreamed! (*Lights candle, and then stands by table to light his pipe.*) You have a good fire here now. My candle has burnt out. May I stop with you? You want to sleep, eh?

VENDALE (*drowsily, to* C. *up*). You can stop here, if you like, till morning comes.

OBENREIZER. Yes—ha! ha! It was a bad dream. See! I was stripped for a struggle!

VENDALE. And armed, too.

447

OBENREIZER (*carelessly*). This? Oh, a traveller's knife that I always carry about me. (*Plays with knife-handle.*) Do you carry no such thing?

VENDALE. No such thing. (R.)

OBENREIZER. No pistols?

VENDALE. No weapons of any kind. (*Seated* R. *as before.*)

OBENREIZER. You Englishmen are so confident. (*To bed, searching.*)

VENDALE. Where are you?

OBENREIZER. You see where I am, dear boy. My candle has burnt out. There's such a little time yet, may I sit here and keep you company?

VENDALE. If you like. Besides, I had something very important to say to you—about—(*sleeping, wakes*) I—I—meant to put it off till the morning.

OBENREIZER. Now, it will relieve your mind. Something about me?

VENDALE (*sleepily*). About you, yes—ah!—to-morrow!—to-morrow! (*Sleeps in chair.*)

OBENREIZER. The laudanum has done its work at last. (*To bed, searches.*) Not there! (*Knife in hand, to table,* L.) Not here! (*At writing-case.*) He must have it on him. (*Crosses to* R.) If I could take it without waking him—without crime! There he lies at my mercy! Marguerite's lover—my rival—who carries more than my life in the pocket of his coat. If that man goes free, I am ruined! (*Bends over* VENDALE, *knife in right hand, searching him with left.*) It is here. Could I but unbutton his coat! (*Loud knock* D. *in* F. OBENREIZER *leaps back, and conceals knife; lights his pipe.*)

VENDALE (*jumps up*). Come in. (*Bewildered.*)

OBENREIZER (*aside*). Another moment, and I——(*Sheathes knife.*)

LANDLORD *enters* D. *in* F. *Lights up.*

LANDLORD. Four o'clock, gentlemen, and the guides are waiting. (*Helps* VENDALE, *sleepy, on with overcoat,* L.)

OBENREIZER (*dresses himself with his clothes brought in by servant—aside*). It is my fate. I must kill him on the road! (*All go up to* D. *in* F.)

(*Scene closes in.*)

SCENE II.—*Exterior of Inn on* 1 G.

Enter, D. *in* F., JEAN PAUL *and* JEAN MARIE *and* LANDLORD.

LANDLORD (L.). Well, my friends, what do you think of the weather now?

JEAN MARIE (C.). I say the weather will do.

JEAN PAUL (R.). I say that it is bad.

LANDLORD. Come, you must make up your mind. The two gentlemen are coming.

Enter, D. *in* F., VENDALE *and* OBENREIZER.

VENDALE (*to* L. C.). Well, I suppose you have explained to the men? Are you ready to cross the mountain?

JEAN MARIE. I don't care, for one.

LANDLORD. You may depend upon these guides, sirs.

OBENREIZER (*aside*). That won't do.

JEAN PAUL. I say no. There's something in the air that looks like snow.

OBENREIZER (*aside*). That's better.

JEAN MARIE. I won't go unless Jean Paul goes.

JEAN PAUL. And I'll not go at all.

OBENREIZER (*to* VENDALE). I suppose you know what all this means?

VENDALE. Indeed, I do not.

OBENREIZER. Part of the trade of the poor devils:—it's to double their pay.

JEAN PAUL. You heard the rushing of the waterfall last night? Snow! You heard an unseen hand try to open the doors? Snow. You heard the far-off thunder? Snow. Yes, you'll have snow enough to bury a man upright, and wind enough to blow the hair off his head! And that won't be long from this;—it will all be before to-night.

OBENREIZER. Part of the profession. Two napoleons will change you.

JEAN PAUL. No! not two thousand would do it.

OBENREIZER (*aside*). He will not go!

JEAN PAUL (*to* VENDALE *leading him to* R. 1 E.). You do not laugh at the guide. Mark! How many peaks do you see?

VENDALE. Two!

JEAN PAUL. There are three!

VENDALE. Why can't I see the other?

JEAN PAUL. Because the storm cloud has already come down upon it. It will bring down tons and tons of snow, which will not only strike you dead but bury you at a blow. Do as you will now. I have done my duty of warning you, and I wash my hands of it.

JEAN MARIE. I'll not go unless the old man will.

LANDLORD. We'll do our best to make you comfortable in the inn, gentlemen.

OBENREIZER. Well, what do you propose? As Shakespeare says, 'Discretion is the better part of valour!' Or will you take my advice? I am mountain-born, and we would only have had to guide those poor devils of guides. If you dare to make the attempt, I will go with you——

VENDALE. The occasion is pressing! I must cross——

OBENREIZER. Yes. It is well to understand one another—friends all. This gentleman——

VENDALE. Must cross.

OBENREIZER. It is settled. We go!

VENDALE. We go! (*They take sticks from guides.*)

JEAN PAUL. Do not rush upon destruction!

OBENREIZER. Never fear!   [*Exit* R. *with* VENDALE.

JEAN MARIE. Stop! here! stop, stop!

LANDLORD (*to* R.). Hi, hi! mind you keep the track! Don't leave the track!

JEAN PAUL. You need not waste your breath. You have seen the last of them.

LANDLORD. Pooh! they are two stout walkers, and one knows the mountains.

JEAN PAUL. That may be, but they are both dead men! (*To* L.)

LANDLORD. We shall see!   [*Exit* D. *in* F.

JEAN PAUL. Come, brother, we must be on our way.

        [*Exit* L., *with* JEAN MARIE.

Thunder distant.—Scene changes.

Scene III.—*Mountain pass—thunder—*Vendale *discovered* c. *front,*
        Obenreizer *up* r. *on stairs, staves in hand.*

Vendale. Is it here that we strike the path again?

Obenreizer. Yes, the track is here again.

Vendale. The snow seems to have passed over.

Obenreizer. The storm will come again!

Vendale. Let us on.

Obenreizer. No.

Vendale. No? why linger here?

Obenreizer. Because we are at the journey's end.

Vendale. Here! how here?

Obenreizer. I promised to guide you to your journey's end! The
    journey of your life ends here!

Vendale. You are a villain!

Obenreizer. You are a fool! I have drugged you! Doubly a fool,
    for I am the thief and forger, and in a few moments shall take
    the proof from your dead body!

Vendale. What have I done to you?   (c.)

Obenreizer (r. c.). Done!   You would have destroyed me, but
    that you have come to your journey's end. You have made me
    what I am! I took that money—I stole it, to give luxury to
    Marguerite! You made me buy the jewels that should outshine
    your gift! You made me lose her love—you would have made
    me lose my liberty and life! Therefore you die!

Vendale. Stand back, murderer!

Obenreizer (*laughs*). Murderer! why, I don't touch you! I need
    not, to make you die! Any sleep in the snow is death. You
    are sleeping as you stand!

Vendale (*violently*). Stand back, base murderer! (*Lifts up his staff,*
    Obenreizer *standing on guard with his staff.*) Stand back! (*Lets
    staff fall, when* Obenreizer *rakes it over to him and throws it off,*
    r.) God bless my Marguerite! May she never know how I died!
    Stand off from me—yet let me look at your murderous face. Let
    it remind me—of something—left to me to say—the secret must
    not die with me—no, no, no! Obenreizer, I must say one thing—
    before I sink in death. Oh! (*Reeling.*)

Obenreizer (*aside*). My courage fails me! (*Advances, knife in
    hand.*)   Give me the paper, or——

451

VENDALE. Never! (*Rushes up set bank to trap, leaps.*) Never!

OBENREIZER (*pauses on bank*). Lost! (*Staggers down to stage.*)
Lost! the—the paper. (*Falling.*) Ah! (*Falls in dead swoon.*
C. *front.*)

> *Music kept up—pause—enter* R. U. E. *by set stage,* MARGUERITE,
> JOEY, *and the two Guides.*

MARGUERITE. Ah, George! (*Comes to* C., *then throws herself on bank,*
looking over.   Music.)

All form picture.

Two Guides.   JOEY. MARGUERITE.   OBENREIZER.
R.   R. C.   C.

CURTAIN

ACT V.

SCENE.—*Interior in Monastery, discovering* JOEY C., a *little up,*
and BINTRY *beside him.*

BINTRY. What next, I wonder? Here's an adventure for a professional man. I've been rattled across the country in the railway,
dragged up the mountains on mule-back, and popped into a
monastery by a monk! This all comes of you, Master Joey!

JOEY. How do you make that out, sir?

BINTRY. Why, could Miss Marguerite have sent for me if you had
not brought her out here, and would she have come out if you
had not brought her? It's all her fault and yours.

JOEY. If it comes to that, Mr. Bintry, would Master George be
living at this moment if we had not been in time to save him on
the mountains?

BINTRY. Is Mr. Obenreizer mixed up in any way in this affair?

JOEY. We found him lying in the snow by the edge of the precipice,
if that's what you call being mixed up with it!

BINTRY. Dead?

JOEY. In a dead swoon!

BINTRY. Did you remark anything?

JOEY. I remarked nothing. At first, I thought Master George was
dead. When I felt of his heart, there was no beat; but my fingers

were so numbed with the cold that perhaps I felt on the wrong side !

BINTRY. You don't comprehend what I am driving at. When will Mr. Vendale be able to travel ?

JOEY. He is able to travel now.

BINTRY. And when will Miss Marguerite be able to travel ?

JOEY. Just so soon as Mr. Vendale is ready to travel, and not before. (*Exchanges glances with* BINTRY, *and both laugh.*)

BINTRY. I see, I see. You mean when they do go out, their first walk will be to the nearest church ?

JOEY. That is about the figure of it, sir.

BINTRY. So far, all is clear. But the rest is not so plain. Now, where is Mr. Vendale ?

JOEY. Here ! in this convent, where the monks brought us after they had picked us up.

BINTRY. Here with Mr. Obenreizer ?

JOEY. But they have not seen one another yet.

BINTRY. What does Mr. Obenreizer say about his ward coming out ?

JOEY. They have not met either. They keep the men and women apart here, sir.

BINTRY. Has Mr. Vendale said nothing out of the common ?

JOEY. No.

BINTRY. Not in any way ?

JOEY. He will not speak. He has something on his mind.

BINTRY. Ah ! then it is he who sent for me by Miss Marguerite ?

JOEY. Then Mr. Vendale will see you at once.

BINTRY. I will go at once.

JOEY (*stops him*). If you 'll excuse me, sir, may I ask you one question first ?

BINTRY. Certainly, as you please !

JOEY. When you left London, how did you leave that precious woman, Miss Goldstraw ?

BINTRY. Leave her ? I didn't leave her ! Mr. Joey, prepare yourself for a great surprise. When Miss Goldstraw heard that Miss Marguerite had come out here after Mr. Vendale, she said she must go into foreign parts as well. And it 's my firm belief, Master Joey, that you are at the bottom of it all !

JOEY (*chuckling.*) Not a doubt on it, sir, not a doubt on it !

BINTRY. Why, he don't seem surprised at all !

JOEY. Why, I knew all along that if I didn't go back to her, she'd come all the way out to me.

BINTRY. Is that your experience of woman, Master Joey?

JOEY. That's my experience of Sarah Goldstraw, sir. Now, what was the beautiful language that she used the last time I saw her? It went this way: 'The separation of a man and a woman is a serious institution, and the sooner they come together again after it, the better for all parties.' There's language! Now, what follows? Why, if Miss Goldstraw has come out to see me, it's all right—all right.

Enter SALLY, R. 1 E. D. *to* C., *up.*

SALLY. If you think I have come here on account of you, I will go back to London again directly!

BINTRY. For that purpose, allow me to offer you my arm, ma'am. (SALLY *takes his arm.*)

JOEY. Just allow me one moment before you walk her off!

BINTRY. Certainly, certainly.

JOEY. There's going to be two marriages. Now, if Mr. Vendale marries Miss Marguerite, who is to marry Miss Goldstraw?

SALLY. Don't you distress yourself on my account.

JOEY (*firmly*). Who is to marry Miss Goldstraw?

BINTRY. Well, you are, I am afraid.

JOEY. Then why are you walking off with her, instead of me?

SALLY. You wait a little and you will be walking off along with me all the rest of your future existence.

BINTRY. Isn't it enough to monopolise your wife after marriage, and not to want to monopolise her before she is your wife?

SALLY. Mr. Joey, I'd like you to remember this: A man had better not give a woman the chance, or it may end in her leaving him at the church door!   [*Exit* D. *in* F.

JOEY (*aside*). Beautiful language!

Enter D. *in* F., FATHER FRANCIS, *with book, and* OBENREIZER *with bag of money, to table* R., *where they put them down.* FATHER FRANCIS *crosses to* L. *to shake* BINTRY'S *hand,* BINTRY *looking at him through eye-glass.*

BINTRY (*aside*). Mr. Obenreizer turned treasurer of the establishment!

OBENREIZER (*to* BINTRY, *who receives him suspiciously*).   You have

arrived safely—so glad! (*Shakes hands.*) Come to see Mr. Vendale?
Make your mind perfectly easy; our old friend is as good a man
as ever. (*Subdued tone.*) You have come on business, I suppose?

BINTRY. Humph! that's impossible to say until I shall have seen
Mr. Vendale.

OBENREIZER. I shared his perils as his fellow-traveller, and yet I
have not seen him yet.

FATHER FRANCIS. You shared his perils, and your sight will remind
him of his perils. This gentleman will remind him of home, and
can see him at once.

JOEY. I'll show you the way, sir. (*At* L. D.)

BINTRY. All right, Joey; I'll follow you at once.

  [*Exit* JOEY L. D., BINTRY *to* R., *to* OBENREIZER, *snuff-box business.*
    Exit quickly, L. D.

OBENREIZER (*aside*). Why has he come here? What can Vendale
have to say to him?

FATHER FRANCIS. Patience, my son; before the night you shall take
the hand of your friend. (*At table.*) Till then you must endure,
for a little longer, my poor company.

OBENREIZER. There is none I could desire better, father. Ah! pardon
me! where does that door (L. D. *in* F.) lead to?

FATHER FRANCIS. Why do you ask?

OBENREIZER. That door puzzles me the more I look at it. No bolt,
no bar, no lock. When I go nearer and listen, I hear something
going 'tick, tick,' like the ticking of a clock.

FATHER FRANCIS. It is a clock in the room.

OBENREIZER. A room there? (*Examines thickness of wall by* R. D.
in F.)

FATHER FRANCIS (*nods*). The door opens by clockwork. One of our
brothers made it after long laborious years. It is the strongest
strong-room in the world. Nothing can move the door till the
time comes, and it opens of itself.

OBENREIZER. A strong-room here! Now, if you were bankers or
jewellers, I could understand the need.

FRANCIS. Are we not bankers of the poor, my son?

OBENREIZER. Oh!

FRANCIS. Then we have to keep our valuables safe.

OBENREIZER. Oh! rare old manuscripts and relics. (*Laughing.*)

FRANCIS. Hush, my son, I speak seriously. The property of the

455

travellers who have perished on the mountain is preserved by us until claimed.

OBENREIZER (*laughs*). What a quantity of waste paper you must have!

FRANCIS. Not so; sooner or later all is claimed.

OBENREIZER. Both by foreigners and natives?

FRANCIS. At the present time we have but one foreign: the Vendale papers (OBENREIZER *starts*) found on an Englishman in the snow.

OBENREIZER (*aside*). The Vendale——(*Checks himself.*) Ah!

Enter, D. in F., staying there, Monk.

MONK. The young English lady desires to speak to you, father.

FRANCIS. Presently, brother, presently. (*Exit Monk D. in F.*) I must put away the money and wait to set the clock. The English travellers will be on the road early. I will make it to open at one o'clock. (*To* OBENREIZER.) We keep regular hours here, and do not often have occasion to alter the hour of the safe's opening.

OBENREIZER (*looks at watch*). It is now a minute to eight. (R. C. *up.*)

FRANCIS. Then in one minute you will see that door open. (R.) (*Music, piano, long-drawn strains on violin—clock strikes eight, L. door in F. opens,* FRANCIS *pushes it back so as not to close, then to table.*)

OBENREIZER. Wonderful!

FRANCIS. So simple, too, in its action. Now, to change the hour. (*Alters the hand.*) At any hour, or part of an hour, that the regulator is fixed, the safe will open. (*To* R.)

OBENREIZER (*to* R.). I see. Don't trouble yourself, father. May I assist you? (*Takes bag of money, puts it in L. room, turns dial hand around, closes door with snap, stands back to it.*) Oh! (*Pretends to snatch at door.*)

FRANCIS. What have you done?

OBENREIZER. My stupidity is inexcusable! I—I leaned against the door and—and——

FRANCIS. You have closed it! (*With vexation of a man who has learnt to suppress emotion pretty well.*) Now it will not open till six to-morrow morning.

OBENREIZER (*aside*). It will open in five minutes!

FRANCIS. And my book is left out! Oh, you have caused me excessive trouble!

OBENREIZER. I am so sorry, father.

456

FRANCIS. The book makes no matter, but the——well, I must go
see the young lady. [*Exit* R. D. *in* F.

OBENREIZER. Ah! the old idiot. How fortunate it was put in his
keeping. (*Watch in hand.*) There's not a minute to be lost. Ah!
the door opens! (*Music,* L. D. *in* F. *opens as before, overhauls
papers.*) This is not it. Not here, not here! I know the receipt
well! What is this? Vendale papers! (*To table, runs over
packet.*) It is not among them. Bah! Eighteen hundred—
twenty-nine years ago! (*Interested.*) What does all this mean?
Certificate of death! a mother—and not a wife! Ah! ah! I
have him! (*Rises, puts paper in breast.*) Ah, Mr. Vendale, I am
prepared to meet you now! (*Closes* L. D. *in* F., *to* L.)

Enter MARGUERITE, R. D., VENDALE D. *in* F., *they embrace.*

OBENREIZER. Marguerite (*to* R. C.), have you no word for *me*?

VENDALE (*keeping* MARGUERITE L. C. *front*). Pardon me, Mr. Obenreizer, you will understand that you can have no further interest
in this lady.

OBENREIZER. Marguerite, what does this mean? Mr. Vendale speaks
in such a tone that I cannot tell whether he is in jest or earnest.

VENDALE. Do not answer. (*To* OBENREIZER.) There can be no
question between us. My object in so far meeting you is to bring
all further proceedings on your part to an end. Mr. Bintry will
tell you how.

OBENREIZER. Marguerite, I hardly need to repeat in what position
I stand towards you. That man has no claim on you—when I
leave the house, you come with me.

BINTRY (*at* R. *table,* R. *side of it*). Mr. Obenreizer, when you are
ready, I am. Will you sign the paper by which you relinquish
all authority over your niece and leave her free to wed Mr. Vendale?

OBENREIZER (C.). Mr. Bintry, your professional enthusiasm leads you
too far, clever as you are. Mr. Vendale and I made an agreement
under which he was bound to double his income. (*To* VENDALE.)
Have you doubled it?

VENDALE. No!

OBENREIZER. Then, more talk is useless. Mr. Bintry, you can put
your paper in the fire.

BINTRY. My paper will get the better of you yet!

VENDALE. I will force you to sign it.

OBENREIZER. Force me! force is a very big word, Mr. Vendale. I beg you to withdraw it. Mr. Bintry, you are fond of curious documents; will you be so good as to look at these?

BINTRY. What? (*Takes papers.*) Impossible!

OBENREIZER. I told you so. Three years ago an English gentleman perished on the mountains, and the papers found on his body were brought here.

VENDALE. How did you come by them?

BINTRY. That it is needless to inquire. (*Examining papers eagerly.*)

OBENREIZER. Twenty-five years ago, a lady living in Switzerland, childless for years, decided on adopting a child, and her sister in England took one out of the Foundling Hospital!

VENDALE. Out of the Foundling!

MARGUERITE. Oh, George, what is this?

OBENREIZER. You shall all have information enough! Here are the written proofs of what I advance. Mr. Bintry, what do you want else?

BINTRY. Proof that the father and mother are living?

OBENREIZER (*gives papers*). They are both dead.

BINTRY. List of the witnesses and their residences who can speak to the facts of the case?

OBENREIZER (*gives papers*). Are they right?

BINTRY. Complete!

OBENREIZER. Ha, ha!

BINTRY (*to* VENDALE). Mr. Vendale, allow me to congratulate you!

VENDALE (*bewildered*). What was the name of the woman in England?

OBENREIZER. Mrs. Miller.

VENDALE. Miller! then we have found the missing man!

MARGUERITE. What *does* all this mean?

VENDALE. Our poor dead friend's last wish on earth is accomplished. All is explained now. (*To* OBENREIZER.) You are the lost Walter Wilding!

OBENREIZER. I — I have not that honour. You are the man! Marguerite, do you know to whom you would have given your hand? To an impostor—a bastard! brought up by public charity!

MARGUERITE. Oh, I never loved you, George, as I love you now!

VENDALE. I the man!

BINTRY. Yes! Ah, ah, Mr. Obenreizer, he is the man who inherits all the fortune of Mr. Wilding. In one breath he has doubled his income, thanks entirely to your exertions. By your own agreement he is free to marry her now. Will you sign the paper? (R. *at table.*)

OBENREIZER (*fiercely*). Never! never!

VENDALE. Then I must force you.

OBENREIZER. Force me!

VENDALE (*shows paper*). What becomes of your authority over her now?

BINTRY. Will you sign?

OBENREIZER (*to* VENDALE *softly*). Does she know?

VENDALE (*same, aside*). She does not.

OBENREIZER (*aside to* VENDALE). Will she ever know, if I sign?

VENDALE (*to table*, R., *to burn receipt in candle*). Never!

BINTRY. I told you my paper would get the better of you at last. (*Points out place to sign.*)

OBENREIZER (*signs while* VENDALE *burns receipt—aside*). So ends the dream of my life! (*Swallows poison from vial.*)

MARGUERITE. What does all this mean?

OBENREIZER. It means that you are free—free to marry him!

MARGUERITE. Free! (*To* VENDALE, L. C.) I don't know what feeling prompts me to do this. (*Approaches* OBENREIZER, C. *front.*) I am going to begin a new and happy life. If I have ever done you wrong, forgive me! If you have ever done me wrong, for George's sake, I forgive you. Ah! you are ill!

OBENREIZER (*sadly taking* MARGUERITE's *hand*). Marguerite, you said once I frightened you! Do I frighten you now?

MARGUERITE. What is the matter? You are looking ill.

OBENREIZER. I am looking at you for the last time, Marguerite! (*Staggers up* C., *when* VENDALE *tries to catch him—fiercely.*) Don't touch me! (*Drops his voice, mildly.*) No, I——Thanks! Farewell! (*Dies.*)

MARGUERITE (*to* VENDALE). George!

JOEY *and* SALLY *enter* D. *in* F., *look down at* OBENREIZER.

CURTAIN

459

POEMS

SONGS FROM 'THE PICKWICK PAPERS'

[1837]

I.—THE IVY GREEN

THIS famous ballad of three verses, from the sixth chapter of *Pickwick*, is perhaps the most acceptable of all Dickens's poetical efforts. It was originally set to music, at Dickens's request, by his brother-in-law, Henry Burnett, a professional vocalist, who, by the way, was the admitted prototype of Nicholas Nickleby. Mr. Burnett sang the ballad scores of times in the presence of literary men and artists, and it proved an especial favourite with Landor. 'The Ivy Green' was not written for *Pickwick*, Mr. Burnett assured me; but on its being so much admired the author said it should go into a monthly number, and it did. The most popular setting is undoubtedly that of Henry Russell, who has recorded that he received, as his fee, the magnificent sum of ten shillings! The ballad, in this form, went into many editions, and the sales must have amounted to tens of thousands.—F. G. K.

OH, a dainty plant is the Ivy green,
That creepeth o'er ruins old!
Of right choice food are his meals, I ween,
In his cell so lone and cold.
The wall must be crumbled, the stone decayed,
To pleasure his dainty whim:
And the mouldering dust that years have made
Is a merry meal for him.
    Creeping where no life is seen,
    A rare old plant is the Ivy green.

Fast he stealeth on, though he wears no wings,
And a staunch old heart has he.
How closely he twineth, how tight he clings,
To his friend the huge Oak Tree!
And slily he traileth along the ground,
And his leaves he gently waves,
As he joyously hugs and crawleth round
The rich mould of dead men's graves.
    Creeping where grim death hath been,
    A rare old plant is the Ivy green.

POEMS

Whole ages have fled and their works decayed,
And nations have scattered been;
But the stout old Ivy shall never fade,
From its hale and hearty green.
The brave old plant, in its lonely days,
Shall fatten upon the past:
For the stateliest building man can raise
Is the Ivy's food at last.
    Creeping on, where time has been,
    A rare old plant is the Ivy green.

II.—A CHRISTMAS CAROL

THE five stanzas bearing the above title will be found in the twenty-eighth
chapter of *Pickwick*, where they are introduced as the song which that hospitable old soul, Mr. Wardle, sung appropriately, 'in a good, round, sturdy
voice,' before the Pickwickians and others assembled on Christmas Eve at
Manor Farm. The 'Carol,' shortly after its appearance in *Pickwick*, was set to
music to the air of 'Old King Cole,' and published in *The Book of British Song*
(New Edition), with an illustration drawn by 'Alfred Crowquill'—*i.e.*, A. H.
Forrester.—F. G. K.

I CARE not for Spring; on his fickle wing
Let the blossoms and buds be borne:
He woos them amain with his treacherous rain,
And he scatters them ere the morn.
An inconstant elf, he knows not himself
Nor his own changing mind an hour,
He'll smile in your face, and, with wry grimace,
He'll wither your youngest flower.

Let the Summer sun to his bright home run,
He shall never be sought by me;
When he's dimmed by a cloud I can laugh aloud,
And care not how sulky he be!
For his darling child is the madness wild
That sports in fierce fever's train;
And when love is too strong, it don't last long,
As many have found to their pain.

A mild harvest night, by the tranquil light
Of the modest and gentle moon,

464

GABRIEL GRUB'S SONG

Has a far sweeter sheen, for me, I ween,
Than the broad and unblushing noon.
But every leaf awakens my grief,
As it lieth beneath the tree;
So let Autumn air be never so fair,
It by no means agrees with me.

But my song I troll out, for CHRISTMAS stout,
The hearty, the true, and the bold;
A bumper I drain, and with might and main
Give three cheers for this Christmas old!
We'll usher him in with a merry din
That shall gladden his joyous heart,
And we'll keep him up, while there's bite or sup,
And in fellowship good, we'll part.

In his fine honest pride, he scorns to hide
One jot of his hard-weather scars;
They're no disgrace, for there's much the same trace
On the cheeks of our bravest tars.
Then again I sing 'till the roof doth ring,
And it echoes from wall to wall—
To the stout old wight, fair welcome to-night,
As the King of the Seasons all!

III.—GABRIEL GRUB'S SONG

THE Sexton's melancholy dirge, in the twenty-ninth chapter of *Pickwick*, seems a little incongruous in a humorous work. The sentiment, however, thoroughly accords with the philosophic gravedigger's gruesome occupation. 'The Story of the Goblins who Stole a Sexton' is one of several short tales (chiefly of a dismal character) introduced into *Pickwick*; they were doubtless written prior to the conception of *Pickwick*, each being probably intended for independent publication, and in a manner similar to the 'Boz' Sketches. For some reason these stories were not so published, and Dickens evidently saw a favourable opportunity of utilising his unused manuscripts by inserting them in *The Pickwick Papers.*—F. G. K.

BRAVE lodgings for one, brave lodgings for one,
A few feet of cold earth, when life is done;
A stone at the head, a stone at the feet,
A rich, juicy meal for the worms to eat;
Rank grass over head, and damp clay around,
Brave lodgings for one, these, in holy ground!

POEMS

IV.—ROMANCE

It will be remembered that while Sam Weller and his coaching-friends refreshed themselves at the little public-house opposite the Insolvent Court in Portugal Street, Lincoln's Inn Fields, prior to Sam joining Mr. Pickwick in the Fleet, that faithful body-servant was persuaded to 'oblige the company' with a song. 'Raly, gentlemen,' said Sam, 'I'm not wery much in the habit o' singin' vithout the instrument; but anythin' for a quiet life, as the man said ven he took the sitivation at the light-house.'

'With this prelude, Mr. Samuel Weller burst at once into the following wild and beautiful legend, which, under the impression that it is not generally known, we take the liberty of quoting. We would beg to call particular attention to the monosyllable at the end of the second and fourth lines, which not only enables the singer to take breath at those points, but greatly assists the metre.'—*The Pickwick Papers*, chapter xliii.

At the conclusion of the performance the mottled-faced gentleman contended that the song was 'personal to the cloth,' and demanded the name of the bishop's coachman, whose cowardice he regarded as a reflection upon coachmen in general. Sam replied that his name was not known, as 'he hadn't got his card in his pocket'; whereupon the mottled-faced gentleman declared the statement to be untrue, stoutly maintaining that the said coachman did *not* run away, but 'died game—game as pheasants,' and he would 'hear nothin' said to the contrairey.'

Even in the vernacular (observes Mr. Percy Fitzgerald), 'this master of words [Charles Dickens] could be artistic; and it may fairly be asserted that Mr. Weller's song to the coachmen is superior to anything of the kind that has appeared since.' The two stanzas have been set to music, as a humorous part-song, by Sir Frederick Bridge, Mus. Doc., M.V.O., the organist of Westminster Abbey, who informs me that it was written some years since, to celebrate a festive gathering in honour of Dr. Turpin (!), Secretary of the College of Organists. 'It has had a very great success,' says Sir Frederick, 'and is sung much in the North of England at competitions of choirs. It is for men's voices. The humour of the words never fails to make a great hit, and I hope the music does no harm. "The Bishop's Coach" is set to a bit of old Plain-Chant, and I introduce a Fugue at the words "Sure as eggs is eggs."'—F. G. K.

I

Bold Turpin vunce, on Hounslow Heath,
His bold mare Bess bestrode—er;
Ven there he see'd the Bishop's coach
A-comin' along the road—er.
So he gallops close to the 'orse's legs,
And he claps his head vithin;

466

POLITICAL SQUIBS

And the Bishop says, 'Sure as eggs is eggs,
This here's the bold Turpin!'

> *Chorus*—And the Bishop says, 'Sure as eggs is eggs,
> This here's the bold Turpin!'

II

Says Turpin, 'You shall eat your words,
With a sarse of leaden b*u*l-let';
So he puts a pistol to his mouth,
And he fires it down his gul-let.
The coachman, he not likin' the job,
Set off at a full gal-lop,
But Dick put a couple of balls in his nob,
And perwailed on him to stop.

> *Chorus* (*sarcastically*)—But Dick put a couple of balls
> in his nob,
> And perwailed on him to stop.

POLITICAL SQUIBS FROM 'THE EXAMINER'

[1841]

In August 1841 Dickens contributed anonymously to *The Examiner* (then edited by Forster) three political squibs, which were signed W., and were intended to help the Liberals in fighting their opponents. These squibs were entitled respectively 'The Fine Old English Gentleman (to be said or sung at all Conservative Dinners)'; 'The Quack Doctor's Proclamation'; and 'Subjects for Painters (after Peter Pindar).' Concerning those productions, Forster says : 'I doubt if he ever enjoyed anything more than the power of thus taking part occasionally, unknown to outsiders, in the sharp conflict the press was waging at the time.' In all probability he contributed other political rhymes to the pages of *The Examiner* as events prompted : if so, they are buried beyond easy reach of identification.

Writing to Forster at this time, Dickens said : 'By Jove, how Radical I am getting ! I wax stronger and stronger in the true principles every day.' . . . He would (observes Forster) sometimes even talk, in moments of sudden indignation at the political outlook, 'of carrying off himself and his household gods, like Coriolanus, to a world elsewhere.' This was the period of the Tory interregnum, with Sir Robert Peel at the head of affairs.—F. G. K.

POEMS

I.—THE FINE OLD ENGLISH GENTLEMAN
New Version
(To be said or sung at all Conservative Dinners)

I 'LL sing you a new ballad, and I 'll warrant it first-rate,
Of the days of that old gentleman who had that old estate;
When they spent the public money at a bountiful old rate
On ev'ry mistress, pimp, and scamp, at ev'ry noble gate,
      In the fine old English Tory times;
      Soon may they come again!

The good old laws were garnished well with gibbets, whips, and chains,
With fine old English penalties, and fine old English pains,
With rebel heads, and seas of blood once hot in rebel veins;
For all these things were requisite to guard the rich old gains
      Of the fine old English Tory times;
      Soon may they come again!

This brave old code, like Argus, had a hundred watchful eyes,
And ev'ry English peasant had his good old English spies,
To tempt his starving discontent with fine old English lies,
Then call the good old Yeomanry to stop his peevish cries,
      In the fine old English Tory times;
      Soon may they come again!

The good old times for cutting throats that cried out in their need,
The good old times for hunting men who held their fathers' creed,
The good old times when William Pitt, as all good men agreed,
Came down direct from Paradise at more than railroad speed. . . .
      Oh the fine old English Tory times;
      When will they come again!

In those rare days, the press was seldom known to snarl or bark,
But sweetly sang of men in pow'r, like any tuneful lark;
Grave judges, too, to all their evil deeds were in the dark;
And not a man in twenty score knew how to make his mark.
      Oh the fine old English Tory times;
      Soon may they come again!

Those were the days for taxes, and for war's infernal din;
For scarcity of bread, that fine old dowagers might win;

468

THE QUACK DOCTOR'S PROCLAMATION

For shutting men of letters up, through iron bars to grin,
Because they didn't think the Prince was altogether thin,
  In the fine old English Tory times;
  Soon may they come again!

But Tolerance, though slow in flight, is strong-wing'd in the main;
That night must come on these fine days, in course of time was plain;
The pure old spirit struggled, but its struggles were in vain;
A nation's grip was on it, and it died in choking pain,
  With the fine old English Tory days,
  All of the olden time.

The bright old day now dawns again; the cry runs through the land,
In England there shall be dear bread—in Ireland, sword and brand;
And poverty, and ignorance, shall swell the rich and grand,
So, rally round the rulers with the gentle iron hand,
  Of the fine old English Tory days;
  Hail to the coming time!   W.

II.—THE QUACK DOCTOR'S PROCLAMATION

Tune—'A Cobbler there was'

An astonishing doctor has just come to town,
Who will do all the faculty perfectly brown:
He knows all diseases, their causes, and ends;
And he begs to appeal to his medical friends.
   Tol de rol:
   Diddle doll:
  Tol de rol, de dol,
   Diddle doll
  Tol de rol doll.

He's a magnetic doctor, and knows how to keep
The whole of a Government snoring asleep
To popular clamours; till popular pins
Are stuck in their midriffs—and then he begins
   Tol de rol.

He's a *clairvoyant* subject, and readily reads
His countrymen's wishes, condition, and needs,

With many more fine things I can't tell in rhyme,
—And he keeps both his eyes shut the whole of the time.
Tol de rol.

You mustn't expect him to talk; but you 'll take
Most particular notice the doctor 's awake,
Though for aught from his words or his looks that you reap, he
Might just as well be most confoundedly sleepy.
Tol de rol.

Homœopathy, too, he has practised for ages
(You 'll find his prescriptions in Luke Hansard's pages),
Just giving his patient when maddened by pain,—
Of Reform the ten thousandth part of a grain.
Tol de rol.

He 's a med'cine for Ireland, in portable papers;
The infallible cure for political vapours;
A neat label round it his 'prentices tie—
' Put your trust in the Lord, and keep this powder dry! '
Tol de rol.

He 's a corn doctor also, of wonderful skill,
—No cutting, no rooting-up, purging, or pill—
You 're merely to take, 'stead of walking or riding,
The sweet schoolboy exercise—innocent sliding.
Tol de rol.

There 's no advice gratis.   If high ladies send
His legitimate fee, he 's their soft-spoken friend.
At the great public counter with one hand behind him,
And one in his waistcoat, they 're certain to find him.
Tol de rol.

He has only to add he 's the real Doctor Flam,
All others being purely fictitious and sham;
The house is a large one, tall, slated, and white;
With a lobby; and lights in the passage at night.
Tol de rol:
Diddle doll:
Tol de rol, de dol,
Diddle doll
Tol de rol doll.   W.

SUBJECTS FOR PAINTERS

III.—SUBJECTS FOR PAINTERS

(After Peter Pindar)

To you, Sir Martin,[1] and your co. R.A.'s,
  I dedicate in meek, suggestive lays,
Some subjects for your academic palettes ;
  Hoping by dint of these my scanty jobs,
  To fill with novel thoughts your teeming nobs,
As though I beat them in with wooden mallets.

To you, Maclise, who Eve's fair daughters paint
  With Nature's hand, and want the maudlin taint
Of the sweet Chalon school of silk and ermine :
  To you, E. Landseer, who from year to year
  Delight in beasts and birds, and dogs and deer,
And seldom give us any human vermin :

  —To all who practise art, or make believe,
  I offer subjects they may take or leave.

Great Sibthorp and his butler, in debate
  (*Arcades ambo*) on affairs of state,
Not altogether ' gone,' but rather funny ;
  Cursing the Whigs for leaving in the lurch
  Our d——d good, pleasant, gentlemanly Church,
Would make a picture—cheap at any money.

Or Sibthorp as the Tory Sec.—at-War,
  Encouraging his mates with loud ' Yhor ! Yhor ! '
From Treas'ry benches' most conspicuous end ;
  Or Sib.'s mustachios curling with a smile,
  As an expectant Premier without guile
Calls him his honourable and gallant friend.

Or Sibthorp travelling in foreign parts,
  Through that rich portion of our Eastern charts
Where lies the land of popular tradition ;
  And fairly worshipp'd by the true devout
  In all his comings-in and goings-out,
Because of the old Turkish superstition.

[1] Sir Martin Archer Shee, *P*.R.A.

POEMS

Fame with her trumpet, blowing very hard,
  And making earth rich with celestial lard,
In puffing deeds done through Lord Chamberlain Howe;
  While some few thousand persons of small gains,
  Who give their charities without such pains,
Look up, much wondering what may be the row.

Behind them Joseph Hume, who turns his pate
  To where great Marlbro' House in princely state
Shelters a host of lacqueys, lords and pages,
  And says he knows of dowagers a crowd,
  Who, without trumpeting so very loud,
Would do so much, and more, for half the wages.

Limn, sirs, the highest lady in the land,
  When Joseph Surface, fawning cap in hand,
Delivers in his list of patriot mortals;
  Those gentlemen of honour, faith, and truth,
  Who, foul-mouthed, spat upon her maiden youth,
And dog-like did defile her palace portals.

Paint me the Tories, full of grief and woe,
  Weeping (to voters) over Frost and Co.,
Their suff'ring, erring, much-enduring brothers.
  And in the background don't forget to pack,
  Each grinning ghastly from its bloody sack,
The heads of Thistlewood, Despard, and others.

Paint, squandering the club's election gold,
  Fierce lovers of our Constitution old,
Lords who 're that sacred lady's greatest debtors;
  And let the law, forbidding any voice
  Or act of Peer to influence the choice
Of English people, flourish in bright letters.

Paint that same dear old lady, ill at ease,
  Weak in her second childhood, hard to please,
Unknowing what she ails or what she wishes;

With all her Carlton nephews at the door,
Deaf'ning both aunt and nurses with their roar,
—Fighting already, for the loaves and fishes.

Leaving these hints for you to dwell upon,
I shall presume to offer more anon.   W.

PROLOGUE TO
WESTLAND MARSTON'S PLAY
'THE PATRICIAN'S DAUGHTER'

[1842]

The Patrician's Daughter was the title bestowed upon a play, in the tragic vein, by a then unknown writer, J. Westland Marston, it being his maiden effort in dramatic authorship. Dickens took great interest in the young man, and indicated a desire to promote the welfare of his production by composing some introductory lines. To Macready he wrote : 'The more I think of Marston's play, the more sure I feel that a prologue to the purpose would help it materially, and almost decide the fate of any ticklish point on the first night. Now I have an idea (not easily explainable in writing, but told in five words) that would take the prologue out of the conventional dress of prologues, quite. Get the curtain up with a dash, and begin the play with a sledge-hammer blow. If, on consideration, you should agree with me, I will write the prologue, heartily.' Happily for the author, his little tragedy was the first new play of the season, and it thus attracted greater attention. Its initial representation took place at Drury Lane Theatre on December 10, 1842, and the fact that Dickens's dignified and vigorous lines were recited by Macready, the leading actor of his day, undoubtedly gave *prestige* to this performance ; but the play, although it made a sensation for the moment, did not enjoy a long run, its motive being for some reason misunderstood. As explained by the Editors of *The Letters of Charles Dickens*, it was (to a certain extent) an experiment in testing the effect of a tragedy of modern times and in modern dress, the novelist's Prologue being intended to show that there need be no incongruity between plain clothes of the nineteenth century and high tragedy.

The Patrician's Daughter : A Tragedy in Five Acts, appeared in pamphlet form during the year prior to its being placed upon the boards. The Prologue was printed for the first time in the *Sunday Times*, December 11, 1842, and then in *The Theatrical Journal and Stranger's Guide*, December 17, 1842. By the kind permission of Miss Hogarth, the lines are here reproduced from the revised and only correct version in *The Letters of Charles Dickens*.

In the preface to the second edition of the play (1842), the author thus acknowledges his indebtedness to Dickens for the Prologue, which, however, does not appear in the book: 'How shall I thank Mr. Dickens for the spontaneous kindness which has furnished me with so excellent a letter of introduction to the audience? The simplest acknowledgment is perhaps the best, since the least I might say would exceed *his* estimate of the obligation; while the most I could say would fail to express *mine*.'—F. G. K.

THE PROLOGUE

(Spoken by Mr. Macready)

No tale of streaming plumes and harness bright
Dwells on the poet's maiden harp to-night;
No trumpet's clamour and no battle's fire
Breathes in the trembling accents of his lyre;
Enough for him, if in his lowly strain
He wakes one household echo not in vain;
Enough for him, if in his boldest word
The beating heart of MAN be dimly heard.

Its solemn music which, like strains that sigh
Through charmèd gardens, all who hearing die;
Its solemn music he does not pursue
To distant ages out of human view;
Nor listen to its wild and mournful chime
In the dead caverns on the shore of Time;
But musing with a calm and steady gaze
Before the crackling flames of living days,
He hears it whisper through the busy roar
Of what shall be and what has been before.
Awake the Present! Shall no scene display
The tragic passion of the passing day?
Is it with Man, as with some meaner things,
That out of death his single purpose springs?
Can his eventful life no moral teach
Until he be, for aye, beyond its reach?
Obscurely shall he suffer, act, and fade,
Dubb'd noble only by the sexton's spade?
Awake the Present! Though the steel-clad age
Find life alone within its storied page,

A WORD IN SEASON

Iron is worn, at heart, by many still—
The tyrant Custom binds the serf-like will;
If the sharp rack, and screw, and chain be gone,
These later days have tortures of their own;
The guiltless writhe, while Guilt is stretch'd in sleep,
And Virtue lies, too often, dungeon deep.
Awake the Present! what the Past has sown
Be in its harvest garner'd, reap'd, and grown!
How pride breeds pride, and wrong engenders wrong,
Read in the volume Truth has held so long,
Assured that where life's flowers freshest blow,
The sharpest thorns and keenest briars grow,
How social usage has the pow'r to change
Good thoughts to evil; in its highest range
To cramp the noble soul, and turn to ruth
The kindling impulse of our glorious youth,
Crushing the spirit in its house of clay,
Learn from the lessons of the present day.
Not light its import and not poor its mien;
Yourselves the actors, and your homes the scene.

A WORD IN SEASON

FROM 'THE KEEPSAKE'

[1844]

The Keepsake, one of the many fashionable annuals published during the early years of Queen Victoria's reign, had for its editor in 1844 the 'gorgeous' Countess of Blessington, the reigning beauty who held court at Gore House, Kensington, where many political, artistic, and literary celebrities forgathered —Bulwer Lytton, Disraeli, Dickens, Ainsworth, D'Orsay, and the rest. Her ladyship, through her personal charm and natural gifts, succeeded in securing the services of eminent authors for the aristocratic publication; even Dickens could not resist her appeal, and in a letter to Forster (dated July 1843) he wrote: 'I have heard, as you have, from Lady Blessington, for whose behalf I have this morning penned the lines I send you herewith. But I have only done so to excuse myself, for I have not the least idea of their suiting her; and I hope she will send them back to you for *The Examiner*.' Lady Blessington, however, decided to retain the thoughtful little poem, which was referred to in the *London Review* (twenty-three years later) as 'a graceful and sweet apologue, reminding one of the manner of Hood.' The theme of the poem, which

POEMS

Forster describes as 'a clever and pointed parable in verse,' was afterwards satirised in Chadband (*Bleak House*), and in the idea of religious conversion through the agency of 'moral pocket-handkerchiefs.'—F. G. K.

A WORD IN SEASON

THEY have a superstition in the East,
    That ALLAH, written on a piece of paper,
Is better unction than can come of priest,
    Of rolling incense, and of lighted taper:
Holding, that any scrap which bears that name,
    In any characters, its front imprest on,
Shall help the finder through the purging flame,
    And give his toasted feet a place to rest on.

Accordingly, they make a mighty fuss
    With ev'ry wretched tract and fierce oration,
And hoard the leaves—for they are not, like us,
    A highly civilised and thinking nation:
And, always stooping in the miry ways,
    To look for matter of this earthy leaven,
They seldom, in their dust-exploring days,
    Have any leisure to look up to Heaven.

So have I known a country on the earth,
    Where darkness sat upon the living waters,
And brutal ignorance, and toil, and dearth
    Were the hard portion of its sons and daughters:
And yet, where they who should have ope'd the door
    Of charity and light, for all men's finding,
Squabbled for words upon the altar-floor,
    And rent the Book, in struggles for the binding.

The gentlest man among these pious Turks,
    God's living image ruthlessly defaces;
Their best high-churchman, with no faith in works,
    Bowstrings the Virtues in the market-places:
The Christian Pariah, whom both sects curse
    (They curse all other men, and curse each other),
Walks thro' the world, not very much the worse—
    Does all the good he can, and loves his brother.

VERSES FROM THE 'DAILY NEWS'

[1846]

THE *Daily News*, it will be remembered, was founded in January 1846 by Charles Dickens, who officiated as its first editor. He soon sickened of the mechanical drudgery appertaining to the position, and resigned his editorial functions the following month. From January 21st to March 2nd he contributed to its columns a series of 'Travelling Sketches,' afterwards reprinted in volume form as *Pictures from Italy*. He also availed himself of the opportunity afforded him, by his association with that newspaper, of once more taking up the cudgels against the Tories, and, as in the case of the *Examiner*, his attack was conveyed through the medium of some doggerel verses. These were entitled 'The British Lion—A New Song, but an Old Story,' to be sung to the tune of 'The Great Sea-Snake.' They bore the signature of 'Catnach,' the famous ballad-singer, and were printed in the *Daily News* of January 24, 1846.

Three weeks later some verses of a totally different character appeared in the columns of the *Daily News*, signed in full 'Charles Dickens.' One Lucy Simpkins, of Bremhill (or Bremble), a parish in Wiltshire, had just previously addressed a night meeting of the wives of agricultural labourers in that county, in support of a petition for Free Trade, and her vigorous speech on that occasion inspired Dickens to write 'The Hymn of the Wiltshire Labourers,' thus offering an earnest protest against oppression. Concerning the 'Hymn,' a writer in a recent issue of *Christmas Bells* observes : 'It breathes in every line the teaching of the Sermon on the Mount, the love of the All-Father, the Redemption by His Son, and that love to God and man on which hang all the law and the prophets.'—F. G. K.

I.—THE BRITISH LION

A NEW SONG, BUT AN OLD STORY

TUNE—'THE GREAT SEA-SNAKE'

OH, p'r'aps you may have heard, and if not, I 'll sing
    Of the British Lion free,
That was constantly a-going for to make a spring
    Upon his en-e-me ;
But who, being rather groggy at the knees,
    Broke down, always, before ;
And generally gave a feeble wheeze
    Instead of a loud roar.

POEMS

Right toor rol, loor rol, fee faw fum,
    The British Lion bold!
That was always a-going for to do great things,
    And was always being 'sold!'

He was carried about, in a carawan,
    And was show'd in country parts,
And they said, 'Walk up! Be in time! He can
    Eat Corn-Law Leagues like tarts!'
And his showmen, shouting there and then,
    To puff him didn't fail,
And they said, as they peep'd into his den,
    'Oh, don't he wag his tail!'

Now, the principal keeper of this poor old beast,
    WAN HUMBUG was his name,
Would once ev'ry day stir him up—at least—
    And wasn't that a Game!
For he hadn't a tooth, and he hadn't a claw,
    In that 'Struggle' so 'Sublime';
And, however sharp they touch'd him on the raw,
    He couldn't come up to time.

And this, you will observe, was the reason why
    WAN HUMBUG, on weak grounds,
Was forced to make believe that he heard his cry
    In all unlikely sounds.
So, there wasn't a bleat from an Essex Calf,
    Or a Duke or a Lordling slim;
But he said, with a wery triumphant laugh,
    'I'm blest if that ain't him.'

At length, wery bald in his mane and tail,
    The British Lion growed:
He pined, and declined, and he satisfied
    The last debt which he owed.
And when they came to examine the skin,
    It was a wonder sore,
To find that the an-i-mal within
    Was nothing but a Boar!

THE WILTSHIRE LABOURERS' HYMN

> Right toor rol, loor rol, fee faw fum,
>   The British Lion bold!
> That was always a-going for to do great things,
>   And was always being ' sold ! '
>
> CATNACH.

II.—THE HYMN OF THE WILTSHIRE LABOURERS

' Don't you all think that we have a great need to Cry to our God to put it in the hearts of our greassous Queen and her Members of Parlerment to grant us free bread ! '—LUCY SIMPKINS, *at Bremhill.*

> OH GOD, who by Thy Prophet's hand
>   Didst smite the rocky brake,
> Whence water came, at Thy command,
>   Thy people's thirst to slake ;
> Strike, now, upon this granite wall,
>   Stern, obdurate, and high ;
> And let some drops of pity fall
>   For us who starve and die !
>
> The GOD, who took a little child,
>   And set him in the midst,
> And promised him His mercy mild,
>   As, by Thy Son, Thou didst :
> Look down upon our children dear,
>   So gaunt, so cold, so spare,
> And let their images appear
>   Where Lords and Gentry are !
>
> Oh GOD, teach them to feel how we,
>   When our poor infants droop,
> Are weakened in our trust in Thee,
>   And how our spirits stoop ;
> For, in Thy rest, so bright and fair,
>   All tears and sorrows sleep :
> And their young looks, so full of care,
>   Would make Thine Angels weep !

479

POEMS

The GOD, who with His finger drew
　　The Judgment coming on,
Write, for these men, what must ensue,
　　Ere many years be gone!
Oh GOD, whose bow is in the sky,
　　Let them not brave and dare,
Until they look (too late) on high,
　　And see an Arrow there!

Oh GOD, remind them!　In the bread
　　They break upon the knee,
These sacred words may yet be read,
　　'In memory of Me!'
Oh GOD, remind them of His sweet
　　Compassion for the poor,
And how He gave them Bread to eat,
　　And went from door to door!

　　　　　　　　　　　　　CHARLES DICKENS.

LINES ADDRESSED TO MARK LEMON

[1849]

DICKENS, like Silas Wegg, would sometimes 'drop into poetry' when writing to intimate friends, as, for example, in a letter to Maclise, the artist, which began with a parody of Byron's lines to Thomas Moore—

> 'My foot is in the house,
> 　My bath is on the sea,
> And, before I take a souse,
> 　Here's a single note to thee.'

A more remarkable instance of his propensity to indulge in parody of this kind is to be found in a letter addressed to Mark Lemon in the spring of 1849. The novelist was then enjoying a holiday with his wife and daughters at Brighton, whence he wrote to Lemon (who had been ill), pressing him to pay them a visit.　After commanding him to 'get a clean pocket-handkerchief ready for the close of "Copperfield" No. 3—"simple and quiet, but very natural and touching"—*Evening Bore*,' Dickens invites his friend in lines headed 'New Song,' and signed 'T. Sparkler,' the effusion also bearing the signatures of other members of the family party—Catherine Dickens, Annie Leech, Georgina Hogarth, Mary Dickens, Katie Dickens, and John Leech.—F. G. K.

NEW SONG

Tune—'Lesbia hath a Beaming Eye'

I

Lemon is a little hipped,
And this is Lemon's true position—
He is not pale, he's not white-lipped,
Yet wants a little fresh condition.
Sweeter 'tis to gaze upon
Old Ocean's rising, falling billers,
Than on the Houses every one
That form the street called Saint Anne's Willers!
 Oh my Lemon, round and fat,
 Oh my bright, my right, my tight 'un,
 Think a little what you're at—
 Don't stay at home, but come to Brighton!

II

Lemon has a coat of frieze,
But all so seldom Lemon wears it,
That it is a prey to fleas,
And ev'ry moth that's hungry, tears it.
Oh, that coat's the coat for me,
That braves the railway sparks and breezes,
Leaving ev'ry engine free
To smoke it, till its owner sneezes!
 Then my Lemon, round and fat,
 L., my bright, my right, my tight 'un,
 Think a little what you're at—
 On Tuesday first, come down to Brighton!

T. Sparkler.

POEMS FROM 'HOUSEHOLD WORDS'
[1850-1851]

The two following poems were discovered recently by means of the Contributors' Book to *Household Words*, to which reference is made in the introductory preface to the present volume. 'Hiram Power's Greek Slave' appeared in that paper on 26th October 1850, and 'Aspire!' on 25th January 1851.—B. W. M.

POEMS

I.—HIRAM POWER'S GREEK SLAVE

THEY say Ideal Beauty cannot enter
The house of anguish.   On the threshold stands
This alien Image with the shackled hands,
Called the Greek Slave: as if the artist meant her
(The passionless perfection which he lent her,
Shadowed, not darkened, where the sill expands)
To, so, confront man's crimes in different lands,
With man's ideal sense.   Pierce to the centre
Art's fiery finger! and break up ere long
The serfdom of this world.   Appeal, fair stone,
From God's pure heights of beauty, against man's wrong!
Catch up, in thy divine face, not alone
East griefs, but west, and strike and shame the strong,
By thunders of white silence, overthrown.

II.—ASPIRE!

ASPIRE! whatever fate befall,
    Be it praise or blame—
Aspire! even when deprived of all—
    It is thy nature's aim.
The seed beneath the frozen earth,
When winter checks the fresh green birth,
    Still yearningly aspires,
    With ripening desires,
And, in its season, it will shoot
Up into the perfect fruit;
    But had it not lain low,
    It ne'er had learn'd to grow.

Aspire! for in thyself alone
    That power belongs of right;
Within thyself that seed is sown,
    Which strives to reach the light;
All pride of rank, all pomp of place,
All pinnacles that point in space,

482

PROLOGUE TO 'THE LIGHTHOUSE'

But show thee, to the spheres,
No greater than thy peers;
But if thy spirit doth aspire,
Thou risest ever higher—higher—
Towards that consummate end,
When Heavenward we tend.

WILKIE COLLINS'S PLAY
'THE LIGHTHOUSE'

[1855]

WILKIE COLLINS composed two powerful dramas for representation at Dickens's residence, Tavistock House, a portion of which had been already adapted for private theatricals, the rooms so converted being described in the bills as 'The Smallest Theatre in the World.' The first of these plays was called *The Light-house*, and the initial performance took place on June 19, 1855. Dickens not only wrote the Prologue and 'The Song of the Wreck,' but signally distinguished himself by enacting the part of Aaron Gurnock, a lighthouse-keeper, his clever impersonation recalling Frédérick Lemaitre, the only actor he ever tried to take as a model.

With regard to 'The Song of the Wreck,' Dickens evidently intended to bestow upon it a different title, for, in a letter addressed to Wilkie Collins during the preparation of the play, he said : 'I have written a little ballad for Mary—"The Story of the Ship's Carpenter and the Little Boy, in the Shipwreck."' The song was rendered by his eldest daughter, Mary (who assumed the rôle of Phœbe in the play); it was set to the music composed by George Linley for Miss Charlotte Young's pretty ballad, 'Little Nell,' of which Dickens became very fond, and which his daughter had been in the habit of singing to him constantly since her childhood. Dr. A. W. Ward, Master of Peterhouse, Cambridge University, refers to 'The Song of the Wreck' as 'a most successful effort in Cowper's manner.'—F. G. K.

I.—THE PROLOGUE

(Slow music all the time ; unseen speaker ; curtain down.)

A STORY of those rocks where doom'd ships come
To cast them wreck'd upon the steps of home,
Where solitary men, the long year through—
The wind their music and the brine their view—

POEMS

Warn mariners to shun the beacon-light;
A story of those rocks is here to-night.
Eddystone Lighthouse!

(*Exterior view discovered.*)

              In its ancient form,
Ere he who built it wish'd for the great storm
That shiver'd it to nothing,[1] once again
Behold outgleaming on the angry main!
Within it are three men; to these repair
In our frail bark of Fancy, swift as air!
They are but shadows, as the rower grim
Took none but shadows in his boat with him.

So be *ye* shades, and, for a little space,
The real world a dream without a trace.
Return is easy. It will have ye back
Too soon to the old beaten dusty track;
For but one hour forget it. Billows, rise;
Blow winds, fall rain, be black, ye midnight skies;
And you who watch the light, arise! arise!

(*Exterior view rises and discovers the scene.*)

II.—THE SONG OF THE WRECK

I

THE wind blew high, the waters raved,
   A ship drove on the land,
A hundred human creatures saved
   Kneel'd down upon the sand.
Three-score were drown'd, three-score were thrown
   Upon the black rocks wild,
And thus among them, left alone,
   They found one helpless child.

---

[1] When Winstanley had brought his work to completion, he is said to have expressed himself so satisfied as to its strength, that he only wished he might be there in the fiercest storm that ever blew. His wish was gratified, and, contrary to his expectations, both he and the building were swept completely away by a furious tempest which burst along the coast in November 1703.

THE SONG OF THE WRECK

A seaman rough, to shipwreck bred,
  Stood out from all the rest,
And gently laid the lonely head
  Upon his honest breast.
And travelling o'er the desert wide
  It was a solemn joy,
To see them, ever side by side,
  The sailor and the boy.

III

In famine, sickness, hunger, thirst,
  The two were still but one,
Until the strong man droop'd the first
  And felt his labours done.
Then to a trusty friend he spake,
  'Across the desert wide,
O take this poor boy for my sake!'
  And kiss'd the child and died.

IV

Toiling along in weary plight
  Through heavy jungle, mire,
These two came later every night
  To warm them at the fire.
Until the captain said one day,
  'O seaman good and kind,
To save thyself now come away,
  And leave the boy behind!'

V

The child was slumbering near the blaze:
  'O captain, let him rest
Until it sinks, when God's own ways
  Shall teach us what is best!'
They watch'd the whiten'd ashy heap,
  They touch'd the child in vain;
They did not leave him there asleep,
  He never woke again.

POEMS

PROLOGUE TO WILKIE COLLINS'S PLAY
'THE FROZEN DEEP'

[1856]

THE second drama written by Wilkie Collins for the Tavistock House Theatre was first acted there in January 1857, and subsequently at the Gallery of Illustration in the presence of Queen Victoria and the Royal Family. As in the case of *The Lighthouse*, the play had the advantage of a Prologue in rhyme by Charles Dickens, who again electrified his audiences by marvellous acting, the character of Richard Wardour (a young naval officer) being selected by him for representation.

The Prologue was recited at Tavistock House by John Forster, and at the public performances of the play by Dickens himself.

It is not generally known that a by no means inconsiderable portion of the drama was composed by Dickens, as testified by the original manuscripts of the play and of the prompt-book, which contain numerous additions and corrections in his handwriting. These manuscripts, by the way, realised £300 at Sotheby's in 1890.

The main idea of *A Tale of Two Cities* was conceived by Dickens when performing in *The Frozen Deep*. 'A strong desire was upon me then,' he writes in the preface to the story, 'to embody it in my own person; and I traced out in my fancy the state of mind of which it would necessitate the presentation to an observant spectator, with particular care and interest. As the idea became familiar to me, it gradually shaped itself into its present form. Throughout its execution, it has had complete possession of me : I have so far verified what is done and suffered in these pages, as that I have certainly done and suffered it all myself.'—F. G. K.

THE PROLOGUE

(Curtain rises; mists and darkness; soft music throughout.)

ONE savage footprint on the lonely shore
Where one man listen'd to the surge's roar,
Not all the winds that stir the mighty sea
Can ever ruffle in the memory.
If such its interest and thrall, O then
Pause on the footprints of heroic men,
Making a garden of the desert wide
Where Parry conquer'd death and Franklin died.

To that white region where the Lost lie low,
Wrapt in their mantles of eternal snow,—

486

PROLOGUE TO 'THE FROZEN DEEP'

Unvisited by change, nothing to mock
Those statues sculptured in the icy rock,
We pray your company; that hearts as true
(Though nothings of the air) may live for you;
Nor only yet that on our little glass
A faint reflection of those wilds may pass,
But that the secrets of the vast Profound
Within us, an exploring hand may sound,
Testing the region of the ice-bound soul,
Seeking the passage at its northern pole,
Softening the horrors of its wintry sleep,
Melting the surface of that ' Frozen Deep.'

Vanish, ye mists! But ere this gloom departs,
And to the union of three sister arts
We give a winter evening, good to know
That in the charms of such another show,
That in the fiction of a friendly play,
The Arctic sailors, too, put gloom away,
Forgot their long night, saw no starry dome,
Hail'd the warm sun, and were again at Home.

Vanish, ye mists! Not yet do we repair
To the still country of the piercing air;
But seek, before we cross the troubled seas,
An English hearth and Devon's waving trees.

A CHILD'S HYMN

FROM 'THE WRECK OF THE GOLDEN MARY'

[1856]

THE Christmas number of *Household Words* for 1856 is especially noteworthy as containing the Hymn of five verses which Dickens contributed to the second chapter. This made a highly favourable impression, and a certain clergyman, the Rev. R. H. Davies, was induced to express to the editor of *Household Words* his gratitude to the author of these lines for having thus conveyed to innumer-

POEMS

able readers such true religious sentiments. In acknowledging the receipt of
the letter, Dickens observed that such a mark of approval was none the less
gratifying to him because he was himself the author of the Hymn. 'There
cannot be many men, I believe,' he added, 'who have a more humble veneration for the New Testament, or a more profound conviction of its all-sufficiency,
than I have. If I am ever (as you tell me I am) mistaken on this subject, it is
because I discountenance all obtrusive professions of and tradings in religion,
as one of the main causes why real Christianity has been retarded in this world;
and because my observation of life induces me to hold in unspeakable dread and
horror those unseemly squabbles about the letter which drive the spirit out of
hundreds of thousands.'—*Vide* Forster's *Life of Charles Dickens*, Book xi., iii.—
F. G. K.

A CHILD'S HYMN

HEAR my prayer, O! Heavenly Father,
  Ere I lay me down to sleep;
Bid Thy Angels, pure and holy,
  Round my bed their vigil keep.

My sins are heavy, but Thy mercy
  Far outweighs them every one;
Down before Thy Cross I cast them,
  Trusting in Thy help alone.

Keep me through this night of peril
  Underneath its boundless shade;
Take me to Thy rest, I pray Thee,
  When my pilgrimage is made.

None shall measure out Thy patience
  By the span of human thought;
None shall bound the tender mercies
  Which Thy Holy Son has bought.

Pardon all my past transgressions,
  Give me strength for days to come;
Guide and guard me with Thy blessing
  Till Thy Angels bid me home.

THE BLACKSMITH

FROM 'ALL THE YEAR ROUND'

[APRIL 20, 1859]

IN the chapter of Forster's *Life of Dickens* dealing with *All the Year Round*, the biographer refers to an article of Dickens's in the first number of that periodical entitled 'The Poor Man and his Beer,' and states how he came to write it.

The Rev. T. B. Lawes of Rothamsted, St. Albans, had interested Dickens in a club that had been set on foot to enable the agricultural labourers of the parish to have their beer and pipes independent of the public-house, and the description of it, says Mr. Lawes, ' was the occupation of a drive between this place (Rothamsted) and London, 25 miles. . . . In the course of our conversation I mentioned that the labourers were very jealous of the small tradesmen, black-smiths and others, holding allotment gardens; but that the latter did so indirectly by paying higher rents to the labourers for a share.' This circum-stance is not forgotten in the verses on the Blacksmith in the same number, composed by Mr Dickens and repeated to me while he was walking about, and which close the mention of his gains with allusion to:

> 'A share (concealed) in the poor man's field,
> Which adds to the poor man's store.'

It is curious to note that no one has identified this poem as Dickens's before, although the indisputable authority quoted above has been available to every one since 1873.—B. W. M.

THE BLACKSMITH

OLD England, she has great warriors,
Great princes, and poets great;
But the Blacksmith is not to be quite forgot,
In the history of the State.

He is rich in the best of all metals,
Yet silver he lacks and gold;
And he payeth his due, and his heart is true,
Though he bloweth both hot and cold.

The boldest is he of incendiaries
That ever the wide world saw,
And a forger as rank as e'er robbed the Bank,
Though he never doth break the law.

He hath shoes that are worn by strangers,
Ye he laugheth and maketh more ;
And a share (concealed) in the poor man's field,
Yet it adds to the poor man's store.

Then, hurrah for the iron Blacksmith !
And hurrah for his iron crew !
And whenever we go where his forges glow,
We 'll sing what A MAN can do.

This book, designed by
William B. Taylor
is a production of
Edito-Service S.A., Geneva

Printed in France